D1106021

# PRESCRIPTION
# FOR SORROW

# Expert Endorsements

"Patrick Hahn's *Prescription for Sorrow* gives a compelling account of some of the most tragic mental health events. His touch is sure and the narrative races along. You may find yourself devouring it in one sitting—and then going back for more. Unless you're definitively on the "other" side before you begin it, you'll likely find yourself recommending it to others."

> **David Healy,** *author of Pharmageddon*
> *Professor Department of Family Medicine, McMaster University.*

"Patrick Hahn's book, *Prescription for Sorrow: Antidepressants, Suicide, and Violence*, is a beautifully written page-turner. Despite being considered an expert on antidepressants, I learned much from it and will certainly be citing it in future work. It should be read by every doctor who prescribes these drugs and by anyone who is considering taking one."

> **Irving Kirsch,** *author of The Emperor's New Drugs*
> *Associate Director of the Program in Placebo Studies at the Harvard Medical School and the Beth Israel Deaconess Medical Center*

"A comprehensive and disturbing analysis of possibly the greatest medical scandal of our times. Patrick Hahn leaves no stone unturned in his search for the truth and the guilty parties."

*John Read*, *editor of Models of Madness*
*Professor of Clinical Psychology at the University of East London*

"A startling tale of psychiatric hubris, corporate greed, and media ineptitude, destined to rival Robert Whitaker's *Anatomy of an Epidemic* as one of the most important books on the rise of antidepressants and societal harm in the twenty-first century."

*Bruce Cohen*, *author of Psychiatric Hegemony*
*Senior Lecturer in Sociology at the University of Auckland*

Also by Patrick D. Hahn

*Madness and Genetic Determinism: Is Mental Illness in Our Genes?*

# PRESCRIPTION FOR SORROW

Antidepressants, Suicide, and Violence

## PATRICK D. HAHN

**Samizdat Health**

Samizdat Health Writer's Co-operative Inc.

Cover Design/Illustration: Billiam James

First Printing, 2020

Title: Prescription For Sorrow: Antidepressants, Suicide and Violence

ISBN: 978-1-989963-09-8

Publisher: Samizdat Health Writer's Co-operative Inc.

www.samizdathealth.org
www.meliponula.wordpress.com

# *Acknowledgments*

Grateful acknowledgement is made to each for the following for their assistance in preparing this book:

To the experts who gave so generously of their time to explain their work to me: Peter Breggin, David Healy, Irving Kirsch, and John Read;

To Wendy, David, Kim, and Michael, who courageously shared their stories of iatrogenic harm;

And to my wife and daughter, for their unwavering support.

# Contents

*Prescription for Sorrow*

# PREFACE

On 14 September 1989, Joseph Wesbecker, a forty-seven-year-old former pressman at Standard Gravure of Louisville, Kentucky, entered his erstwhile place of employment armed with a Polytech AK47S semi-automatic rifle, a Sig Sauer P226 9mm pistol, two MAC 11 9mm machine pistols, a Smith & Wesson .38 revolver, a bayonet, and over a thousand rounds of ammunition. Wesbecker opened fire, killing eight employees and wounding twelve more. He also shot up the water sprinklers, and a police officer responding to the scene would later recall the place ran with what looked like rivers of blood.[1]

Wesbecker's surviving victims later recalled his blank stare—"totally dehumanized,"[2] as one described it. Others remembered hearing him laughing as he proceeded from room to room, dealing out death to his former colleagues.[3]

Wesbecker kept firing, pumping bullets into already dead bodies, the slaughter finally ending only when he turned the Sig Sauer on himself and shot his own face off.[4] An autopsy revealed his blood contained therapeutic levels of two drugs—lithium, which is commonly prescribed for bipolar disorder, and a new antidepressant drug released by pharmaceutical company giant Eli Lilly the year before, called Prozac.[5]

The survivors of the massacre banded together and filed suit against Lilly. On 12 December 1995, a jury voted nine-to-three to acquit the company on all charges. Lilly's CEO, Randall Tobias, told the Associated

Press "We have proven in a court of law, just as we have to more than 70 scientific and regulatory bodies all over the world, that Prozac is safe and effective."[6]

The AP article did not mention that just before the trial began, Tobias's wife had committed suicide, shortly after starting on the company's blockbuster drug.[7]

One could scarcely have been alive and conscious anywhere in the Western world any time in the past twenty-five years and not have been aware of a raging controversy surrounding antidepressants, suicide, and violence—a controversy that shows no sign of abating. During that same period, prescriptions for antidepressants have skyrocketed, and the companies that manufacture them—and also manufacture and control the evidence purporting to show that these nostrums are safe and effective—have grown to be, in the words of psychiatrist David Healy, "the most profitable organisations on the planet."[8]

So what is the story? Do these drugs drive people to suicide, or do they not? What about homicide? Are they addictive? Do they even help with depression?

In an effort to find answers to these questions, I have examined the scientific literature, trial transcripts, government documents, and news accounts, and listened to psychiatrists, psychologists, patients, and their family members. I have reconstructed the story of how these drugs came on the market and how they have stayed on the market, piecing together events month by month and sometimes day by day.

This is an account of staggering corporate mendacity and greed, and of news media which all too often behave like lapdogs rather than watchdogs. But it is also a tale of courageous doctors, reporters, litigators, and ordinary men and women whose lives were turned upside-down by these drugs—all of whom were relentless in their drive to uncover the truth. It's a story that affects every one of us, and you are invited to come along and share in what I have learned.

# CHAPTER I

# THE BEGINNING

Everybody who knew Nick agreed on one thing—the lad had talent.

Like many a talented young man, Nick dreamed of being a star. And, like many a talented young man, he found the world was coldly indifferent to his dream. A producer took an interest in his work and he recorded a couple of albums, but sales were miniscule. Nick hated touring and refused to give interviews, and without that there wasn't much hope of building up an audience.[9]

Nick had always been a loner, hard to get to know, but now he was spending increasing amounts of time sequestered in his drab little bedsitter apartment, smoking hashish and brooding, neglecting his appearance and hygiene. He went to a doctor who prescribed medication for his condition, but it didn't seem to help.[10]

Like many a young person with broken dreams, Nick moved back home to live with his parents, who by all accounts wanted to help but were at a loss as to how to do so. Nick would get up and leave without giving anyone the slightest notice, borrowing his parents' car without asking and driving for miles until he ran out of petrol—an apt metaphor for a life going nowhere. He toyed with the idea of pursuing a more conventional career, enrolling in a computer programming course and even speaking to an Army recruiter, but he never followed through on either of these initiatives.[11]

On the evening of 24 November 1974, Nick went to bed early. His mother would later say, "I remember him standing at that door, and I said to him 'Are you off to bed Nick?'"[12]

That was the last time anyone ever saw him alive.[13]

### The Search for a Psychic Energizer

The *Epic of Gilgamesh* is mankind's oldest written narrative, having first been inscribed on clay tablets sometime in the seventeenth century BC.[14] The eponymous hero was a Sumerian warrior-king who lived probably over a thousand years before his story was first written down.[15] Towards the end of the tale, he watches helplessly as his best friend, the Paleolithic savage Enkidu, dies of a lethal disease. Unable to accept the finality of death, the hero stands guard over his erstwhile comrade's dead body until it actually begins to decompose.

Shattered with grief, the hero walks into a bar and pours his heart out to the waitress, who gives him the only advice she can: to enjoy life while it lasts, knowing full well that everything will be taken away from him all too soon.

So depression has been with us since before the beginning of written history. It is only within the span of a single lifetime that this condition has come to be regarded as a chronic brain disease, which can and should be treated with drugs. The first drug marketed specifically as an antidepressant, iproniazid, was not introduced until the end of 1957.

Iproniazid is a derivative of hydrazine, a molecule first synthesized in 1875 by the chemist Emil Fischer of the University of Strasbourg,[16] and used by the Nazis as fuel to power their V-2 rockets during World War Two. At the end of the war, large stockpiles of the chemical became available at bargain-basement prices, and drug companies went to work to find uses for hydrazine derivatives.[17]

One of these, iproniazid, was first synthesized by scientists at Hoffman-LaRoche in Nutley, New Jersey. This compound was found to kill the bacillus that caused tuberculosis, first in vitro and later in mice,[18] and finally in human patients.[19] The new drug was approved for that use and marketed under the trade name Marsilid.

However, the drug produced some interesting side effects. Supposedly, patients were "dancing in the wards."[20] In fact the effects were more complicated, and not always benign.

Some patients exhibited reduced fatigue, increased appetite, and decreased need for sleep, but others experienced recurring nightmares, violent outbursts, hallucinations, delusions, and manic psychosis. Patients with pre-existing psychiatric problems found those problems got worse on iproniazid. Other toxic effects included hypotension, dizziness, dysphagia, and dyspnea. Between fifty and seventy percent of patients given the drug had to be taken off it because of these effects.[21]

All this hardly amounted to a ringing endorsement of iproniazid, but some psychiatrists thought the drug had potential as a treatment for depression. However, the results obtained in the first trials on mental patients were disappointing. An August 1953 study described the results of a study which tested iproniazid on a heterogeneous group of eleven patients. Some of them seemed to improve in mood somewhat, but this result was soon overshadowed with constant complaints about vertigo. None of the patients remained on the drug for more than three weeks.[22]

The following November, another study reported the results of a trial of iproniazid on a group of thirty mental patients, all female. These patients were rated on a number of metrics including weight gain or loss, table manners, dress and person, behavior towards aides and nurses, and attitudes toward electroshock (!). Compared to the patients given placebo or nothing at all, those given the new drug exhibited tiny improvements in some of these areas, but the investigators themselves concluded "The differences between the groups were never great enough to be of practical significance."[23]

Meanwhile, Nathan Kline, a psychiatrist at Rockland State Hospital in upstate New York who had studied the effect of the tranquilizer reserpine on mental patients, decided that something needed even more urgently than a tranquilizer was a "psychic energizer" for the depressed. In 1955 he addressed the American Psychoanalytic Association on the subject. Delivering his pitch in the language of Freudian jargon with which his audience was intimately familiar, he described what a psychic energizer would do:

> *The plethora of id energy would make large amounts of energy easily available to the ego so that there would be more than enough energy available for all tasks. Such a situation would result in a sense of joyousness and optimism. As the dose was raised to the point where the id drives threatened the integrity of the ego, anxiety would appear. If the dose was raised still further, one would expect the id pressure finally to cause a rupture of ego defenses so that clinical neurosis or psychosis would ensue, depending upon the specific ego weakness which would determine its line of fracture.*[24]

The following year Kline spoke with a researcher at Warner Laboratories who mentioned that iproniazid nullified the tranquilizing effects of reserpine, at least in mice. Kline decided that this was the psychic energizer he was looking for.

Kline and his colleagues tested the drug on seventeen chronically depressed female patients and found that four exhibited "appreciable response," seven "some response," one a "transient response," two no response, and the remaining three had to be taken off the drug because of unfavorable side effects. In other words, approximately seventy percent of these women exhibited at least "some response."[25]

There was no placebo group, but in modern-day antidepressant trials, typically something like thirty-five to forty percent of patients respond to a placebo,[26] meaning that three or four patients would have to be treated with iproniazid to get one additional patient to respond.

Kline and his colleagues presented their results in April of 1957 at the regional conference of the American Psychiatric Association in Syracuse, New York, and within a year's time the drug had been given to some 400,000 patients.[27] Kline was later awarded the Lasker Prize (sometimes called the "American Nobel") for his work.[28]

Iproniazid belongs to a class of drugs known as monoamine oxidase inhibitors.[29] These drugs catalyze the breakdown of monoamines, an important class of biological molecules including serotonin and norepinephrine. Both of these substances serve as neurotransmitters, or molecules that relay messages between nerve cells.

Iproniazid was later withdrawn from the market, due to reports of sometimes fatal liver toxicity. Other MAO inhibitors have been introduced and still are prescribed, but all drugs of this class come with a host of dietary restrictions. Consumption of foods rich in the trace amino acid tyramine (such as aged cheeses, pickled foods, wine, and smoked meats) can precipitate a hypertensive crisis which can (rarely) result in fatal cerebral hemorrhaging. The MAO inhibitors are not considered first-line treatment, and generally are reserved for patients considered unresponsive to other types of antidepressants.

Around this same time iproniazid was being studied for its potential as an antidepressant, Swiss psychiatrist Roland Kuhn was busy testing some antihistamine compounds developed by the firm J.R. Geigy, for a variety of psychiatric complaints. One such drug, known as G 22355, showed special promise in treating depression. Kuhn referred to the new drug as a "thymoleptic."[30] In 1958 Geigy released G 223555, or imipramine as it was now known, under the trade name Tofranil.[31]

Kuhn stressed that imipramine was most effective for so-called "endogenous" depression, as opposed to "reactive" depression, or depression judged to have arisen from some external cause. Anticipating the arguments of the modern-day psychopharmaceutical industry, with its rallying cry of "It's nobody's fault,"[32] he wrote:

> *It has at last been recognized that the vital depressive disturbances can be traced back to childhood...We know too about the child whose sluggish and tearful behavior is often mistaken for laziness...The symptoms are sleeplessness, anxiety, tiredness and thus failure in school in spite of high intelligence, neglect of school homework, the 'sitting in front of a blank page' because the child can think of nothing to write. Other common symptoms are playing hooky, enuresis or encopresis; in short, many that are today still interpreted by child psychiatrists as due to environmental damage, poor upbringing, or neurosis.[33]*

### A Simplistic Theory

Imipramine belongs to a class of drugs known as tricyclics, due to their three-ringed structure. Another tricyclic antidepressant, amitriptyline, was introduced to the market in 1961 under the trade name Elavil. These drugs block the reuptake of neurotransmitters (such as serotonin and norepinephrine) from the synapse, or the gap between two nerve cells.[34]

Since both MAO inhibitors and tricyclics are thought to increase the activity of neurotransmitters (including serotonin and norepinephrine), this led researchers, including the Nobel-Prize winning neuroscientists Arvid Carlsson and Julius Axelrod,[35] to propose that this increase explains the therapeutic effects of these drugs. From there it was only a short step to proposing that depression is caused by a deficiency of neurotransmitters.

This view, which came to be known as the "chemical imbalance" hypothesis, initially was no more than that—a tentative working hypothesis, as its proponents themselves made clear. Leo E. Hollister, Chief of Medical Services at the Veterans Administration Hospital in Palo Alto, warned against simplistic views of the etiology and treatment of mental disorders, in a paper published at the very dawn of the modern psycho-pharmaceutical era:

> *The success of psychopharmaceutical agents in treating emotional disorders has led to the belief that only more (or more powerful) drugs are needed to solve the enigma of mental illness. It should be emphasized that little, if any, hard facts support this wild speculation. As yet, we have no convincing evidence that the drugs do more than control abnormal behavior and lessen the symptoms of psychopathology. Big as this achievement is, it is not enough. There is no drug yet known that will remove a patient from a stressful environment or influence human behavior and thought as much as persons and ideas do. Insight into the causes of emotional illness will be obtained more readily if all investigators keep constantly in mind both the sociopsychological and the biological factors involved.*[36]

Unfortunately, these words of caution were all but forgotten in the decades that followed.

At the time the chemical imbalance hypothesis was proposed, there were only a handful of molecules know to function as neurotransmitters. Today over a hundred such molecules are known. Meanwhile a half a century of research has failed to produce any convincing evidence that depression (or any other of the conditions commonly treated by psychiatrists) is caused by a deficiency or an excess of serotonin or any other neurotransmitter. This simplistic theory cannot possibly be true,[37] and yet it has been relentlessly promoted by psychiatrists and drug companies.[38]

## A Two-Edged Sword

From the beginning it was apparent that antidepressant drugs were a two-edged sword. A 1966 article by George Krieger, Chief of Psychiatric Services at the Veterans Administration Hospital in Palo Alto, reported that the rate of hospital suicides soared after antidepressants and tranquilizers were introduced—and that the suicide rate closely tracked per-patient spending on these drugs.[39]

Psychiatrists David Avery and George Winokur looked at the rate of suicide attempts by patients admitted to the Iowa State Psychiatric Hospital for depression during the ten-year period between 1959 and 1969.[40] They found that suicide attempts were more likely among patients with one or more prior suicide attempts than those with none. No surprise there.

The surprise came when they compared patients with one or more prior suicide attempts (who presumably were more impaired) and who were not given antidepressant therapy, with patients who had no prior suicide attempts (and who were presumably less impaired) who did receive antidepressants. The suicide attempt rate among the less impaired patients who received antidepressants was higher than that of the more impaired patients who did not get them. The suicide attempt rate was higher still among the less impaired patients who received "adequate" antidepressant therapy.

Moreover, the tricyclics represented a two-edged sword, because the difference between a therapeutic dose and a lethal dose is a narrow one. A 1987 paper in the *British Medical Journal* calculated the toxicity index, or the number of overdose deaths per million prescriptions, for different classes of antidepressant drugs. Every one of the tricyclics had a significantly higher toxicity index than the mean for all antidepressants.[41]

In plain English, these drugs didn't just put some patients into a suicidal state—they were actually being used by patients as a means to commit suicide. One tricyclic, amitriptyline, was implicated in half of all antidepressant overdose deaths in the United States and the United Kingdom.[42]

But these reports were mere harbingers of a gathering storm.

§

And what about Nick, the troubled young man we met at the beginning of this chapter?

On the night of 24 November 1974, Nick Drake died from an overdose of amitriptyline—the same drug he had been prescribed to help him with his problems. By the time the family housekeeper discovered his body the next morning, he had already been dead for hours.[43]

While virtually unknown in his lifetime, Nick has acquired something of a cult following in the years after his death, and is best remembered for his third and final album *Pink Moon*. In 2014 the readers of *MOJO* magazine voted him one of the most important artists of the last twenty years,[44] despite the fact that he had been dead for twice that length of time. He was twenty-six years old when he died.

# CHAPTER 2

# THE PROZAC ERA

## A Promise Made

More than any other drug, Prozac has come to epitomize the modern-day psychopharmaceutical era. Fluoxetine (the generic name for Prozac) belongs to a class of drugs known as selective serotonin reuptake inhibitors, or SSRI's. Other SSRI's include citalopram (Celexa), escitalopram (Lexapro), fluvoxamine (Luvox), paroxetine (Paxil, Seroxat), and sertraline (Zoloft).

The term "Selective Serotonin Reuptake Inhibitor" implies a drug with a very specific mode of action, a sort of "magic bullet" for mental illness. In fact, all it means is that the drug does not act on the norepinephrine system of the brain.[45] What it is doing to any of the dozens of other chemical substances known to act as neurotransmitters in the human brain is anybody's guess.

And despite their alleged selectivity, these drugs have been touted for a dizzying variety of human woes, including depression, anxiety, eating disorders, phobias, obsessions, compulsions, drug and alcohol addiction, migraine headaches, social phobia, schizophrenia, post-traumatic stress disorder, panic disorder, attention deficit/hyperactivity disorder, borderline personality disorder, and something called "premenstrual dysphoric disorder."

One notable property of SSRI's is that they are much safer in overdose than the older antidepressants, notably the tricyclics. It was hoped that the use of these drugs would lead to a lowered rate of suicide for depressed patients.

Industry giant Eli Lilly obtained FDA approval for Prozac for the treatment of depression at the end of 1987.[46] This was followed by a massive media campaign to pitch this new drug. The public was saturated with the message that this and similar dugs corrected a chemical imbalance, just like insulin for diabetes, along with seemingly ubiquitous offers of free "depression screening."[47]

Prozac was not the first SSRI to be released on to the market—that honor belongs to zimelidine.[48] Nor was it the first SSRI to stay on the market—that honor belongs to Luvox. But Prozac became a cultural icon as no other drug has before or since, lending its name to works of nonfiction (*Listening to Prozac, Talking Back to Prozac, Prozac Backlash*), memoirs (*Prozac Diary, Prozac Nation*), a musical (*The Prozac Sisters*), and a video game (*Virtual Prozac*). In the words of one psychiatrist, "Prozac was on 'Nightline' when you went to sleep and on the 'Today' show when you woke up."[49] Indeed, the very sound of the word "Prozac" conveys images of power, of action, of crackling, zapping bolts of electricity.

The first longform article about the new drug appeared in *New York* on 18 December 1989—three months after the Standard Gravure Massacre. Titled "Bye-Bye Blues: A New Wonder Drug for Depression,"[50] the piece began with the story of Rachel, an unhappily single professional whose boyfriend had left her to marry another woman and have a child with her. Rachael cried every morning on the commuter train to work and even contemplated suicide. But after trying Prozac, a seemingly miraculous change ensued:

> *The most amazing thing happened. I found myself humming little tunes at work. I'd walk down the hall humming something from The Sound of Music.*[51]

Other users offered similar testimonials:

*I'm so efficient. I've never been able to handle so much at work.*[52]

*The Prozac has allowed me to achieve new levels of insight.*[53]

*My supervisor jumps up and down and hugs me, she's so pleased with me.*[54]

In fairness to author Fran Schumer, she offered a more balanced view than many subsequent media treatments of Prozac did. She noted that other drugs, such as Xanax, were once ballyhooed in a similar fashion, and turned out to have serious, even fatal, toxic effects.[55] She also mentioned that Prozac had already been associated with a wide range of toxic effects including crying jags, anxiety, insomnia, convulsions, nausea, stomach pain, headaches, skin rash, dry mouth, constipation, sexual dysfunction, and uncontrollable agitation—and that other, even more serious rare adverse events not detected in clinical trials could manifest themselves as millions took the drug.[56]

The possibility that Lilly might hide serious adverse events that occurred in trials of the drug was not considered.

The article also offered these curiously backhanded words of praise from one psychopharmacologist:

*Prozac is incredibly easy to prescribe. You can teach a chimpanzee to prescribe it.*[57]

On 26 March 1990, *Newsweek* ran a cover story titled "The Promise of Prozac,"[58] featuring a larger-than-life image of the Prozac capsule (or "pulvule," as Lilly called it) hovering over the landscape. On the first page, we meet Susan A., who "has spent most of her life fighting with people— her parents, her neighbors, her co-workers, her husband." Susan had suffered bouts of depression and bulimia, abused drugs and alcohol, and twice tried to kill herself—but once again, after trying Prozac, a seemingly miraculous change ensued:

> *Within a month, Susan had given up psychotherapy in favor of school and a full-time job. She had also given up tranquilizers and street drugs... 'I actually like Mom & Dad now, I'm well-liked at work, I don't ruminate on negatives, my marriage is five times better.'*[59]

The article noted that Prozac had already become the nation's most prescribed antidepressant, with annual sales projected to top $1 billion by 1995. "Nearly everyone has something nice to say about the new treatment,"[60] the article gushed, before concluding:

> *We're only beginning to fathom the mind's exquisite chemistry... Who knows? Maybe wit and insight will eventually come in capsule form. For now, the good news is that afflicted people are escaping their torment.*[61]

Three days later, an article singing the praises of Lilly's new wonder drug appeared in the *New York Times*. Titled "New Antidepressant is Acclaimed but Not Perfect," the article noted that Prozac had already become the most widely prescribed antidepressant in America, despite its selling price of $1.50 a pill, several times more than that of any competing drug. Then, after informing readers "All antidepressants work by restoring the balance of neurotransmitter activity in the brain," the piece concluded with these words of reassurance from an eminent doctor:

> *Prozac is not like alcohol or Valium. If you take penicillin but you don't have pneumonia, it won't do anything for you.*[62]

## Being Tortured from the Inside Out

Not everyone was so sanguine about all this. On 10 February 1990, a few weeks before the *Newsweek* cover story came out, Martin Teicher and his colleagues at the Harvard Medical School published a paper in the *American Journal of Psychiatry* describing six case histories of patients who developed intense, violent suicidal preoccupation after starting Prozac.[63] None of the patients was suicidal when he or she began taking the drug, none of them could articulate why he or she felt that way, and in every case the suicidal preoccupation disappeared shortly after discontinuing Prozac. Teicher and his co-authors asserted that this syndrome developed in 3.5% of patients given the drug.

In February of the following year, researchers at the State University of New York Health Science Center described two patients who became suicidal after starting Prozac.[64] A twenty-eight-year-old woman had recurrent suicidal thoughts and fantasized about jumping out a window. A fifty-eight-year-old man tried to hang himself with a rope. Neither of these patients had any prior history of mania, hypomania, or suicidal ideation or behaviors, and in both cases the suicidal obsession ceased soon after Prozac was stopped.

The next month, researchers at the Yale University Child Study Center reported six cases of children, three boys and three girls all between the ages of ten and seventeen, who exhibited emergent suicidality or self-harm after being started on Prozac for obsessive-compulsive disorder. One twelve-year-old boy experienced a violent nightmare of murdering his classmates until he himself was shot. He awakened with difficulty, and even afterward the dream continued to feel "very real" to him.

Subsequently he became depressed and suffered obsessional thoughts of hurting himself. The Prozac was stopped and these obsessional feelings gradually dissipated. He was re-started on Prozac, and the suicidal feelings returned again. He was taken off Prozac and put on the tricyclic antidepressant clomipramine, and the suicidal feelings went away once more.[65]

In August, a young psychiatrist at North Wales Hospital named David Healy published an account of a sixty-seven-year-old man who developed intense suicidal preoccupation sixteen days after starting Prozac. The patient had decided to throw himself into a quarry, and left the house only to return five hours later, claiming that the only thing that prevented him from carrying out his plan was his inability to find a suitable location.[66]

For the next five days he was tormented by images of slashing his own wrists or electrocuting himself by means of inserting a pair of scissors into the electric mains with one hand while holding on to a grounded metal tap with the other. The following morning he arose and decided to put an end to it all by drowning himself. The sea was shallow and he had to walk out several hundred yards before he reached neck depth, at which point he changed his mind and walked back. The Prozac was discontinued, and he was released two weeks later "fully recovered." He was not able to provide any explanation for these destructive thoughts and behaviors.[67]

That December, Anthony Rothschild and Carol A. Locke, also of the Harvard Medical School, published an account of three patients (all of whom had a previous history of suicide attempts or suicidal ideation) who made serious suicide attempts while taking Prozac.[68] A twenty-five-year-old woman jumped off a roof and sustained a subdural hematoma and compound fractures of her arms and legs. A forty-seven-year-old man jumped off a cliff but his fall was broken by a tree and he sustained "only" a minor concussion. A thirty-four-year-old woman jumped off a roof; her fall was broken by a balcony and she sustained "only" a fractured femur.

In each case the symptoms disappeared when Prozac was discontinued, and re-appeared when the drug was resumed. In two of these cases, the drug was resumed a second time, and the addition of the drug propranolol, which is known to antagonize the action of Prozac, caused the feelings of agitation and suicidality to abate.[69]

In the conclusion, the authors stated:

*Patients need to be reassured that the overwhelming symptoms being experienced are side effects of the medication and are treatable. Our patients had concluded that their illness had taken such a dramatic turn for the worse that life was no longer worth living.*[70]

In July of the following year, researchers at the West Los Angeles Medical Center reported cases histories of five patients, all women, none of whom had a history of significant suicidal behavior, and all of whom experienced uncontrollable agitation, or akathisia, along with suicidal thoughts after starting Prozac.[71] In each of the five cases the akathisia and suicidal ideation stopped after discontinuing the drug.[72]

"Akathisia feels like you are being tortured from the inside out," psychiatrist Peter Breggin once told me. "People often can't find the words to describe how it feels."

The *Diagnostic and Statistical Manual IV*, the American Psychiatric Association's official catalog of psychiatric disorders, recognizes akathisia as a risk factor for suicide.[73] Another pernicious feature of this condition is that patients can easily mistake this condition for a resurgence of their mental illness, rather than a drug effect.[74]

In many of these cases in the aforementioned studies, patients were started on a standard twenty milligram dose of Prozac, and the violent agitation and suicidality either first appeared or became worse after the dose was titrated upwards to two or three times that.

In short, several lines of evidence all pointed to a cause-and-effect relationship between Prozac and violent suicidal agitation.[75] The effect appeared after the drug was administered (challenge), disappeared when the drug was discontinued (dechallenge), and re-appeared upon re-exposure to the drug (rechallenge). The relationship between the drug and its purported effect was dose-dependent, and the suicidal agitation was reversed by antidote. Moreover, the plausibility of these studies was supported by the fact that all came from eminent investigators in the field, from several different institutions—eliminating the possibility that these results stemmed from the bias of one researcher or even one center.

These researchers included some of the most senior names in clinical psychopharmacology. These were men and women who had seen depression and agitation and suicidality before. It was obvious from the urgent tone of these articles that this was something new, something that demanded an explanation.

## That's All Gone

On 21 September the FDA held a one-day hearing on the link between Prozac and suicidal and homicidal violence. By that time, defendants in at least twenty criminal cases had pled insanity on the grounds that they had been under the influence of the drug at the time they committed their crimes, and the FDA had received over 14,000 adverse event reports concerning the drug—including 500 suicides.[76]

The atmosphere at the hearing was tense. The chairman, Daniel Casey, showed up wearing a bulletproof vest.[77] One witness after another got up and told heartbreaking stories of loved ones lost to suicidal and homicidal violence:

> MELINDA HARRIS: *"Unfortunately with my dad we didn't have time to notice too many changes, except that he became withdrawn and agitated. But by that time it was too late. He got up at nine o'clock in the morning, took a twelve-inch butcher knife out of the kitchen drawer and stabbed himself violently in the abdomen once, and then proceeded to do it twice."[78]*

> MARIA MALAKOFF: *"My husband just committed suicide four months and 20 days ago in front of our four kids and myself… He came back on April 30th and he just blew his brains out in front of all of us."[79]*

DAVID MONEYMAKER: *"I had two sons: David Lee, age eight, and Billy, sixteen, a wife of 20 years, but that's all gone. I'll tell you why... After being on Prozac for 21 days, my wife shot and killed both of these two boys right there. She turned the gun to herself and shot herself twice. Now she's in jail for murder."*[80]

SUSAN WILLIAMS: *"My sister did commit suicide in front of [her daughter] Lindsey. Another woman [at the hearing today] spoke of hollow-point bullets. That's what my sister used... My sister never would have killed herself in front of this little girl. She would never have done that. Prozac induced her to do that."*[81]

Despite this testimony, after the hearing a panel of expert advisors voted six to three that there was no sound evidence that Prozac or any other antidepressant drug caused suicidal or violent behavior.[82] Interestingly, the panel was not asked to vote on whether there was any evidence that Prozac or any other antidepressants *decreased* the rate of suicide.

Five of the nine members of the panel had received waivers allowing them to participate, despite their ties to the drug companies.[83]

Afterwards, Paul Leber, Head of the Central Nervous System Division of the FDA, advised Lilly to carry out an experimental study to assess definitively whether Prozac causes suicidality. Lilly representatives met with the FDA several times to discuss the matter further, and the protocols were drawn up, but the proposed study was never carried out.[84]

### Straw Men

The backlash to the backlash began even before the FDA hearing took place. On 8 July 1991, *Forbes* published a diatribe titled "Junk Science in the Courtroom" by author Peter Huber.[85] The essay was a masterpiece of guilt-by-association, beginning with Huber's opening salvo: "Ever wonder about Princess Di's recent affair with Elvis Presley?" He then tells his readers about the jury that awarded $1 million to a psychic after she claimed a CAT scan destroyed her clairvoyant abilities (an appalling decision, to be sure, but one that was overturned by the judge) before getting down to business:

> *A tentative (and cautiously phrased report), based on observations on a total of six patients, suggested a possible link between Prozac, a widely used antidepressant, and an increase in suicidal tendencies.[86]*

Huber goes on to attack biological psychiatry's favorite straw man opponent:

> *But trial lawyers, in a bizarre alliance with the Church of Scientology, have launched a huge campaign to smear Prozac and its manufacturer, Lilly, and to drum up litigation.[87]*

Huber bemoans the abandonment of the Frye Rule, that required an expert witness to report only views that are generally accepted in the scientific community, and blasts the "charlatans" apparently running amok in the courtrooms of America, likening their views to those of witch hunters in the Middle Ages, to Lysenkoism in the Soviet Union under Stalin, and to the "junk science of the Nazis." He implores judges to "look toward consensus in the scientific community"[88]—apparently unaware that Lysenkoism and the junk science of the Nazis *were* the "consensus in the scientific community" in their respective nations at the time—and that much of the junk science of the Nazis was manufactured by psychiatrists, possessed of impeccable academic credentials, and national and even international reputations.[89]

One month later, the *Saint Petersburg Times* published a letter from Lilly company official E.A. West, who also attacked biological psychiatry's number one straw man:

> *For nearly two years, the Church of Scientology had focused its longstanding vendetta against psychiatry and psychotropic drugs*

*on the antidepressant Prozac... This fringe group has repeatedly misrepresented scientific studies of Prozac during its campaign to discourage people from seeking psychiatric treatment they desperately need.[90]*

West goes on to kick over a couple more straw men, asserting:

*Moreover, it appears that many depressed patients have simply chosen not to seek any treatment for this life-threatening disorder that has long been the subject of social ridicule. The Scientologists seemed to be realizing their goal of restigmatizing a disease that affects millions of Americans.[91]*

All this begs the questions of whether antidepressant treatment lowers the death rate for this "life-threatening disorder"—and whether stigma is reduced by claims that depressed people have a "disease" which can and should be treated with brain-altering drugs. In fact, since the time that West authored this missive, a mountain of empirical evidence has accumulated showing that such claims increase stigma.[92]

The very same day the FDA hearings took place, a piece appeared in *BMJ* titled "Fluoxetine and Suicide: A Meta-Analysis of Controlled Trials of Treatment for Depression."[93] Authored by Charles Beasley and eight other Lilly employees, the article reviewed evidence from seventeen double-blind clinical trials involving 3,065 patients and concluded that Prozac did not cause an increase in suicidal ideation, suicidal acts, or completed suicides (the authors reported that there was one completed suicide in the trials, during the placebo washout period).[94]

The year 1993 saw the release of *Listening to Prozac* by psychiatrist Peter Kramer, who reeled off a series of anecdotes about patients who found this marvelous drug made them "better than well."[95] Dr. Kramer recounted his astonishment at learning how the effects of these pills extended to "social popularity, business acumen, self-image, energy, flexibility, sexual appeal..."[96] and coined the term "cosmetic psychopharmacology"[97] for these astounding transformations. While never explicitly claiming these outcomes were typical, Kramer did very little to disabuse readers of that notion. The book became an international best-seller.

In February of the following year, *Newsweek* weighed in with another cover story with the provocative title, "One Pill Makes You Larger, and One Pill Makes You Small," which offered readers these words of wisdom:

> *It's gone beyond Prozac. Now the same scientific insights that led to the development of Prozac are raising the prospect of made-to-order, off-the-shelf personalities.*[98]

The article went on to discuss a new drug-in-development said to improve learning and memory in rats and then, going preposterously beyond the available evidence, burbled "Who could criticize a drug that stamps the rules for long division into your child's head after a single lesson?"[99]

## A Poisonous Atmosphere

Meanwhile, a rash of lawsuits had been filed against Lilly, alleging that company's blockbuster drug had been the cause of violence and suicide. These lawsuits were combined into one huge multidistrict case, and Paul Smith, a forty-five-year-old trial lawyer from Dallas, emerged as the lead counsel.[100] Psychiatrist Peter Breggin was retained as an expert witness for the plaintiffs.[101] Dr. Breggin had already risen to national prominence with his book *Toxic Psychiatry: Why Therapy, Empathy, and Love Must Replace the Drugs, Electroshock, and Biochemical Theories of the "New Psychiatry"*[102] and he was a frequent guest on talk shows. But at that point he had had very little experience in the courtroom.

The first of these cases to go to trial was *Fentress v Lilly*, filed by the survivors of the Standard Gravure massacre. The plaintiffs knew they had an uphill battle ahead of them. As Paul Smith himself said, "It was Lilly's best case of the bunch, and our worst."[103] The shooter, Joseph Wesbecker, had been a troubled and troubling figure, with a history of violence and personal problems that began long before he had ever heard of Prozac.

His was a hardscrabble upbringing—his father died when he was just a year old, and his grandfather, who had stepped into the role of father figure for young Joseph, died just a year after that, leaving his mother to care for him as best as she could. For a time they stayed in the home of his maternal grandmother, along with his mother's nine brothers and sisters. At the age of six, Joseph watched as his grandmother was taken away to a mental hospital; the boy never saw his grandmother again. His own mother was diagnosed with depression and given electroshock treatment, and Joseph himself spent part of his childhood in an orphanage.[104]

Joseph had a history of behavioral problems and poor academic performance. He sometimes carried a starter pistol to intimidate people, and he and a friend were accused of pointing that gun at two girls while two of their friends had sex with the girls. Joseph was convicted and, at the age of sixteen, sentenced to six weeks in adult prison. He denied the charges, and was pardoned after serving just a few days. Joseph ended up dropping out of school, although he did later earn his GED.[105]

As a grown man, Joe Wesbecker tried to make a go out of being a solid citizen, and for a while he succeeded. He went to work as a pressman, learning his trade and working hard, marrying and fathering two children. He saved and invested his money, and accumulated a sizeable nest egg.

But then his first marriage ended in divorce, and then his second marriage ended the same way. He attempted suicide at least twice. His older son suffered from scoliosis, and the younger one had a history of exposing himself sexually and threatening suicide. In addition, Wesbecker found himself engaged in bitter and prolonged legal wrangling with his first ex-wife.[106]

Meanwhile, the printing trade was suffering the same maladies that seemed to be affecting every category of blue-collar job, jobs that once were a source of pride and stability to millions of American men: corporate takeovers and concomitant raiding of pension funds, pay freezes, massive downsizing, and punishing workloads for those who remained. Three pressmen now were operating presses that used to be manned by ten, and sixty-four-hour work weeks were routine. In his book *The Power to Harm*, author John Cornwell describes the pit of misery Standard Gravure had become: rampant drug and alcohol abuse, harassment, intimidation, vandalism, and fistfights. The atmosphere had become so poisonous pressmen were bringing guns to work and openly threatening each other.[107]

The atmosphere may have been poisonous in another way, literally so, due to the chemicals used in the plant. Wesbecker himself became convinced that toluene, a solvent employed in the printing process, had caused long-term brain damage to himself and his fellow workers.[108]

Wesbecker had been under the care of the psychiatric profession going back at least as far as 1984, and over the years he had been prescribed a veritable cornucopia of medications. Towards the end of his tenure at Standard Gravure, he began neglecting his appearance and personal hygiene, and he spoke of using a model airplane loaded with explosives to ignite the vast stores of chemical solvents and blow the place to smithereens.[109]

By 6 August 1988, his last day of work, it was obvious to those around him that Wesbecker was cracking up. Someone had even placed a sign on a company bulletin board: "Problems? Call Wesbecker—585-NUTS." Two days after Wesbecker's last day on the job, his new psychiatrist, Lee Coleman, diagnosed him with schizoaffective disorder.[110]

Wesbecker applied for long-term disability payments and was awarded $391.21 per month, from which $78.00 would be deducted for health insurance. By May of 1989, Dr. Coleman was maintaining him on a cocktail of Lithium, Trazadone, Restoril, Halcion, and Soma.[111]

On 10 August of that year, at the behest of Dr. Coleman, Wesbecker started taking a drug released just the year before, called Prozac. Wesbecker had actually tried the new drug the previous year, but had discontinued it after only a couple of days. Wesbecker's second ex-wife, who still slept with him occasionally, noticed the drug changed him; he seemed more fidgety and would get up in the middle of the night and pace around.[112]

Just over a month after starting Prozac, Wesbecker returned to Dr. Coleman's office in an agitated state, telling his doctor the new drug had helped him to "remember" an incident that took place a year before, in which Wesbecker had been forced to perform oral sex on his foreman while his co-workers watched. Wesbecker sobbed uncontrollably after relating this bizarre story.[113]

No such incident ever took place. Wesbecker was clearly delusional by this point. Alarmed, Dr. Coleman urged his patient to check into a mental hospital, but Wesbecker refused. Coleman then asked him to discontinue the Prozac, and to return the following week.[114]

Three days after that, the Standard Gravure massacre took place.

Wesbecker had a lot of problems over the years, but never had he become frankly psychotic until he began taking Lilly's blockbuster drug. On the other hand, the plaintiffs' case was complicated by one obvious fact: Prozac had not been the only toxic influence in Joe Wesbecker's life.

Moreover, the plaintiff's attorneys were seriously outgunned. They were facing a company with projected revenues of $6.5 billion for the year 1995, with $1.7 billion of that expected to come from Prozac. Even bigger sales receipts were expected in the future, now that the drug had been approved for use in over seventy countries.[115]

But at the same time, Lilly had acquired PCS Inc., the largest pharmacy benefits manager in the United States, a bold move but one that left the company with $2.5 billion in debt. The number of Prozac-related lawsuits by this time had swollen to 160, and a victory for the plaintiffs could result in Lilly being swamped with lawsuits.[116] This was a case Lilly could not afford to lose, and they went at it with everything they had.

Attorneys for Lilly interviewed nearly 400 witnesses who had known Wesbecker in one way or another, a process that took four years, with some depositions going on for as long as three to four days, assembling what may be the largest file ever assembled on a spree killer, looking for anything in Wesbecker's life to point the finger at besides Prozac.[117]

As Cornwell remarks, there was a certain irony in these tactics being employed by a pharmaceutical company that had amassed a fortune by promoting a paradigm that seemed to view the patient not so much an individual person with a history than as a bag of neurochemicals. There was also irony in the company going to such lengths to attack the very patient for whom their drug had once been prescribed to help.[118]

But Smith had a potential ace in the hole. In 1985, Lilly was charged by the US Department of Justice for failing to report four deaths and six additional cases of serious illness resulting from its new anti-inflammatory drug, Oraflex. Lilly's Chief Medical Officer, William Shedden, pleaded guilty to fifteen misdemeanor counts and could have received a maximum of fifteen years in prison. In fact, he served no time, and the company paid a fine of $25,000.[119] Attorneys for the defendants had argued in pre-trial motions that testimony regarding the Oraflex incident would be inflammatory and prejudicial to Lilly, and Judge John Potter agreed, but Smith knew if he could ever find a way to introduce the Oraflex evidence, this could turn out to be the chink in Lilly's armor that could lead to the company's undoing.

### Ad Hominem Attacks

The trial began on Monday 26 September 1994—almost exactly five years after Wesbecker's murderous rampage. In his opening statement on Friday 30 September, Lead Counsel Paul Smith laid the foundation for his case against Lilly:

> *The FDA didn't test Prozac. Food and Drug Administration didn't test Prozac, the National Institute of Mental Health didn't test Prozac. The Centers for Disease Control didn't test Prozac.*

*Lilly and Company tested Prozac. The inventor of the drug, the proponent of the application for food and drug approval tested the drug. What I mean by that is that Lilly invented the drug, Lilly designed the test that would be performed on the drug. Lilly chose the investigators who would test the drug. Lilly chose the sites where the drug would be tested. Lilly set up the rules and guidelines for what people could be included in the test. The tests were conducted exclusively by Lilly. The trial process was done by Lilly at their guidance, direction and control.*

Clearly, Smith was trying to goad the other side into asserting Lilly's trustworthiness in such matters—giving him an opening to introduce the Oraflex evidence.

On Sunday 2 October, the day before trial testimony began, a candlelight vigil was held in front of the courthouse by self-described sufferers of depression. One of the protestors told a reporter "We hope this lawsuit doesn't take our drug away."[120]

That same day, an article appeared in the *New York Times Magazine* titled "Good Health: Out of the Darkness." The piece began by bashing Dr. Breggin, expert witness for the plaintiffs, accusing him of "sleight of hand" in claiming in his book *Talking Back to Prozac*[121] (which he co-authored with his wife, Ginger Breggin) that the benefits of antidepressants were wildly exaggerated:

*The probability that these effects are due to chance, as the Breggins claim, is less than one's chance, on the average day, of being struck by lightning.*[122]

In fact the Breggins made no such claim. What they said was that the purported benefits of antidepressants in clinical trials are virtually indistinguishable from those of placebo—and subsequent research has borne out this claim in spades.[123]

The remainder of the article consisted of a love letter to Prozac in particular and antidepressants in general:

*Medical science does have much more to learn about these drugs, and research continues. Meanwhile, a formerly suicidal elderly man takes some real pleasure in every day; a young mother who became obsessively afraid to leave her home within weeks after her baby was born is freed from her mental prison; an addict is able to stop using cocaine.*[124]

We are never told whether these are accounts of actual human beings or fictional "composite cases." There then follows the single most self-revealing sentence in the entire piece:

*New [beneficial] effects of the drugs are reported so frequently that one hesitates to mention them for fear of sounding like a hawker of snake oil.*[125]

After this the author goes on to tout the benefits of antidepressants for long-distance runners and household pets, and then describes the salubrious effects he himself has experienced:

*One time of day I am reminded of the medicine is when I first wake up and stumble out of the driveway to pick up the newspaper... I am as troubled as ever by the news, but I am more likely to do something, like call a senator or send a few dollars to Rwanda.*[126]

Apparently even starving children in Third-World hellholes are reaping the benefits of these new miracle drugs.

One week after the *NYT* piece ran, an article appeared in *Time* which also painted a largely unflattering portrait of Dr. Breggin, beginning with the tag line "His critics say he's crazy." The piece went on to inform readers:

*For the past few decades, researchers have worked to show that psychiatric disorders are triggered by chemical imbalances in the brain that can be rectified with medication. Breggin, by contrast, clings to an old-fashioned view: the emotional problems that land a person on a psychiatrist's couch result from traumas caused by outside forces, like sexual abuse during childhood...*

*This bizarre notion take no account of mountains of evidence to the contrary. But, like a slick lawyer, Breggin has answers for every argument.[127]*

Since then a mountain of evidence has accumulated demonstrating that serious mental illness is indeed the product of traumas caused by outside forces, like sexual abuse during childhood.[128]

The article also blasted Dr. Breggin for claiming that the shrunken brains observed in schizophrenics is due to the action of so-called antipsychotic drugs. Again, since then a mountain of evidence has accumulated demonstrating that Breggin was absolutely right.[129]

Why the sudden full-court press in the mainstream media to discredit the plaintiff's expert witness? The *Time* article itself gives us a hint:

*Breggin has infuriated Prozac's manufacturer, Lilly, prompting the firm to deluge journalists with material intended to discredit the maverick psychiatrist.[130]*

## A Substantial Factor

On 17 October, while cross-examining Lilly's Chief Scientific Officer Leigh Thompson, Lead Counsel Paul Smith introduced into the evidence a memo written to Thompson by Claude Bouchy, head of the German affiliate of Lilly, concerning Lilly's instructions to code suicide attempts as "overdoses" and suicidal ideation as "depression":

*I do not think I could explain to the BGA [the Bundesgesundheitsamt, or the German equivalent of the FDA] to a judge, to a reporter, or even to my family why we would do this, especially on*

*the sensitive issue of suicide and suicidal ideation, at least not with*
*the explanations that have been given to our staff so far.*

Dr. Thompson tried to explain away this memo as merely an attempt to reconcile two different coding systems of two different countries, but it was obvious from Bouchy's anguished tone that this was about something more than a mere bookkeeping matter.

Then Dr. Breggin took the stand. Step by step, he laid out the case against a company which persistently ignored the warning signs that its miracle drug in fact had a stimulant profile very similar to that of amphetamines or PCP.

He began with the animal testing back in the 1970's. Cats given the drug began to hiss and growl, and dogs became markedly aggressive. One perturbed pooch bit a technician attempting to give it its daily dose.

In one of the Phase I studies, a doctor administered the drug to just two patients. One of the two became suicidal and was placed on neuroleptic medication. In Phase II testing, the drug was given to seventy-seven patients, and five had serious clinical events including one case of manic psychosis, and one case of paranoid psychosis (just as Wesbecker had after starting the drug).

Clinicians working for Lilly authorized the use of tranquilizers (benzodiazepines or chloral hydrate) in Phase III trials to try to control the agitation caused by Prozac. Somewhere between a third and a half of patients in the Phase III trials ended up getting tranquilizers. Moreover, when these patients were dropped from the analysis, there was no difference between the effects of the drug and those of placebo. In effect, what the FDA ended up approving was not Prozac but a combination of Prozac and tranquilizers.

Dr. Breggin noted that FDA psychiatrist Richard Kapit advised the agency that the most common toxic effects of Prozac were anxiety, nervousness, insomnia, dizziness, and nausea. "With the exception of dizziness," Breggin added, "That's your typical amphetamine profile."

Dr. Breggin tallied up the results: thirty-eight percent of patients on Prozac experienced agitation, as opposed to nineteen percent on placebo. In addition, 1.2 percent of those of Prozac suffered from mania, as opposed to only 0.3 percent on comparator drugs and none on placebo. These alarming results become even more alarming in light of the facts that 1) this was with the use of concomitant use of tranquilizers, and 2) patients with a diagnosis of manic depression or bipolar disorder (like Joe Wesbecker) were excluded from these trials.

Dr. Breggin noted that Dr. Kapit had recommended to the FDA that the prescribing information for Prozac include a warning that the drug could cause worsening depression in some patients. This recommendation was not implemented.

Even more damning, Dr. Breggin reported that Lilly's own investigators reported twelve suicide attempts for patients given Prozac in Phase III trials, as opposed to two for those on comparator drugs and one on placebo, and that six of the twelve Prozac-associated suicide attempts were re-classified as something less serious by the company.

Dr. Breggin also discussed concerns by German regulators that the drug had an amphetamine-like profile. Ultimately the drug was approved for use in that country, but the prescribing information included a warning that patients should be watched for signs of suicidality during the first few weeks of treatment and might need concomitant tranquilizing medication.

Dr. Breggin's final assessment: Prozac was a "substantial factor" in the Standard Gravure massacre, and that Lilly was negligent in not fully informing the FDA and the public about the hazards of the drug.

## Blind Faith

After that, Lilly brought in a phalanx of eminently credentialed experts—doctors, professors, neuroscientists—in an effort to discredit Dr. Breggin's testimony. The last of these was Paul Granacher, a board-certified forensic psychiatrist from Lexington, Kentucky, whose testimony began Thursday, 1 December. Prozac, in Dr. Granacher's expert opinion, "is perfectly safe and acceptable for use in the treatment of depression in human beings," and "played no role whatsoever in the actions that Joseph Wesbecker took at Standard Gravure."

Dr. Granacher's testimony continued on Tuesday 6 December:

> *Antidepressants uniformly reduce violence. They don't increase violence.*
>
> *There is not a single medical article in all the world literature of the advanced nations that do this kind of research: Europe, Soviet Union, Japan, United States, Australia, New Zealand, South America, that shows that any antidepressant has ever caused homicides in any human being on this planet, not a single medical article stating that.*
>
> *Every antidepressant ever developed to be used in a human being uniformly reduces aggression…*

During cross-examination, the following exchange took place between Lead Counsel Paul Smith and Dr. Granacher:

> PAUL SMITH: *It wasn't interesting to you as to who was used in the clinical trials, what group of patients were used?*
>
> DR. GRANACHER: *No, sir. It's an FDA-approved drug. I don't need to know that.*
>
> PAUL SMITH: *You base your blind faith on the FDA?*
>
> DR. GRANACHER: *They've forgotten more about approving drugs that I ever knew.*
>
> PAUL SMITH: *And your blind faith in Lilly's character and reputation in reporting the accuracy of these trials to the FDA?*

DR. GRANACHER: *I don't have any opinions about Lilly. I have opinion about what the FDA said about Lilly's product and whether or not it was approved for use in humans. And if the FDA approved it, that's good enough for me.*

As questioning continued, Smith established that Dr. Granacher had not seen any of Lilly's in-house data collected during the development of Prozac, then asked:

PAUL SMITH: *Would it be interesting for you to know that in 1984, the BGA had reservations regarding the CNS side effects of Prozac, that there had been patients complaining of psychosis and hallucinations?*

Edward Stopher asked to approach the bench, and complained that Dr. Granacher was unfairly being questioned about documents he had never seen. Judge Potter dismissed the jury for lunch and the hearing continued in the judge's chambers.

Smith argued that by saying "If it's good enough for the FDA, it's good enough for me," Dr. Granacher had opened the door to the Oraflex evidence that he had sought since the beginning of the trial. Judge Potter cautioned Smith that he was still enjoined from introducing that evidence, but added that he would consider allowing him to do so.

Back in the courtroom, Smith continued his cross-examination of Dr. Granacher, confronting him with company memos and BGA documents stating the drug caused hostility and suicidality in depressed patients, along with the BGA's 1984 assessment that Prozac was "totally unsuitable" for treatment of depression. Granacher stuck by his position that the FDA knew best, and afterwards Judge Potter dismissed the jurors for the day and once again met with counsel for both sides in his chambers.

By that time Smith's voice was failing him, due to a bout of flu, but his assistant, Nancy Zettler, argued forcefully for the introduction of the Oraflex evidence:

*Clearly, Lilly has opened the door for this evidence. Its purpose is to rebut their constant, with just about every witness they've put on who's not a layperson, injection of testimony as to Lilly's glowing reputation within the scientific community as well as within the FDA.*

*The other purpose for the Oraflex evidence is that it demonstrates that the FDA is not the be-all and end-all of determining a drug's safety and efficacy.*

*Their major defense in this case is that the FDA approved this drug.*

*A lot of this stuff with Oraflex is the exact type of thing that happened in this case; that they had things from outside the United States that they simply did not report to the FDA until they were caught.*

Stopher threatened to move for a mistrial if the Oraflex evidence was introduced. Judge Potter ruled against him, but he gave Stopher time to file a writ of mandamus to the Kentucky Supreme Court to block the evidence from being introduced.

The following morning was taken up with rebuttal evidence not connected to the Oraflex case. Then Judge Potter order a short recess, which unexpectedly lasted the rest of the day.[131] The next day attorneys for both side met with Potter in chambers. Had Smith and Zettler finally obtained the opening in the company's defenses they had sought for so long? Was this checkmate for Eli Lilly?

## With Prejudice

Lead Counsel Paul Smith began by informing Judge Potter that both sides had agreed to waive the introduction of any more evidence in the case and go directly to the closing arguments, reserving the Oraflex evidence for the penalty phase of the trial, assuming there was one. Potter then asked for a discussion off the record.

What happened next depends on whose version of events you believe. Judge Potter says he asked if any money had changed hands, and everyone present denied it. Other participants later gave different versions of that conversation. At any rate, Potter brought the jurors in for their final instructions before the closing arguments, and then dismissed them until the following morning.

Back in Judge Potter's chambers, Edward Stopher demanded that Dr. Breggin's testimony be stricken from the record, citing the 1993 US Supreme Court *Daubert* ruling that expert testimony be restricted to theories that are "generally accepted in the scientific community." Nancy Zettler forcefully countered that that point had already been argued during the pre-trial phase, and Potter denied the motion.

The closing arguments were delivered on Friday 9 December. The following Monday, the jury returned its verdict: Prozac played no role in the Standard Gravure Massacre. The vote was nine to three, the bare minimum required by Kentucky law to avoid a mistrial.

The next day, Eli Lilly's stock price closed at $62.63, up one dollar from the day before. One of Lilly's lawyers told the Louisville *Courier-Journal* "We feel like this is a complete vindication of the drug."[132]

On 25 January of the following year, Potter entered the final judgement: the case was dismissed "with prejudice," meaning it could not be re-opened.[133]

But that was not the end of the story.

## A Serious Lack of Candor

As rumors swirled around him, Judge Potter became increasingly suspicious that something rotten was in the air. On 19 April of the following year, he published a motion to change the verdict from "dismissed" to "settled," and he ordered lawyers for both sides to attend "show cause" hearing before the Kentucky Court of Appeals to determine if there had been a secret settlement. The two erstwhile opposing teams joined forces, and retained the services of a local law firm to try to block the hearing.[134]

The hearing was held on 8 June. In a document filed with the court, Judge Potter asserted "Lilly sought to buy not just the verdict, but the court's judgement as well." Nevertheless, a week later the court issued a writ of prohibition, ruling that Judge Potter did not have the authority to order a hearing on the matter.[135] Undaunted, he appealed to the Kentucky Supreme Court.

A Friend of the Court brief filed by Judge Potter asserted that there had been a secret agreement between the two sides. In exchange for not presenting the Oraflex evidence, the plaintiffs would be paid a certain sum (or a "sum certain," in lawyerse) in three annual installments. The size of that sum was never publicly disclosed, but a lawyer representing one of the plaintiffs in an unrelated divorce case said "The amount boggles the mind."[136] The agreement also stipulated that neither side would appeal the verdict, and that the plaintiffs must never publicly acknowledge the existence of the agreement.

Smith had told Judge Potter in chambers that he wanted to reserve the Oraflex evidence for the penalty phase of the trial. But there never would have been a penalty phase to this trial, since both sides had already agreed on a settlement, win or lose. And two of the jurors John Cornwell spoke to after the trial were furious when they learned that evidence had been withheld from them, asserting it probably would have made a "huge difference" in the outcome.[137]

On 23 May 1996 the Kentucky Supreme Court dissolved the writ of prohibition, declaring "In this case, there was a serious lack of candor with the trial court and there may have been deception, bad faith conduct, abuse of the judicial process and even fraud."

Armed with this new ruling, Judge Potter set a hearing to take sworn testimony regarding the secret settlement for 27 March 1997. But, the scheduled hearing never took place. On 24 March, lawyers for both the plaintiffs and the defendants presented Potter with a new motion showing the case was dismissed "as settled." Three days later Judge Potter dismissed himself from the case, stating that "the focus should be on the log, not on the person trying to roll it over."[138]

The trial itself had been largely overshadowed by the concurrent O.J. Simpson media circus, and this coda went virtually unnoticed by the mainstream media.

Nearly twenty-five years after the verdict in *Fentress v Lilly* had been handed down, Dr. Breggin discussed the case with me:

> *If Wesbecker hadn't been put on Prozac, there's no reason to believe he would have become a mass murderer. He did have violent thoughts toward people at work, but it didn't rise to the level of psychosis until Prozac pushed him over the edge.*

Dr. Breggin made it clear he did not believe Dr. Coleman was guilty of malpractice:

> *He had no strong reason to suspect that this drug was going to take somebody who was potentially violent and tip him over the edge. So I thought the he conducted himself within the standard of care at the time.*
>
> *But I think if the doctor had not given Prozac this wouldn't have happened, and that the Prozac pushed him over.*

On 11 September 2019, the *Courier-Journal* published a story marking the thirtieth anniversary of the Standard Gravure shooting.[139] The article revealed the size of the settlement: $20 million (worth over $40 million in today's dollars), to be split between the survivors and their lawyers. Two of the victims stated that they had felt compelled to accept the settlement because they had suffered terrible injuries that would have prevented them ever from working again. Nancy Zettler, the plaintiff's attorney who had forcefully argued for the inclusion of the Oraflex evidence, told the *Courier-Journal* that she had not been involved in the settlement but had heard the same figure from two of the plaintiffs. Judge Potter (now retired) declined to comment.

The piece also informed readers, "Prozac is still prescribed across the US and is considered safe if used as directed…"[140]

## A New Phenomenon

On 4 March 1993, sixty-four-year-old William Forsyth of Kaanapali Hillside, Hawaii, took a serrated kitchen knife and stabbed his wife of thirty-seven years to death, inflicting at least fifteen wounds in the process. He then affixed the knife to a stool and impaled himself on the blade, ending his own life. Their grown son discovered their lifeless bodies in a pool of blood later that day. This was ten days after the elder Forsyth had started taking Prozac for his depression.[141]

William Jr., a charter boat captain in Maui, and his sister Susan retained the services of the law firm Baum, Hedlund, Aristei, Guilford, & Downey and filed suit against Lilly. This was only the second Prozac lawsuit to go to trial (*Fentress v Lilly* was the first). Every single one of the others had either been dropped or settled out of court.[142]

Meanwhile, bad news continued to pile up for the drug companies in general and Lilly in particular. In January of 1995, *BMJ* published a study by epidemiologist Herschel Jick and his colleagues that looked at the correlation between antidepressant prescriptions and suicide rates in the United Kingdom. They found that, after controlling for age and sex, the suicide rate for patients in primary care with no history of suicidality who were prescribed Prozac was twice that of those given the tricyclic antidepressant dothiepin, at the time the most widely prescribed antidepressant in the UK.[143] This was worrisome, given that one of the selling points of SSRI antidepressants such as Prozac was that they were safer in overdose, and presumably should have led to a lowering of the suicide rate.

In May of 1997, as *Forsyth v Lilly* was wending its way through the courts, Baum Hedlund contacted psychiatrist David Healy and retained his services as expert witness for their pending case.[144] Dr. Healy, it will be recalled, authored one of the first clinical case histories of Prozac-induced agitation and suicidality.

Around this same time, Dr. Healy conceived of a study that would assess the effect of Zoloft on healthy subjects. Twenty volunteers (nine men and eleven women) were recruited from the staff of the North West Wales District General Hospital Psychiatric Unit. None of these volunteers had a history of psychiatric treatment.[145]

Two of the women given Zoloft developed clear suicidal ideation. One of these women experienced nausea, lethargy, panic, jaw pain, restlessness, and agitation. When the dose was increased, she began fantasizing about hanging herself by the neck from a beam from the bedroom ceiling. She said she never had such thoughts before, and she reported an abnormal lack of concern about the prospect of her loved ones discovering her lifeless corpse. These feelings disappeared completely upon discontinuing the drug.[146]

The other woman fared worse. At first she reported a stiff jaw, nausea, malaise, restlessness, agitation, anxiety, vivid emotions, racing thoughts, and ruminations, followed by recurring nightmares of having her throat slit. Feeling as if she were under the control of some alien force, she decided the only course of action left open to her was to go out and hurl herself in the path of a car or a train. Just as she was about to leave her home, the telephone rang and she snapped out of her suicidal trance.[147]

Months later, these two women were still experiencing distress at how easily they had lost their sense of themselves. Dr. Healy would later estimate the probability of two healthy women with no significant financial, legal, or interpersonal problems becoming suicidal within a two-week period as less than one in a million. Nevertheless, these startling results would be dismissed by experts as mere "anecdotes."[148]

On Tuesday, 9 March of 1999, Dr. Healy was called to testify in *Forsyth v Lilly*. Just as they did with Dr. Breggin in *Fentress v Lilly*, lawyers for the defense argued strenuously that Healy not be allowed to testify, again citing the *Daubert* rule. Again, the judge dismissed their arguments.

Andy Vickery served as Lead Counsel for the plaintiffs. Under his questioning, Dr. Healy began by discussing the Jick study, which showed the suicide rate for patients in primary care treatment for depression taking Prozac was more than twice that of those who were taking the reference antidepressant, dothiepin. This worked out to 189 suicides per 100,000 patient-years. For comparison, the suicide rate for all patients in primary care treatment for depression was 15.8 per 100,000.

In other words, the suicide rate for those taking Prozac was twelve times greater.

The following day, Dr. Healy rendered his expert judgement: 1) Prozac causes some people to become violent, 2) Prozac causes some people to develop akathisia, 3) Prozac-induced akathisia can lead to suicide and violence, and finally 4) Prozac-induced akathisia led directly to the death of Forsyth and his wife.

Dr. Healy went on to discuss the importance of the controlled clinical case studies by Teicher and others in establishing the link between Prozac and violence:

> *What was reported and what the court needs to bear in mind, what was so striking for those of us from the outside when we read the report was clearly you had very, very senior people who knew what depression was like, who knew what suicidal ideation in people who were depressed was like, we know suicidal ideation happens in the case of people who were depressed, but what we are witnessing here is something new that we have not seen before, not to this degree, not this intensity... I do not think you would get senior psychiatrists of this kind interested to write an article just about*

*depressed people being suicidal. This would not be research news.*
*They were reporting what they believed to be a new phenomenon.*

The day after that, Dr. Healy noted that Prozac usually is not prescribed to patients who are severely depressed—the ones most likely to commit suicide. The twelve-fold increase in suicide with Prozac was, if anything, an underestimate.

He also noted that the ferocity with which Forsyth dispatched his wife was not of the sort seen in cases of premeditated murder, but it was perfectly consistent with a state of drug-induced agitation, the kind Prozac had been found to produce.

During cross-examination, the attorney for Lilly hammered away at the plaintiffs' expert witness, trying to blow up every challenge and change of circumstances the elder Forsyth had encountered in late middle age as evidence of his raging pathology, but Dr. Healy stood firm.

Despite all this, the jury in the case found Lilly not guilty. Noting that over thirty-five million people worldwide had been prescribed Prozac, company spokesman Edward West told a reporter "Medicine doesn't enjoy that type of use unless it's both safe and effective."[149]

### Lines of Evidence

In September, Dr. Healy attended a meeting of the European College of Neuropsychopharmacology in London, in which two separate presenters reported that the rate of suicide attempts for patients on SSRI's was three times that for those on older types of antidepressants. Extrapolating from these figures, Healy calculated that, out of forty million people worldwide who had taken Prozac, this would amount to 40,000 extra suicides.[150]

Dr. Healy also checked the FDA's Adverse Event Reporting System, which by October of 1999 had logged over 2,000 Prozac-associated suicides. This system is thought to capture between one and ten percent of adverse drug events, which would indicate somewhere between 20,000 to

200,000 Prozac-associated suicides. In addition, the ratio of male to female suicides was one-to-one instead of the usual three-to-one, indicating that some abnormal factor was cutting across natural responses.[151]

A third line of evidence was the Jick figure of 189 suicides for every 100,000 patients. Set against the background rate of suicide for patients in primary care depressive treatment, this would mean an extra 40,000 or more Prozac-associated suicides.[152]

Data from three different sources converged on three very similar figures, suggesting that Prozac had caused one suicide for every day the drug had been on the market.[153]

Around that same time, Dr. Healy published a piece in the *International Journal of Risk and Safety in Medicine* titled "A Failure to Warn" in which he made use of information revealed in the *Fentress* and *Forsyth* cases to blast the 1991 meta-analysis by Charles Beasley and his colleagues at Eli Lilly, purporting to show that Prozac does not increase the risk of suicide:

> *This analysis covering 3,065 patients, was festooned with eponymous statistical tests and had the appearance of scientific rigour. It later became clear that most Prozac trials had been omitted from the meta-analysis, so that the 3,065 patients had been drawn from a clinical trial database of approximately 27,000 patients, that within the trials analysed, up to 5% of patients had dropped out for akathisia-like symptoms and had been omitted and no mention was made of approximately 198 US and 94 non-US Prozac-associated suicides. No mention was made of the benzodiazepines co-prescribed with fluoxetine to minimise drug-induced agitation.[154]*

The paper had first been rejected by *BMJ*, the same journal that had published the Beasley meta-analysis in the first place.[155]

In March of the following year, Dr. Healy published a piece in the *Hastings Center Report* in which he pointed out that increasing proportion of the clinical trials literature was ghost-written, and as consumption of antidepressants had soared, so had the incidence of depression. By then the estimated incidence of depression had risen from something like fifty people per million to over 100,000 per million, and depression had become the number one cause of disability and economic disadvantage. He also summarized the evidence that Lilly's blockbuster drug drove some people to kill themselves, concluding "Thus there are good grounds to conclude that Prozac can trigger suicidality."[156]

It turned out that Lilly was one of the biggest funders of the Hastings Center, and after the article was published they withdrew their support. The center had the article re-reviewed, and one of the reviewers said Dr. Healy's only mistake was he didn't go far enough in his criticisms.[157]

In April of 2000, a meta-analysis of the risk of suicidality in randomized clinical trials of five antidepressants (not including Prozac) by Arif Khan and his colleagues appeared in *Archives of General Psychiatry*. The rate of completed suicide in patients given antidepressants was twice that of patients given placebo, although the difference did not rise to the customary (but wholly arbitrary) five percent level of significance.[158]

The authors concluded "Our data indicate that depressed patients in clinical trials who are assigned to placebo treatment are not at greater risk for suicide"[159]—rather an odd way of spinning the results, especially given that none of these trials was designed to detect a difference in suicide rates.[160]

Three months later, Dr. Healy presented the results of the healthy volunteer study at the British Association for Psychopharmacology meeting at Cambridge. During the poster session he was approached by Charles Nemeroff, Chair of Psychiatry at Emory University at Atlanta and key opinion leader for the psychopharmaceutical industry, with financial ties to Lilly, Pfizer, SmithKline Beecham, Pharmacia, and Forest Laboratories—

all manufacturers of SSRI's. This was the man who had been profiled on the cover of *The Economics of Neuroscience* as the "Boss of Bosses."[161]

Nemeroff bluntly told Dr. Healy that he would face serious consequences to his career by publicizing such results, adding that in the previous few weeks he had been approached on several occasions and asked if he would testify in legal actions against Healy.[162]

## The Ultimate Insider

On Thursday 30 November of that same year, Dr. Healy addressed the Department of Psychiatry at the University of Toronto, on the occasion of the department's 75th birthday. Healy had already been offered the position of Professor and Head of the Mood and Anxiety Disorders Program within the department's Center for Addiction and Mental Health. David Goldbloom, Physician-in-Chief at the CAMH, had urged him to give his current employer one month's notice rather than three. "We need to get you here within weeks rather than months,"[163] he wrote to Healy in an email.

Indeed, Dr. Healy was in the last stages of obtaining his visa and had already picked out his new office furniture when he gave his talk,[164] titled "Psychopharmacology & the Government of the Self." Some of his remarks follow:

> *Modern pharmaceutical companies and corporations have grown to be the most profitable organisations on the planet. There has been a change from companies run by physicians and chemists to companies run by business managers who rotate in from Big Oil or Big Tobacco. The companies are advised by the same lawyers who advise Big Oil and Big Tobacco and other corporations.*
>
> *In the case of tobacco industry, it now seems clear that the legal advice in the face of the problem of smoking was not to research the hazards of smoking, as to do so would increase the legal liabilities*

*of the corporations involved... And the same lawyers who advise the pharmaceutical corporations are the lawyers for the tobacco corporations...Advice like this would convert prescription-only arrangements into a vehicle to deliver adverse medical consequences with impunity.*

*I happen to believe that Prozac and the other SSRI's can lead to suicide. These drugs may have responsible for one death every day that Prozac has been on the market in North America. In all likelihood many of you will not agree with me on this—you haven't seen the information I have seen. However we can all agree that there has been a controversy about whether there may be a problem or not. What I believe you also have to agree with is the fact that since the controversy blew up there has not been a single piece of research carried out to answer the question of whether Prozac does cause suicide or not. Designed, yes—carried out, no.[165]*

These were strong words indeed. But what was even more startling was the identity of the man who uttered them. This was not someone who could be dismissed as a crank or an outsider. This was someone who had conducted clinical trials for the drug companies, and lectured at symposia organized by the drug companies, and testified as an expert witness on behalf of the drug companies. David Healy was the ultimate insider.

The lecture received the highest rating from audience, which was made up of some 200 people across the board in the Mental Health Services.

Dr. Nemeroff was also at the meeting, and he is known to have spoken later that day to Dr. Goldbloom, Dr. Healy's prospective new boss.[166] When Healy met later that night with Goldbloom, Healy recalls, Goldbloom was "apoplectic."[167]

Dr. Healy later told the CBC, "I saw a man who was more worked up than I've seen almost anyone else before ever. He seemed to me to be at a risk for stroke he was so worked up. It's an extraordinary switch to have happened just during the course of a few hours."[168]

This was all the more surprising, given that Dr. Healy had made no secret about his views on the toxic effects of Prozac and the other SSRI's. He had said many of the same things in his book *The Antidepressant Era*,[169] and furthermore the previous April Dr. Goldbloom had written to him in an email "When the position was offered to you, your views on the toxicity of fluoxetine were well-known."[170]

The following Tuesday, Dr. Healy had been scheduled to give the same lecture at Cornell University. A senior figure in American psychopharmacology called senior figures at that institution, telling them that Healy was "manic-depressive, violent, and a peddler of junk science" and suggesting that the lecture be canceled.[171]

The lecture was held as scheduled, and was received enthusiastically. Dr. Healy then returned to his home in Wales to find an email from Dr. Goldbloom informing him that the job offer at the University of Toronto had been rescinded.[172]

# CHAPTER 3

# THE PAXIL ERA

### An Effective Drug Treatment

On 13 February 1998, sixty-year-old Donald Schell of Gillette, Wyoming, took two guns and shot his wife and daughter and nine-month-old grand-daughter dead. Each victim took at least three shots to the head. He then turned one of the guns on himself and ended his own life.[173] This was two days after Don Schell had started taking SmithKline Beecham's block-buster drug Paxil.

Paxil is one of several brand names for paroxetine, which like Prozac is a member of class of drugs known as selective serotonin reuptake inhibitors, or SSRI's. In the UK paroxetine is sold under the trade name Seroxat.

Paroxetine was developed in 1975 by the Danish firm Ferrosan, which in 1980 sold the rights to the Beecham Group. In 1989 the Beecham Group merged with SmithKline Beckham to form SmithKline Beecham, which in 2001 merged with Glaxo Wellcome to form GlaxoSmithKline, at the time the largest drug company on the planet.

Paxil was approved by the FDA for treatment of depression at the end of 1992.[174] Before a drug can be approved, the FDA requires drugmakers to submit two controlled studies demonstrating it has significantly greater benefits than those produced by placebo. In the case of Paxil, nine trials had to be performed to get the two positive ones.[175] For some reason, the company never mentioned this fact in its advertising. Nevertheless, in the first year of the new millennium, six years after its launch, Paxil became GSK's first drug to top $1 billion in annual sales.[176]

Meanwhile, Tim Tobin, son-in-law of the late Donald Schell, retained the services of Baum Hedlund and filed suit against GSK. Again Andy Vickery served as Lead Counsel for the plaintiffs, and again Dr. Healy was retained as an expert witness. The trial was scheduled for May of 2001, just a few months after the Center for Addiction and Mental Health at the University of Toronto had rescinded its job offer to Healy, who would later write "I could envisage a situation where my first question on the witness stand would be about being sacked from the University of Toronto... I had little option but to do something."[177]

On 15 February 2001, Dr. Healy wrote to the Chair of the Ethics Committee at the CAMH. He mentioned the events of the previous year, when Lilly withdrew its funding of the Hastings Center after its publication of his article critical of Prozac. Noting that the CAMH also received a great deal of money from Lilly and other drug companies, Healy pointed out that these circumstances had the potential to create bad publicity for the CAMH and the University of Toronto. He also mentioned that he was already scheduled to speak at a meeting in Toronto that April, and that this could provide an opportunity to talk things over before the matter got out of hand.[178]

The Chair of the Ethics Committee didn't even bother to reply.[179]

Dr. Healy contacted the Canadian Association of University Teachers, who wrote to the President of the University of Toronto, expressing their concerns. The President dismissed their concerns out of hand.[180]

The case of *Tobin v SmithKline* began in the US District Court of Cheyenne, Wyoming, on 18 May 2001.[181] Dr. Healy had filed a request months before that to be allowed to review GSK's secret files, but he did not actually gain access to them until two days before he had to file his final report.[182]

Dr. Healy was led to a long room with a series of files containing over a quarter of a million sheets of paper. He later told the BBC "When I saw what I was actually faced with, my heart literally sank, and I had no real idea how I'd be going about trying to find out what I could learn from this."[183]

Nevertheless, Dr. Healy persevered, and on 22 May 2001 he gave his expert opinion to the jury: 1) Paxil caused some patients to become suicidal or homicidal, and 2) Without Paxil, the Tobin family massacre never would have taken place.

Under Andy Vickery's questioning, Dr. Healy walked the jury through the evidence that the SSRI's, Paxil included, caused agitation and violence: clinical case studies, challenge-dechallenge-rechallenge studies, and dose response studies. He went on to describe the healthy volunteer studies—two of which were administered by none other than Dr. Healy himself. In these studies, as many as half of the volunteers had to drop out early due to agitation—in some cases after a single dose of Paxil.

He went on to discuss the epidemiological studies, including one he had first learned about a couple of years previously at the European College of Neuropsychopharmacology meeting in London, which showed a tripling of suicide attempts on Paxil.

"I nearly fell out of my chair," Dr. Healy recalled.

He reiterated his point that still no one had ever carried out a study designed specifically to test whether Paxil or any other SSRI caused suicide, even though the protocol for just such a study had been drawn up years before. He also countered the It's-the-disease-not-the-drug argument advanced by the defense by asserting that Schell suffered from mild depression, nowhere near the severity expected to lead to suicide and homicide.

Dr. Healy testified that he did prescribe antidepressants to his patients, including SSRI's, including Paxil. But he also made it clear that prescribers could not possibly do their jobs without proper warnings of serious side effects—warnings that SmithKline Beecham failed to provide. Doctors, and their patients, needed to be alert for possible side effects like agitation and suicidality, and to understand that these could be drug effects, rather than manifestations of the underlying condition.

Not surprisingly, Charles Preuss, one of the attorneys for GSK, disagreed with Dr. Healy's assessment. In his closing statement, he went for broke:

> *Unfortunately, as we have learned, there is a stigma to mental illness. Many men think it is unmanly, think they can handle it and control it on their own. It's something they're embarrassed about so they keep it from other people, even their own families. Don Schell was one of those people who felt the stigma of mental illness.*
>
> *The result is that many people who need help with mental illness do not get help... Others go undertreated. 60 percent of individuals who are untreated commit suicide. Don Schell was one of those that was untreated or undertreated.*
>
> *As we have learned, Paxil is a treatment for depression. It is a safe and effective medication for depression and anxiety. It has been used successfully for millions of people over the past eight years. It reduces anxiety, it reduces depression, and it reduces aggression. Simply put, it saves lives...*
>
> *Given time to be effective, Paxil could have saved four lives in Gillette in February of 1998...*
>
> *It would be wrong to change that label, based on what the evidence shows. The consequence would not be good for mental illness. It would not be good for the people of Wyoming. It would cause people not to see doctors because they're afraid of homicide/ suicide. It would cause doctors not to want to prescribe.*

The message was clear: if you find in favor of the plaintiffs, you will have blood on your hands.

The jurors didn't buy it, and on 7 June 2001, they found GSK guilty and ordered them to pay $6.4 million to the survivors of the Tobin family massacre.[184] This was the first ever verdict for the behavioral effect of any drug.[185]

## Study 329

The next month, a paper titled "Efficacy of Paroxetine in the Treatment of Adolescent Major Depression: A Randomized Controlled Trial"[186] appeared in the *Journal of the American Academy of Child and Adolescent Psychiatry*, the highest-ranked journal in the field of child mental health and the second-highest-ranked in pediatrics.[187] This was SmithKline Beecham's Study 329 of Paxil, probably the most infamous clinical trial ever conducted.

The leading author on the paper was Martin Keller, Head of the Department of Psychiatry at Brown University and one of the key opinion leaders in his chosen field. During the years 1993-1998 alone, Dr. Keller had brought in over $14 million in research funding for his department.[188]

He also was no stranger to controversy. In 1994, Dr. Keller had been investigated by the Rhode Island State Police and the Attorney General's office for allegedly double-billing his expense accounts. The investigation was dropped after the university agreed to handle the matter internally. Keller was ordered to pay back $918 to Brown.[189]

A January 7 1996 article in the *Boston Globe* by reporter Alison Bass claimed that the Massachusetts Department of Mental Health had paid $218,000 to the Brown University Department of Psychiatry for research that was never performed. Several Brown employees listed as having done research planning or training for the project told the *Globe* that they had never actually been involved, but then changed their minds after "consulting" with Dr. Keller.[190] The Massachusetts Attorney General's office launched an investigation, and the US Attorney General's Office and US Postal Service mail fraud investigators also began looking into the matter.[191]

The following June, another *Globe* article by Bass reported that five former Brown employees complained in a letter to University President Vartan Gregorian that they had suffered various forms of retaliation, including being stripped of their job duties or denied promotions, after blowing the whistle on Dr. Keller.[192]

The Commonwealth of Massachusetts filed a civil lawsuit against Brown, and the university was ordered to pay back over $300,000 in damages. Daniel Amigone, the Massachusetts DMH official who awarded the contract, was demoted.[193]

An October 1999 article in the *Globe* by Bass revealed that, for the year 1998 alone, Dr. Keller had been paid over half a million dollars in consulting fees, much of it from pharmaceutical companies whose products he had touted in peer-reviewed journal articles and professional meetings. The article also stated that Keller had failed to disclose the full extent of his financial ties to the drugmakers, either to Brown University or to the American Psychiatric Association, which sponsored meetings where Keller presented his findings.[194]

Nevertheless, let's take a look at the findings reported by Dr. Keller and his co-authors. Study 329 was the largest study ever conducted on the effects of an SSRI on children. The study group consisted of a group of adolescents between twelve and eighteen years of age, each of which had been diagnosed with major depression of at least eight weeks in duration. Ninety-three of these youths received paroxetine while eighty-seven were given placebo. Subjects were assessed by means of the Hamilton Rating Scale for Depression (HAM-D), a questionnaire consisting of twenty-one items with possible scores ranging from zero to fifty-two; the higher the score, the more severe the depression.[195]

The Results section of the paper listed two primary outcome measures: 1) response, defined as a HAM-D score of eight or less, and 2) change in the HAM-D total score. For the latter outcome, there was no significant difference between children given paroxetine and those given placebo. For response, sixty-three precent of the youths given paroxetine were judged to have "responded," as opposed to fifty percent of the controls.[196]

In addition, the paper listed six other outcome measures. For three of these, patients given paroxetine were judged to have done better than those on placebo, while for the other three there was no difference.[197]

Serious adverse events were reported for eleven patients given paroxetine, as opposed to two for those given placebo. The serious adverse events for youths given paroxetine included "emotional lability," (five patients), conduct problems or hostility (two patients), euphoria (one patient), and headache (one patient). The authors stated "Only headache (1 patient) was considered by the treating investigator to be related to paroxetine treatment."[198] The logic underlying this conclusion was not explained.

The paper concluded, "Paroxetine is generally well tolerated and effective for major depression in adolescents."[199] A GSK memo to its own sales staff was more exuberant: "Paxil demonstrates REMARKABLE Efficacy and Safety in the treatment of adolescent depression."[200]

### Vindication

That same month, the CBC program *News and Current Affairs* aired a segment titled "Hard to Swallow" on the Toronto affair. In an interview, Paul Garfinkel, President and CEO of the CAMH, dismissed the concerns raised by Dr. Healy during his lecture the previous November, stating, "Frankly we'd be about as concerned about aspirin as Prozac." The show also revealed that the Mood Disorders Program received over fifty percent of its funding from the drug companies, and the CAMH had received a grant of $1.5 million from Lilly.[201]

Presenter Peter Mansfield mentioned that on the day Dr. Healy delivered his lecture in Toronto, a number of people from the Centre were visiting Lilly's headquarters in Indianapolis. Dr. Garfinkel categorically denied there was a connection:

> *Let me set the record straight on Dr. Healy's so-called conspiracy theories. We have never ever made an offer or rescinded an offer based on the impact of an external donor.*[202]

On 4 September, a letter signed by twenty-seven senior authorities in the field was sent to the President of the University of Toronto, protesting the withdrawal of Dr. Healy's job offer at the CAMH. The signatories included the Nobel-Prize-winning neuroscientists Arvid Carlsson and Julius Axelrod, along with former presidents of the American Psychiatric Association, the American College of Neuropsychopharmacology, and a range of other psychiatric and psychopharmacological organizations throughout the world, including Europe, North and South America, China, and Japan.[203] The president dismissed their concerns, and on the 24th of that same month Healy filed suit against the University for breach of contract and libel, seeking $9.4 million Canadian for damages.[204]

On 26 April 2002, Dr. Healy and the University of Toronto settled out of court for an undisclosed sum.[205] Healy was also awarded a three-year appointment as a Visiting Professor in the Department of Psychiatry, and agreed to accept assurances that the drug companies had played no role in the withdrawal of the original offer.[206] Canadian Association for University Teachers President Vic Catano said "We see the settlement as a complete vindication for Dr. Healy."[207]

### Cracks in the Façade

That same month, the first cracks began to appear in the façade of the *JAACAP* paper by Dr. Keller and his colleagues. The *JAACAP* published a letter from psychiatrist Mitch Parsons, who wanted to know how Keller et al. were justified in concluding that the high rate of serious adverse events (including emotional lability, worsening depression, suicidal ideation and gestures, conflict problems, and behavioral disturbances) in the children given paroxetine was not related to their treatment.[208]

Keller and two of his colleagues replied that those events were all related to a variety of situational factors such as arguments with boyfriends or parents or torments by peers[209]—ignoring the obvious point that insofar as any of this was true, that means that the treatment group and the placebo group were not comparable, which would call into question the validity of the entire study.

The next month, *JAACAP* published a letter to the editor by psychiatrist Jon Jureidini and clinical pharmacologist Anne Tonkin, both of Australia. The authors pointed out Keller and his colleagues had played fast and loose with their own outcome variables in the 2001 *JAACAP* paper. In the Materials and Methods section, "response" was defined as HAM-D score of eight or less OR fifty percent reduction in baseline HAM-D score. There was no significant different between paroxetine and placebo for that outcome. But in the Results section, "response" was re-defined as simply HAM-D score of eight or less. So in fact there was no significant difference between paroxetine and placebo for either of the two originally specified primary outcome measures.[210]

No justification was offered for changing the definition of one of the two primary outcomes, nor was this change even noted.

In conclusion, Drs. Jureidini and Tonkin stated "Given that the research was paid for by GlaxoSmithKline, it is tempting to explain the mode of reporting as an attempt to show the drug in the most favorable light."[211]

The same issue of *JAACAP* published a reply from Dr. Keller and eight of his co-authors, which read, in part:

> *Drs. Jureidini and Tonkin argue that the reviewers failed to understand and appropriately critique the article (and by exten-*

*sion that the editor was not up to the task) and that the authors of the original article swerved from their moral and scientific duty under the influence of the pharmaceutical industry. By extension, they covertly argue that the reader who agrees with them is intellectually and morally superior while a reader who does not agree with their position shares the cognitive and moral failing of the rest of us. We say that this article and body of scientific work is a matter for thoughtful and collegial discussion and say in addition that their emperor has no clothes.[212]*

Sales of Paxil continued to rise unabated, reaching a total of $3.3 billion for that year, up from $2.7 billion for the year 2001 and $2.3 billion for 2000.[213]

### Seroxat Prevents Suicide

The year 2002 was an auspicious time for GSK. Prozac had just gone off-patent, and GSK had set its sights on having Paxil take its place as the world's best-selling antidepressant. Company officials submitted an application to the FDA requesting approval for Paxil for treatment of depression in children and adolescents. Congress had recently passed the Best Pharmaceuticals for Children Act, granting a six-month patent extension to companies testing their drugs on children, regardless of the results of such testing. (Oddly enough, there was no requirement that companies that found their drugs were not safe and effective in children to inform prescribers, or the general public.) In the case of Paxil, such an extension could be worth millions to GSK.

Even if a drug is not approved for a given indication or a given population, doctors are free to prescribe pretty much any drug they think will help, to any patient. That's called off-label prescribing, and it's perfectly legal. What's not legal is for drug companies to promote off-label prescribing. That is a point we shall return to later.

On 28 August 2002, two American trial lawyers, Don Farber and Skip Murgatroyd of the Baum Hedlund law firm, met with Steve Galson, the FDA deputy director of drug evaluation and research. Farber and Murgatroyd had requested the meeting after discovering GSK internal documents indicating that GSK had been coding suicidality in children as "emotional lability."[214]

On 6 October *Newsweek* weighed in again with yet another cover story, "Young and Depressed,"[215] just in time for World Mental Health Day. The cover featured a photograph of a winsome-looking young woman, clutching a Raggedy Ann doll and gazing soulfully into the camera lens, along with the tagline: "3 million kids suffer from it. What you can do." Inside, the article told a tale of a dire situation:

> *Without treatment, depressed adolescents are at high risk for school failure, social isolation, promiscuity, 'self-medication' with drugs or alcohol, and suicide—now the third-leading cause of death among 10-to-24-year-olds... A recent report from the Centers for Disease Control found that 19 percent of high-school students had suicidal thoughts and more than 2 million of them actually began planning to take their own lives.[216]*

Fortunately, we are assured, help is on its way. The article mentions a University of Pittsburgh professor of child psychiatry who is conducting a study "looking at newer medications, including Effexor and Paxil, that may help kids whose depression is resistant to Prozac."[217]

On 10 October, the FDA contacted GSK, demanding to know why the company had coded self-harm and suicidality in Paxil trials under the category of "emotional lability."[218]

We might never have known the full extent of GSK's campaign of deception were it not for the intrepid reporting of Shelley Jofre and her colleagues at the BBC news magazine *Panorama*. On 13 October, *Panorama* aired the documentary "Secrets of Seroxat,"[219] which featured

Jofre's interview with Alistair Benbow, Head of European Clinical Psychiatry for GSK. When Jofre asked him about the Tobin family massacre, Dr. Benbow replied:

> *There is no reliable clinical evidence that Seroxat causes violence, aggression or homicide. This tragic, tragic case is something that occurs from time to time in patients who are depressed... We remain firmly convinced that Seroxat did not cause the tragic events in this case.* [220]

Jofre also asked Dr. Benbow why the information from GSK's own healthy volunteer studies was being kept secret from the public. He explained:

> *You are not a clinician or a healthcare professional...Your GP is a clinician. If he asked to see some of the data, then of course he could see the data, if it was appropriate.* [221]

But Dr. Healy later contradicted Dr. Benbow's version of the way things are done:

> *Not only can you not see what I've seen, but I've made notes on those as well, and you can't even see my notes. And it seems extraordinary to me that the only way that anyone can get to see things like this is through a legal case.* [222]

After the episode aired, producers were flooded with 1,400 emails and 67,000 telephone calls from viewers claiming to have been harmed by paroxetine. One missive after another told of paranoia, hallucinations, self-harm, nightmares about murdering children, self-mutilation, violence, and completed suicides. One viewer recalled that he felt as if his skull was boiling from the inside after taking the drug. *Panorama*, which had never before repeated a topic, subsequently aired three more episodes about paroxetine. [223]

Six weeks after the program aired, Health Minister Hazel Blears announced an intensive review of paroxetine. But the following March the review committee had to be disbanded when it was revealed that over half of its members owned shares in GSK.[224]

That same month, Dr. Healy re-analyzed the data on antidepressants (including paroxetine) and suicide from the 2000 meta-analysis by Khan and his colleagues that had concluded that these drugs do not increase the rate of suicidal acts.[225] But this time, Healy made some important adjustments.

First, Dr. Healy noted that patients who respond well to the drug obviously tend to be kept on the drug for longer periods of time, so he analyzed the data on suicidal acts in terms of absolute number of patients, rather than patient-years, which skews the numbers in favor of those who respond well.[226]

Second, many drug trials are preceded by what is called a "placebo washout period," in which all subjects are given a placebo, and those that respond well to it are removed from the trial. After examining FDA documents, Dr. Healy discovered that some of the suicides said to have occurred in the placebo arm of the trial in fact occurred during the placebo washout period.

Since the patient population in the washout period is not the same as that of the trial itself, including these suicides is a violation of the very essence of a randomized clinical trial, which dictates that the placebo and treatment groups both comprise a random selection drawn from the same group of patients. Moreover, since there is no requirement that trials be conducted on drug-naïve patients, some of the effects seen during the placebo washout period may in fact be drug withdrawal effects. Accordingly, Healy removed placebo washout suicides from his analysis.[227]

Finally, Dr. Healy's analysis included data for the antidepressants citalopram and Prozac, not available to Khan and his co-authors.[228]

After making these adjustments, Dr. Healy found that on a per-patient basis, compared to placebo, the seven antidepressants were associated with a doubling of the rate of suicidal acts and a whopping nearly seven-fold increase in the rate of completed suicides.[229]

Can this be true? If anything, these results probably underestimate the increase in risk, because actively suicidal patients are routinely excluded from antidepressant trials.

As Dr. Healy later put it, graphically and succinctly, "When it comes to dead bodies in current psychotropic trials, there are a greater number of them in the active treatment groups than in the placebo groups. That is quite different from what happens in penicillin trials or trials of drugs that really work."[230]

The mendacity of the pharmaceutical companies went beyond the mere shifting of the occasional dead body from the placebo washout period to the trial itself. Entire studies were deep-sixed if they failed to serve the interests of the drugmakers.

On 31 May of that year, a *BMJ* article by Hans Melander and his colleagues revealed just how serious the problem was. The authors reviewed forty-two studies submitted to the Swedish drug regulatory agency for the approval of five SSRI antidepressants. Twenty-one of these studies showed a statistically significant drug effect, while the remaining twenty-one did not. Of the twenty-one that had shown a significant effects, all twenty-one appeared as stand-alone publications in the scientific literature—in fact, several were published more than once. Of the twenty-one that had not shown a significant effect, only six appeared as stand-alone publications. Others were pooled with positive studies so that the overall results showed a positive drug effect, and four of the negative studies had never seen the light of day in any form.[231]

The authors' (rather restrained) conclusion was "Any attempt to recommend a specific serotonin reuptake inhibitor from the publicly available data only is likely to be based on biased evidence."[232]

Meanwhile, the bad news continued to pile up for GSK. "Emails From the Edge," the second installment in the *Panorama* series on paroxetine, aired on 11 May 2003. Producers had sent extensive questionnaires to all 1,400 viewers who had emailed the network after the first episode aired. Of these viewers, 239 replied, and the producers retained Alfred White of the Royal College of Psychiatrists to examine these responses in detail.

"The first impression is that the vast majority should not have been on drugs in the first place," Dr. White told *Panorama*. "There were hardly if any that I saw that I felt convinced that they had an illness which would be appropriate." In addition, fully one-third of the respondents said they had been put on the drug after a five-to-ten-minute consultation, two-thirds said doctors had given them no warning that stopping the drug would be difficult, and one-third said the experienced self-harm or suicidal thoughts that they had never had before.

Obviously stung by these attacks, GSK produced an internal memo in an attempt to buck up its sales staff. Titled "Science with a Conscience,"[233] the cover of the pamphlet featured a color photograph of a somber-looking teenage boy, along with the notice "FOR INTERNAL GSK USE ONLY." Inside, the document poses an interesting question to readers: "If you are depressed, who should you consult? A TV presenter or a doctor?" (The option "Neither of the above" was not provided.) This is followed by a series of talking points, which include:

> *Seroxat is not addictive.*[234]

> *Seroxat prevents suicide by treating depression and helping to reduce suicidal thoughts.*[235]

> *1 in 7 people with serious depression commit suicide.*[236]

> *There is no compelling evidence that Seroxat is linked to an increase in suicide and self-harm.*[237]

*Data shows that Seroxat will reduce violence and help prevent self-harm.*[238]

On 22 May 2003, GSK contacted the FDA and the MHRA (the Medicines and Healthcare Products Regulatory Agency, the British equivalent of the FDA), and submitted unpublished data showing that Paxil doubled the rate of suicidal and violent acts in children in clinical trials, and that the majority of healthy volunteers experienced withdrawal symptoms upon discontinuing Paxil, even after exposure for as little as two weeks.

On 10 June, the MHRA responded by issuing a warning that no one under the age of eighteen should be prescribed Paxil. Ten days later the FDA followed suit.[239]

### Commercially Unacceptable

On 27 October, the FDA released a "Talk Paper" which warned of reports of suicidal ideation and suicide attempts in pediatric antidepressant trials. They noted that none of the antidepressants besides Prozac had been judged to be effective for use in children, then hastily added "Failure to show effectiveness in any particular study in pediatric MDD, however, is not definitive evidence that the drug is not effective because *trials fail* for many reasons." (italics added)[240]

The phrase "trials fail" seemed a strange choice of words, as if the purpose of a drug trial is not to determine whether or not a given drug is safe and effective, but rather to secure official approval of that drug—regardless of whether or not it be safe and effective.

The paper also announced that a hearing would be held on the matter the coming February.[241]

Around this time *Panorama* came into possession of a tranche of GSK internal documents. The provenance of these documents has never been revealed publicly, and nobody who is in a position to know is saying anything, but they included an internal position paper by Julie Wilson of the Central Medical Affairs Team regarding Study 329 that showed that as far back as October 1998, SmithKline Beecham had known that Paxil was ineffective at treating depression in adolescents:

> TARGET: *To effectively manage the dissemination of these data in order to minimise any potentially negative commercial impact.[242]*

> *It would be commercially unacceptable to include a statement that efficacy had not been demonstrated, as this would undermine the profile of paroxetine.[243]*

> *Positive data from Study 329 will be published in abstract form at the ENCP (Paris, November 1998) and a full manuscript of the 329 data will be progressed.[244]*

This manuscript became the 2001 *JAACAP* paper of Dr. Keller and his colleagues.

The FDA scheduled a hearing on the link between antidepressants and suicidality in children and teenagers for Monday, 2 February 2004. Twelve days before that, the FDA Task Force on SSRIs and Suicidal Behavior in Youth released its preliminary report. The Task Force included three of the authors of the *JAACAP* paper: Graham Emslie, Karen Wagner, and Neal Ryan.

With proper scientific caution, the authors stated that they did not have access to much of the unpublished data, and so their conclusions should be regarded as tentative.[245] They reviewed clinical trials for five antidepressants in youth and concluded:

> *The rates [of suicidality] appear to be lower in the clinical trials, by virtue of the exclusion [of suicidal youths] and perhaps the therapeutic care and attention delivered during a treatment trial, and do not occur at rates that permit detection of a specific beneficial effect of medication.[246]*

That was an odd way of spinning the results, given that Table 2 of the preliminary report shows a clear excess of suicidality for every one of the antidepressants except Prozac.[247]

The authors also made much of the fact that not a single completed suicide occurred in the treatment arm in any of the trials[248]—ignoring the fact that no suicides occurred in the placebo arm either, and the obvious corollary that therefore leaving children undrugged does not increase their risk of suicide.

On Sunday 1 February, the day before the hearing was to be held, the *San Francisco Chronicle* reported that the agency had forbidden FDA medical officer Andrew Mosholder from presenting his findings from a review of twenty clinical trials of Paxil and seven other antidepressants involving over 4,000 children.[249]

Dr. Mosholder's review concluded that, considered as a group, the eight antidepressants nearly doubled the rate of suicidality in adolescents. The worst offenders were Effexor and Paxil, each of which was associated with a near tripling of the rate of suicidality in youths. Noting that none of the antidepressants besides Prozac had ever been judged effective in treating depression in youths in clinical trials, Mosholder recommended that all of the antidepressants except for Prozac be banned for use in children.[250]

Dr. Mosholder declined to be interviewed for the article.[251]

The hearing was held as scheduled the next day. Again, one speaker after another told heartbreaking stories of lives shattered by these drugs:

> TOM WOODWARD: *"Our oldest child, Julie, hung herself after 7 days on Zoloft... The doctors we spoke with stressed that Zoloft was safe and had very few side effects. The possibility of violence, self-harm, or suicidal acts was never raised. The two and a half pages we received with the Zoloft never mentioned self-harm or suicide... Instead of picking out college for our daughter, my wife and I had to pick out a cemetery plot for her."[252]*

MARK MILLER: *"We lost our 13-year-old son, Matt, in the summer of 1997... Matt's doctor, a man we know through court testimony to have been a well-paid spokesman for Pfizer, gave us Zoloft. He said, 'Take these for a week, call me back when you know how Matt is doing.' Matt didn't have a week. He hung himself from a bedroom closet hook, barely higher than he was tall."*[253]

SARA BOSTOCK: *"My daughter Cecily had only been taking Paxil for two weeks before she died, during which time her condition greatly worsened. By the day of her death, she was pale, unable to sleep, almost unable to converse, and in a frightened, agitated state, jumped at the slightest noise. That night she got up and without turning any lights, went into our kitchen only 40 feet from where I was half asleep. She stabbed herself twice in the chest with a large chef's knife... This was a young woman who had everything to live for. She had just completed applications to grad school and received a large pay increase the month before. She had a boyfriend who loved her and scores of wonderful friends."*[254]

ROBERT FRITZ: *"My daughter, Stephanie Raye Fritz, was taking Zoloft. We weren't told of any risk of increasing suicidal tendencies or increased suicide attempts. She hung herself on the evening of November 11th in her bedroom after finishing her homework. She showed no signs of increased depression or imminent suicidal thoughts, and in fact was still recruiting people to see her sing the following month."*[255]

DENNIS WINTER: *"Less than four months ago, [our daughter] Beth, a 22-year-old recent graduate from the University of Rhode Island, she graduated summa cum laude, she was a beautiful child who was loving, from a very tight, close family, never any instance of alcohol or drug abuse, never any problem, a wonderful student, a wonderful girl, a loving sister to her brothers and sisters, committed suicide after being on Paxil for seven days.*"[256]

PAMELA WILD: *"On September 9, 2001, in a state of confusion and hopelessness, I put a .38 Special Smith and Wesson revolver under my chin and pulled the trigger. In going through withdrawal from Paxil, I lost all ability to cope and reason and, without realizing it, became suicidal... The front of my face was blown away, leaving a hole large enough to encompass a man's fist. The bullet miraculously only took two-thirds of my tongue, most of my mandible and my cheek bones. The maxilla was shattered. The orbit of my left eye was broken and forced the eyeball out onto what remained of my left cheek. It completely destroyed my hard and soft palate along with my nose and sinus cavity. I am blessed though. I may not be able to taste and smell, but at least I lived. I can see, talk, and I can hear. But more surprising than any of those, I have brain function. I truly believe my life was spared for a reason. That reason is so I can prevent others from experiencing what I experienced."*[257]

The same day the FDA hearing was held, the above-mentioned position paper by Julie Wilson of the CMAT was released at a press conference by Dr. Healy, who had obtained it from *Panorama*.[258] The *Canada Medical Association Journal* published excerpts from this paper on 2 March.[259] On the 23rd of the same month, the FDA issued a public health advisory stating that patients taking antidepressants can become suicidal in the first weeks of therapy, and physicians should watch patients closely when first giving the drugs or changing dosages.[260]

On 31 March, the *Chronicle* reported that the FDA had launched an investigation to try to determine who leaked the information that Dr. Mosholder's findings had been suppressed at the hearing of 2 February. The article also reported that Senate Finance Committee Chair Charles Grassley was "very troubled" that the FDA may have withheld critical information about the risks of these drugs to children, adding "Even more troubling is the possibility that the FDA started an investigation to find out which staffer let the public know. From what I know now, that person or persons might deserve a medal."[261]

Meanwhile, Rose Firestein, a prosecutor working for the Consumer Fraud Protection Bureau of the New York State Attorney General's office, discovered the above-mentioned CMAT memo in the course of a Google search.[262] Here was the smoking gun she had been looking for, revealing SmithKline Beecham's intent to spin the negative results from Study 329 into something positive. On 2 June, her boss, Attorney General Eliot Spitzer, filed suit against GSK, accusing the company of fraud by illegally promoting the off-label use of Paxil in adolescents. This was the first time a public official had ever filed a lawsuit against a drug company.[263]

GSK CEO Jean-Pierre Garnier played the victim card, telling the *Sunday Telegraph*:

> *There is a certain amount of bullying in these tactics.[264]*

> *It's becoming too easy for many people to attack the pharma industry and hold the pharma industry to standards that are higher than anywhere else. I don't have a problem with standards but I do have a problem with extortion.[265]*

> *Can a company control the millions, and I mean millions, of memoranda that are written by, in our case, 110,000 people? What are the odds that stupid memos were written? What are the odds that memos asking the company to do things against company policy will be written? The odds are 100 per cent.[266]*

> *Of course we didn't follow this advice. Of course we didn't selectively publicise the data. This is not a smoking gun. It's a stupid memo.[267]*

Dr. Garnier did not specify what action had been taken against the author of the aforementioned "stupid memo."

While not admitting guilt, GSK agreed to pay $2.5 million to settle the case and to post the results of all its clinical trials published since 2000 on a website.[268] In an interview Spitzer made it clear his office was not passing judgement on whether Paxil was safe and effective. "I'm certainly not the person to determine whether Paxil is appropriate or not for any given patient," he told the *New York Times*. "But what I can do is ensure the information to doctors is fair and complete so that those equipped to make this determination can do so."[269]

Meanwhile, the FDA had commissioned a team of experts at Columbia University to re-analyze the studies Dr. Mosholder had already reviewed, and they reached the same conclusions as Mosholder had.[270] On 13 September 2004, an FDA advisory committee voted fifteen to eight to mandate a black box warning all antidepressants, stating that these drugs increase the risk of suicidality in children and adolescents.[271]

On 23 September, the House Energy and Commerce Committee held a hearing on antidepressants and suicidality in children. Robert Temple, director of the FDA's office of medical affairs, was called upon to testify before the committee. Some of the members pointed out that most studies had failed to show antidepressants were effective for treating depression in youths, and when they asked Dr. Temple why the FDA didn't just ban the drugs for use in children, he responded with a curiously backhanded defense of antidepressants: "More than 50 percent of all trials in adults fail, too. We don't know why."[272] The possibility that the drugs don't work seems not to have been considered.

In April of 2006, a GSK internal review concluded that Paxil was associated with an increased risk of suicide-related events in younger adults. The next month, GSK issued a "Dear Doctor" warning letter to prescribers, informing them that Paxil was correlated with an increased frequency of suicidal behavior in young adults either with or without

Major Depressive Disorder, and also in adults of all ages who did have MDD. The same warning was inserted into the class labeling section in the prescribing information for Paxil.

The letter from GSK tried hard to minimize their own findings, pointing out that the differences observed did not rise to the level of statistical significance—neatly sidestepping the question of whether any of the trials were sufficiently powered to detect such differences. The letter also pointed out that suicidality is itself a symptom of psychiatric illness—sidestepping the question of whether Paxil decreases or increases suicidality.

The summer issue of *Ethical Human Psychology and Psychiatry* for that year featured an article by Dr. Breggin titled "How GlaxoSmithKline Suppressed Data on Paxil-Induced Akathisia: Implications for Suicidality and Violence."[273] In it, Breggin revealed information he had obtained while serving as an expert witness in another case of Paxil-induced suicidality and violence, *Lacuzong v GlaxoSmithKline*.

On 29 April 1997, thirty-five year old Reynaldo Lacuzong drowned his two small children, and then himself, in the bathtub of his home in San Jose, California. The bodies were found by the children's mother shortly before midnight.[274] This was three days after Mr. Lacuzong started on Paxil.[275]

We have already seen that akathisia is both a well-known toxic effect of SSRI antidepressants and a well-known risk factor for suicide. In the course of his pre-trial investigation, Dr. Breggin determined that Smith-Kline Beecham (the forerunner of GSK) systematically eliminated the term "akathisia" from its studies, instead coding this reaction as "agitation," "anxiety," "nervousness," "tremor," etc.[276]

The term "akathisia" was entirely absent from the US studies, although there were thirteen acknowledged cases of akathisia in non-US trials. Of these thirteen patients, there was one suicide attempt and one completed suicide.[277]

## My Life Changed Forever

On 13 December 2006, the FDA Psychopharmacologic Drugs Advisory Committee convened yet another hearing. Andrew Leon, a psychiatric researcher at Cornell Weill Medical College and a member of the FDA review panel, told the *New York Times* "Sitting up there and having the public yell that you're killing their children is no fun. But I suppose that has become a part of the process now."[278]

Tom Laughren, Director of the Division of Psychiatry Products at the FDA, gave the introductory remarks. He began by noting that two years previously, the committee had considered the possibility that antidepressants could cause suicidality in children—deliberations which had resulted in the FDA black box warning. Now the committee had undertaken the task of deciding whether these same drugs could cause suicidality in adults, and had reviewed 372 placebo-controlled trials of antidepressants involving almost 100,000 patients.[279]

Dr. Laughren also mentioned two papers that had recently appeared in *BMJ* that were of particular relevance to the day's deliberations:

> *The first paper, by Fergusson, et al., 2005, was a systematic review that was focused on data available from published reports of controlled trials of antidepressants in adults being treated for depression and other indications. What they found was a twofold increase in the risk of suicide attempts in users of SSRI's compared to placebo or other interventions, but no difference when you compare SSRI's to tricyclic antidepressant use. There was no difference, however, in completed suicides across these trials.*
>
> *There were serious limitations to this review, most important being the lack of any safety information on, roughly, 58 percent of the patients who were eligible for the analysis.*
>
> *The second paper, Gunnell et al., was also a systematic review. This focused on data that was available to the MHRA and*

*summaries that they published on their website... What they found was that the odds ratio for SSRI's to placebo was greater than one for self-harm but less than one for suicidal ideation and neither finding was statistically significant. Again, there was no difference across the treatment groups for completed suicide.*[280]

After the introductory remarks, it was the public's turn to speak. Once again, one witness after another told stories of lives shattered by these drugs:

ELLEN HANSON: *"[My husband] Scott was prescribed Paxil because he was having difficulty adjusting to our having triplets. He had no history of being suicidal. His Paxil dosage had been doubled about three weeks before his death... I found my husband hanging from a tree. I had to reach out and touch his hand to see if this was even real. I cut him down with a rope and I cut the rope off his neck. I held him in my arms until the police came... I didn't know that Paxil could cause someone to become suicidal until the policeman who arrived on the scene said 'Oh, no, not another one' when I told him he was taking Paxil."*[281]

SUZANNE GONZALEZ: *"Four pills into Paxil, [my husband] woke up, within hours he shot himself in the head. He did this less than 10 feet from where my son was sleeping."*[282]

BEVERLY HATCHER: *"On August 18, 2003, my mother, the late Ms. Barbara Jean Darden, was prescribed Paxil. On September 2, 2003, one day before her youngest daughter's birthday, she took her life. She was only on Paxil for 16 days. My mother had no history of depression."*[283]

MICHELLE MOORE: *"I will never forget the moment I had to tell [my children] their father died. It was the worst and difficult moment of my life. They screamed in horror... I returned from home, after him being on Paxil for one day and Prozac for the previous three days, and found him dead."*[284]

Sarah Bostock: *"Five years ago, my life changed forever when my 25-year-old daughter, Cecily, stabbed herself [to death] after three weeks on Paxil."*[285]

Kim Witczak: *"This is Woody, my husband of almost 10 years. Woody was outgoing, gregarious, smart, and full of energy. Everyone loved him. But to me he was simply Woody, my best friend and the one that greeted me every day 'Hello Sunshine.' He was the guy I was supposed have a family and grow old with. However, on August 6, 2003, that day it changed. I became a widow. Woody was found dead hanging from the rafters of our garage of Zoloft-induced suicide at age 37. Woody wasn't depressed. He had no history of depression or suicidality."*[286]

Next Dr. Healy stepped forward to the microphone. Brandishing the panel's report in one hand, he addressed the members in the clipped cadences of an Oxbridge don, a rising edge of anger in his voice:

*Hello colleagues. Could you have a look at the first slide there? 'Truth is stranger than fiction. Well, of course it is,' said Mark Twain. 'Fiction has to make sense.' The question is, what would Mark Twain have classified this posting from the FDA as—truth or fiction?*

*That's the distribution of suicidal acts that happened in the registration trials of these three drugs here. But slide two—and I don't know how to move the slides forward—yeah—this is how the company reports, FDA reviews of the drug, and journal articles report those acts.*

*You referred earlier to the Fergusson et al. article, on which I am a co-author. We had to cope with this. We didn't undo this particular bit of bias to come to the results we had. The results we had would have been worse if we had undone this.*

*You referred to the MHRA article. Well, MHRA included three placebo suicides that weren't on placebo in clinical trials. People who a week after going on Prozac went on to commit suicide.*

*Dr. Laughren has an article from 2001, in which he is the sole author, that repeats this mistake. Dr. Laughren, in this particular document here, gives you no hint that all of the articles that he refers to showing that there is no increase in risk, also repeats the mistake that you see here.*

*This is the most interesting slide. This one you won't have seen perhaps. This is data from three and a half years ago. This is data from FDA that FDA put in the public domain. This shows you a clearly, statistically significant increased risk of suicide.*

*FDA said three and a half years ago 'But we can get this risk to go away if we control for age and sex.'*

*Now, controlling for age and sex in controlled RCT's, to begin with, suggests you're doing something awfully odd, that the clinical trials were invalid to begin with. The FDA also said that we can control for location, as if that actually makes a difference. And this year FDA reported that when you look at the clinical trials that happened in the US here, the placebo-controlled trials, that there were fewer people who went on to actually commit suicide.*

*I am sure you know that there are clinical trialists here in the US who have ended up in jail for entering fake patients into this clinical trial program.*

*Fake or bogus patients do all sorts of interesting things. They get well on treatment. They don't commit suicide. It is just incon- venient for the audit trail if they do.*[287]

Then Dr. Breggin laid it on the line:

*Fifteen years ago I warned the FDA, and I warned the country, in Toxic Psychiatry, that antidepressants were causing an amphetamine-stimulant-like syndrome that was resulting in violence and murder. In 1994 in Talking Back to Prozac I warned the country and the FDA again, this time with tons now of scientific data on the same issues.*

*During that period of time I was asked to be, and this is very relevant to your deliberations, the scientific advisor for all the combined Prozac suits, almost two hundred of them. So I got to look at all the sealed data that Lilly didn't want anybody else to see.*

*So about twenty books later now, and a few dozen different scientific studies and innumerable, innumerable product liability suits where I've looked at sealed data, I've come to tell you that you're evaluating junk. You're evaluating carefully edited, expurgated data that I've seen and you haven't. This is a most remarkable circumstance that you have resources, people who have been inside the drug companies who can tell you what's happening inside the drug companies and of course you've avoided it. All the documents I'm going to discuss now are on my website, www.breggin.com, and they've all been given to you, sent to you, via the committee.*

*In 1985, the Germans asked Lilly to review all of its controlled clinical trials, Phase II Phase III, for suicidality. The company came up with twelve suicide attempts on Prozac, one on alternative antidepressant, and one on placebo. A raging signal, which the company did not report to the Germans, did not report to the FDA, and did not report at the 1991 hearings.*

*In addition, the company hid suicidal data. When it would get an incoming suicide [attempt] from the field, it would reclassify it as depression, it would reclassify it as "no drug effect." Claude Bouchy, who was in Germany, working for Lilly, wrote an ashamed memo to the Central Office, saying How could I explain this to, quote, my family, to, quote, a judge? But, he said, of course we would go along with what the company said.*

*And as for akathisia, the company was very clever. It didn't code akathisia. So none were reported. It wasn't an available term. I found innumerable cases of akathisia, combing through the company files, that were never never reported.[288]*

Afterwards, the committee voted to extend the black box warning on suicidality to young adults up to twenty-five years of age.[289] No explanation was offered as to why the effect supposedly turns itself off after the twenty-fifth birthday.

The amended warning also informed prescribers "Depression and other serious psychiatric disorders are themselves associated with increases in the risk of suicide"[290]—rather an odd formulation, one that begs the question of whether these drugs make that risk go up or down.

The next month, the fourth *Panorama* episode about Paxil aired. Titled "Secrets of the Drug Trials," the show painted a disturbing picture of corporate venality on the part of GSK.

### Ghostly Presences

On 29 January 2007, *Panorama* aired "Secrets of the Drug Trials," which detailed the behind-the-scenes attempts to spin the results of SmithKline Beecham's Study 329 of Paxil in adolescents, which formed the basis of the 2001 *JAACAP* paper. The show extensively quoted SmithKline Beecham internal documents obtained by the law firm Baum Hedlund:

*The possibility of obtaining a safety statement from this data was considered but rejected.[291]*

*The best which could have been achieved was a statement that although safety data was reassuring, efficacy had not been demonstrated.[292]*

> *Consultation of the marketing teams confirmed that this would be*
> *unacceptable commercially.[293]*

Karin Barth Menzies, a partner at Baum Hedlund, told *Panorama* "They figured out ways that they could downplay the risks, blow up out of proportion the supposed benefits or the good sides of the study and really downplay the negative."[294]

This task fell to Sally K. Laden of Scientific Therapeutics Information, Inc. She had not taken part in the study design nor the collection of data, but it was to her that GSK assigned the task of presenting the data from Study 329 in the best light possible. The manuscript she produced became the *JAACAP* paper. Ms. Laden was not listed as an author on that paper, although the fine print at the bottom of the first page states "Editorial assistance was provided by Sally K. Laden, M.S."[295]

Not everyone at GSK was happy with the job she did. "She's going too far in burying bad news," one memo protested. Another stated "It seems incongruous that we state it [is] safe yet we report so many serious adverse events."[296]

But these voices of caution were ignored. In a memo to Dr. Keller, Ms. Laden stated that all the necessary materials for submitting the paper were enclosed, right down to the cover letter. "Please re-type on your own letterhead," the memo helpfully advised. "Revise if you wish."[297]

So what exactly was Dr. Keller's role in preparing the paper? In a deposition taken on 6 September 2006, he explained:

> *I've reviewed data analytic tables. I don't recall how raw it was...*
> *Huge printouts that list items by item number. You know, item*
> *numbers, and variable numbers, and don't even have words on*
> *'em. I tend not to look at those. I do better with words than I do*
> *with symbols.[298]*

The term "ghost writer" has been used to describe Ms. Laden's role. As Dr. Healy explained to me "Most medical articles—when I say 'most,' I mean over ninety percent—that are done on patent drugs, that's drugs that are recently released, that the company is in the business of marketing—will be ghostwritten." He went on to argue that the term "ghost writer" has been misapplied: "The ghosting actually applies to the fact that you've got a bunch of workers there who haven't even seen the data. Their names are there on the authorship line, but they are ghostly presences. They're not real, if you see what I mean."

In May of that year, the FDA contacted GSK and instructed them to delete the Paxil-specific language they had added to the Class Labeling section of the prescribing information for that drug, and replace it with uniform language. A series of back-and-forth emails ensued, culminating with this missive from the FDA:

> *The Agency has reviewed your proposed changes, and we do not believe that your product specific analysis should be included in the class labeling revisions since the labeling is targeted at the class of drugs. If you would like to discuss this matter further, please submit a formal meeting request.*

The requested meeting apparently never took place.

## A Major Milestone

In 2008, a year after "Secrets of the Drug Trials" aired, *The International Journal of Risk and Safety in Medicine* published a paper by the aforementioned Jon Jureidini and his co-authors which re-analyzed the data from Study 329, using secret documents obtained by Baum Hedlund. Dr. Jureidini and his colleagues found the mendacity of the authors of the *JAACAP* paper went even further than had previously been recognized. The original study protocol listed two primary outcome measures as well as six secondary outcomes. *There was no significant difference between Paxil and placebo for any of these eight outcomes.*[299]

Investigators then looked at nineteen more outcome measures, and found that in four of these nineteen there were a statistical difference which favored Paxil, while in the remaining fifteen there were not. In plain English, Paxil did better than placebo for four out of twenty-seven outcomes looked at, or fifteen percent of the total.

The practice of switching endpoints has a name: Hypothesizing After Results Are Known (HARK). This practice has been likened to shooting an arrow and drawing a target around wherever it lands and then calling yourself a marksman.

In addition, while the *JAACAP* paper reported that five youths given Paxil had experienced "emotional lability" (in fact, all five had self-harmed or reported emergent suicidal ideation), Dr. Jureidini and his colleagues found an additional three such cases buried in the patient-level data. While the original paper had claimed that Paxil is "generally well-tolerated and effective for major depression in adolescents," Jureidini et al. concluded the results were "negative for efficacy and positive for harm."

The bad publicity continued to pile up for GSK. On 3 October of that year, an article in the *New York Times* revealed that for the period 2000-2007, Charles Nemeroff, the man *The Economics of Neuroscience* had styled the "Boss of Bosses," had accepted almost a million dollars from GSK, almost none of which he had reported to Emory University, where he was Chair of the Department of Psychiatry. The University announced that Dr. Nemeroff had agreed to "voluntarily" step down as Chair pending resolution of the issues.[300]

In August of the following year, a paper in the *Journal of Clinical Psychiatry* showed the risk of suicide attempt more than tripled in the first fifty-five days of antidepressant therapy—confirming Dr. Healy's argument that analyzing data in terms of patient-years, rather than per-patient, systematically underestimates the risk of suicide.[301]

On 11 September 2010, *Forbes* reported that GSK had paid out a total of $390 million to settle lawsuits brought on behalf of patients (or their surviving relatives) who had attempted or completed suicide while on Paxil.[302]

In December of 2010, a study published by Thomas J. Moore of the Institute for Safe Medication Practices and his colleagues tabulated violence case reports as a percentage of all serious events reported to the FDA over a five-year period. A total of 484 drugs were looked at, including eleven antidepressants. For most of these drugs, there were either no violence case reports, or at most one or two.[303]

The eleven antidepressants (including Paxil) stood out from the pack with a whopping 578 violence case reports, or thirty percent of the total. Only the stop-smoking drug Chantix had a stronger violence signal.[304]

On 2 July 2012, the United States Department of Justice announced that GSK agreed to plead guilty and pay $3 billion to resolve accusations of fraud and failure to report safety data for a number of its drugs, including illegal promotion of off-label prescribing of Paxil. This was the largest health care fraud settlement in US history.[305]

A story in the *New York Times* revealed that during the years 1997-2005 (the period covered by the $3 billion settlement with the Department of Justice in 2012) Paxil brought in $11.6 billion for the company—and remember, Paxil was only one of several drugs covered by the settlement.[306]

In a press release, Deputy Attorney General James M. Cole triumphantly proclaimed:

> *Today's multi-billion dollar settlement is unprecedented in both size and scope. It underscores the Administration's firm commitment to protecting the American people and holding accountable those who commit health care fraud.*[307]

Deputy Secretary of Health and Human Services Bill Corr joined in the chorus:

> *Today's settlement is a major milestone in our efforts to stamp out health care fraud. For a long time, our health care system has been*

*a target for cheaters who thought they could make an easy profit at the expense of public health, safety, taxpayers, and the millions of Americans who depend on programs like Medicare and Medicaid. But thanks to strong enforcement actions like those we have announced today, that equation is rapidly changing.*[308]

The day the agreement was announced, GSK's stock price went up.[309]

That same year, Thomas Laughren, who chaired the 2006 FDA hearing on antidepressants and suicide, left the FDA and became an expert witness for the SSRI manufacturers.

But the saga of Study 329 still was not over.

## It's Shameful

Peter Doshi is an Assistant Professor of Pharmaceutical Health Services Research at the University of Maryland, an Associate Editor at *BMJ*, and a leading advocate for clinical trial transparency. On 13 June 2013, a paper authored by Dr. Doshi, along with Dr. Healy and several others, appeared in *BMJ*. The authors noted that they had obtained access to 178,000 pages of previously confidential drug company documents pertaining to clinical trials which either had never been published in the scientific literature or which had been misreported. They called upon the sponsors of the trials to publish the unpublished ones and to correct the misreported ones. They further stated that if the sponsors failed to do so, the data would be considered "public access data" that others would be allowed to publish.[310]

The article, titled "Restoring Invisible and Abandoned Trials: A Call for People to Publish the Findings" amounted to a manifesto demanding a new era of clinical trial transparency. The authors specifically mentioned GSK's Study 329 of Paxil as an example of a misreported trial in need of restoration.[311]

After GSK made it clear they would not retract or correct the paper, Dr. Healy set about the task himself, along with Dr. Jureidini and several others. Through GSK's website, the authors had access to 5,000 pages of appendices along with 77,000 pages of individual patient-level data—information never before made available to independent researchers.[312]

GSK provided two members of the RIAT team a portal with access to a remote desktop, a cumbersome arrangement which the team members came to call "the periscope." They could not download or print off the data, and the system repeatedly blocked them from accessing the data at all. Appendix H contained over 77,000 pages with up to four different versions of a given patient's records, and researchers had to open multiple spreadsheet tables simultaneously, copying, pasting, and cross-checking in a highly restrictive space.[313]

As previously noted, the authors of the original *JAACAP* paper added new outcomes to those specified by the original study protocol—outcomes more favorable to SmithKline Beecham's product. Since the authors of the re-analysis could not find any document justifying these post-hoc changes, they analyzed only the eight outcomes originally specified by the study planners. And, since the study was not powered to detect harms, they reported all serious adverse events without analyzing them for statistical significance.[314]

The RIAT team submitted the paper to *BMJ*, but the road to publication was a rocky one, with the journal's editors demanding no less than seven revisions. Every time they complied with the journal's demands, a whole new set of demands was thrust upon them. Nevertheless, they persisted.[315]

The re-analysis, published in *BMJ* on 16 September 2015, actually held few surprises, although the authors did uncover three more instances of self-harm or suicidal behavior among the youths given Paxil, bringing the total to eleven (they also uncovered one additional case of self-harm among the youths given placebo). The authors concluded that paroxetine was ineffective in the treatment of major depression in adolescents, and moreover was associated with a clinically significant increase in harm. Of even greater significance was the following statement which appeared in *BMJ*, possibly the most prestigious medical journal in the world: "Published conclusions about safety and efficacy should not be read as authoritative."[316]

In an accompanying editorial, Dr. Doshi pointed out that none of the original Study 329 paper's twenty-two authors had made the slightest attempt to correct the scientific record. The paper remained without so much as an erratum, and none of the authors—many of whom are university professors and/or prominent members of professional societies—have been disciplined by any of the institutions with which they are affiliated. He also blasted Brown University and the American Academy of Child and Adolescent Psychiatry for failing to demand a retraction of the paper. Doshi noted that the Academy received between $500,000 and $1 million a year, or somewhere between five and twenty percent of its revenue, from the drug companies.[317]

The next day the *Chronicle of Higher Education* published a lengthy story on the re-analysis, which quoted Dr. Keller: "Nothing was ever pinned on any of us."[318]

Two months later, Dr. Keller and eight of his colleagues replied to Dr. Doshi's editorial in a statement sent to a number of media outlets which said, in part:

> *In the interval from when we sat down to plan the study to when we approached the data analysis phase, **but prior to the blind being broken,** the academic authors, not the sponsor, added several additional measures of depression as secondary outcomes... The secondary outcomes were decided **by the authors prior to the blind being broken.** (Emphasis in the original)[319]*

Keller and his co-authors also stated their intention to write a more detailed letter to the editor of *BMJ*, rebutting the claims and accusations made in the article by Dr. Healy and his colleagues.[320]

In a response published on the website Study329.org, Dr. Healy stated:

> *[T]he correspondence we have with GSK, which will be available on Study329.org as of Sept 16 and on the BMJ website, indicates clearly that we made many efforts to establish the basis for introducing secondary endpoints not present in the protocol. GSK has been unwilling or unable to provide evidence on this issue, even though the protocol states that no changes will be permitted that are not discussed with SmithKline. We would be more than willing to post any material that Dr. Keller and colleagues can provide.*[321]

On a cold rainy October morning, less than a month after the *BMJ* paper came out, I met with Dr. Doshi in his office in downtown Baltimore. He told me "Here we have a fundamentally ethical issue about research and scientific integrity and Brown University—my university, my alma mater—will not confirm or deny whether it's actually looked into the case. It's shameful, right?"

I asked Dr. Doshi about the in-depth letter Dr. Keller and his co-authors had promised to submit to *BMJ*. "To my knowledge, we haven't received that letter yet," he told me. "I'm very concerned that we are going to see the various actors that have institutional responsibility for this story remain in the position of potentially stonewalling and not getting involved. That's my biggest worry."

The promised letter was published on 18 January of the following year:

> *In the interval from when we planned the study to when we approached the data analysis phase, but **prior to the blind being broken**, the academic authors, not the sponsor, added additional measures of depression as secondary outcomes... Taking this into consideration, and **in advance of breaking the blind**, we added secondary outcome measures agreed upon by all authors of the paper... [S]econdary outcomes were decided by the authors **prior to the blind being broken**. (Emphasis added)*[322]

By this time Dr. Keller and his colleagues had publicly asserted at least five times that the additional outcomes had been agreed upon prior to the blind being broken, without providing a shred of documentation in support of this assertion.

Drs. Jureidini and Healy, along with the other co-authors of the re-analysis, replied:

> *In spite of multiple requests, neither GSK nor Keller and colleagues have ever produced this analytic plan, suggesting that either it does not exist, or that it contains information unsympathetic to their claims.*[323]

In an email dated 17 April 2019, Dr. Doshi confirmed that there still had been no correction, no retraction, no apology, and no erratum from any of the twenty-two authors of Study 329. I wrote back to ask him if Keller and his colleagues had ever provided any documentation of their contention that the decision to include the additional outcomes was made before the blind being broken. Here is his reply:

> *I certainly have not seen it. There is also important slippage in such a concept because depending on how the analysis worked, analyses could have been done prior to the blind being broken that would allow knowledge of whether or not the study groups (drug vs placebo) were separating. Therefore it remains a possibility in my mind that the investigators knew there was no difference from placebo and added additional endpoints before the blind was broken.*
>
> *Best, Peter*

None of this seems to have harmed Dr. Keller's career noticeably. He had already stepped down from the position of Department Head back in 2009,[324] and was awarded the title of Professor Emeritus.[325] The multinational mass media and information firm Thomson Reuters named him one the world's most influential scientific minds of 2015.[326]

Dr. Healy summed up matters thusly to me: "This isn't a paper about an antidepressant being given to kids. This is a paper about access to data, and in the absence of access to data you have to assume that industry's mode of operation in this trial is the standard industry approach towards harms, and that it applies to all drugs, for all indications, for all age groups, and at this point we will be concluding you cannot trust the academic literature, you cannot trust the clinical study reports, and you can't trust the FDA. The only way forward from here is to demand access to all the data."

A paper published the year before in *BMJ Open* confirmed all this.[327] The authors examined clinical trial summaries for three antidepressant drugs and three antipsychotic drugs that had been posted on the website clinicalstudyresults.org, sponsored by the Pharmaceutical Research and Manufacturers of America, or PhRMA (the website has since been taken down).

When the authors compared the data from clinical trial summaries with that in published journal articles, the results were nothing short of shocking: over forty percent of serious adverse events were not reported in journal articles, and the majority of deaths and suicides were not, either. The authors concluded, with considerable understatement, "Access to complete and accurate data from clinical trials of drugs currently in use remains a pressing concern."

The need for transparency became even more clear in the light of another case in which Dr. Healy would play a central role as expert witness.

### An Absolutely Wonderful Guy

"He was an absolutely wonderful guy."

That's how Wendy Dolin of Chicago remembers her late husband Stewart.

"We met when we were fifteen and sixteen," she told me. "We were together for forty-two years. He was an unbelievable dad, an unbelievable husband, and a devoted friend."

Stewart had been head of the US Corporate Securities Group for the law firm Reed Smith, managing hundreds of lawyers. He enjoyed travel, skiing, hiking, and an occasional cigar.[328] He and his wife had loads of good friends, and their two by-then grown children were out of the house and successfully pursuing their own lives. The house was paid off, and they were debt-free. At the age of fifty-seven, life for the Dolins was sweet.

All that changed on 15 July 2010, when Stewart leaped off a station platform and into the path of a moving commuter train in downtown Chicago. He died of multiple injuries.[329] This was six days after his trusted family doctor and long-time friend Marty Sachman had prescribed GSK's blockbuster drug Paxil for anxiety.

Stewart's death left those who had known him bewildered—although it is not as if his life had been trouble-free. The law firm where he had worked had recently been swallowed up by a much larger one, bringing Stewart new responsibilities and new headaches, such as the unenviable task of downsizing many of his former co-workers, including the son of a close family friend. Stewart himself had difficulties in adapting to the new corporate culture, and recently had received mixed performance reviews along with a salary cut.

On the other hand, problems of this sort are not exactly unheard of, especially among late-middle-aged men in this era of corporate restructuring. They don't usually lead to suicide.

But there were warning signs, if only anyone had known how to interpret them correctly. The day before his death, he had called his therapist to schedule a same-day appointment, during which he became so agitated that the therapist had called him the next day to urge him to ask his doctor to prescribe a sedative. The last time Wendy had dinner with her husband, he had barely been able to remain seated. And a witness has reported seeing Stewart pacing back and forth on the station platform moments before he jumped.[330] When a family friend called Wendy and told her "Akathisia killed Stewart," she didn't even know what the word "akathisia" meant. But when she googled "akathisia, Paxil, and suicide," the first item that came up was Dr. Breggin's 2006 article about how GSK had hidden data on Paxil-induced akathisia and suicidality.

Wendy decided to fight. She retained the services of not one but two law firms: Baum Hedlund, the same firm that had represented the survivors of the Tobin family massacre, and Rappaport Law Offices.

But her lawyers told her right away there was a potential problem with the case: while Stewart had been *prescribed* Paxil, he had never actually *taken* Paxil. Illinois law stipulates that unless a prescription expressly states "brand name only," the pharmacist must fill the prescription with a cheaper generic version whenever it is available—in this case, a generic version of paroxetine manufactured by Mylan, Inc.[331]

This placed the case in a bizarre sort of legal no-man's-land. GlaxoSmithKline had nothing to do with the manufacturing, distribution, or sale of the pills which Wendy's lawyers claimed led to Stewart's undoing. On the other hand, generic drug makers such as Mylan by law cannot change a single word of the product labeling unless the patent-holder (in this case GSK) receives FDA approval for the change. Courts historically have been reluctant to hold patent-holders responsible for damages done by generic versions of their products.[332] It seemed as though nobody could be held responsible for the failure to warn Dr. Sachman, and Stewart, of the drug's potential to cause life-threatening complications—specifically, akathisia and suicide.

That hurdle was cleared in March of 2014, when Judge James Zagel of the US District Court denied a summary motion by GSK's lawyers to have the case dismissed (the same judge threw out the charges against Mylan).[333] The case against GSK was allowed to proceed.

## Awfully Scary Things

*Dolin v GlaxoSmithKline* began on 14 March 2017. During opening arguments, David Rappaport of Rappaport Law Offices charged that going back as far as 1989, SmithKline Beecham and later GSK had concealed information about suicidality and suicide attempts in its clinical trials of Paxil. The next day, lawyers for GSK countered that the company could not be held at fault because on four separate occasions the FDA had denied requests from GSK to be allowed to change its warning label.

But this argument was refuted the next day when Brent Wisner of Baum Hedlund showed jurors a video deposition from 9 January 2006 of then-CEO Jean-Pierre Garnier, taken in the course of another wrongful death suit filed by a woman whose brother killed himself after taking Paxil. In the course of the deposition, Dr. Garnier was asked if a reasonable and prudent manufacturer had a responsibility to warn prescribers of serious adverse events. He of course agreed. Next he was asked if it was possible for a drug company to add new information to a warning label without first obtaining permission from the FDA. Garnier replied:

> *Yes, but in practice you don't want to do that… The next day the FDA might come back and say 'Well, we didn't like the way you did this, you'll have to redo it.' So it's considerably disrupting, that's why most companies go through the FDA first, in practice, but you are right, there's a legal way for us to go directly to the public.*[334]

So GSK's own former CEO was in effect saying that 1) GSK had a responsibility to warn prescribers of serious adverse events; and 2) They did not need permission from the FDA to do so.

That same day, Dr. Healy took the stand. Under Wisner's questioning, Healy explained three means by which SSRI's can lead to suicide: 1) akathisia, or a state of emotional turmoil; 2) emotional blunting, or a numbing of the parts of the brain that normally inhibit us from acting out in a destructive manner; and 3) psychotic decompensation, throwing some people into an openly psychotic state (as we have already seen in the case of Joe Wesbecker).

Dr. Healy told jurors that the SSRI's were associated with particularly violent kinds of suicide:

> *With the SSRIs in particular, you get a range of awfully scary things. People who have set fire to themselves. People who filet themselves, literally skin themselves. You get people who murder others, murder their wives and children and then themselves... You're doing things that are not just violent, but at odds completely with the norms for them. You know, there's been some awful things like people killing themselves with a nail gun to the head.*

Wisner went on to produce a 2006 GSK memo to Thomas Laughren, then-Director of the FDA's Division of Psychiatry Products:

> *In adults with MDD [Major Depressive Disorder], all ages, there was a statistically significant increase in the frequency of suicidal behavior in patients treated with paroxetine compared with placebo.*

Eight of the eleven suicide attempts on Paxil were in patients past the age of twenty-four—the upper cutoff age limit for SSRI-induced suicidality, according to the FDA. All told, the odds ratio for suicide attempts for adult patients on Paxil was a staggering 6.7 times greater than for those on placebo.

Dr. Healy then walked the jurors through all the ways GSK had hidden this signal:

- Suicide attempts during the placebo washout period were incorrectly listed as occurring in the placebo arm of the trials

- Suicide attempts were analyzed in terms of Patient Exposure Years, rather than on a per-patient basis, biasing the results in favor of those patients who did well on Paxil

- Suicide attempts occurring after the trial was over were recorded as occurring in the placebo arm (some of these after the patient had been prescribed another SSRI, Prozac)

- Concurrent medications were allowed in the trials, including antihistamines which have a similar mode of action to SSRI's and which could obscure any signal resulting from Paxil

- Suicidal ideation, suicide attempts, and completed suicides were coded under the meaningless label "emotional lability"

- Suicidal ideation and suicide attempts were coded under the same label, thus allowing data on suicidal ideation to drown out the signal from the much rarer but far more serious category of suicide attempts

- Data on suicidality and self-harm were excluded from the published reports (as we have already seen, in the case of Study 329)

## Aside from That, Mrs. Lincoln, How Did You Enjoy the Play?

The next day David Ross took the stand. Dr. Ross was the Director of Public Health Pathogens Programs with the United States Department of Veterans Affairs and an Associate Professor of Clinical Medicine at the George Washington University School of Medicine. Prior to that he had worked for the FDA for ten years, reviewing new drug applications.

Under questioning from Wisner, Dr. Ross offered this damning assessment:

- Paxil is associated with an increased risk of suicide in adults over the age of twenty-four.

- GSK was not upfront about the risk.

- GSK had the ultimate responsibility for the content of the paroxetine label.

- GSK had a duty to warn prescribers about the suicidal behavior induced by Paxil.

- GSK did not warn prescribers of this risk.

Dr. Ross also noted that most FDA funding comes not from taxpayer dollars but from "user fees" paid by the same drug companies whose products are being assessed by the agency. In addition, he informed jurors that two suicides listed as "placebo suicides" actually occurred during the washout phase. These patients, Ross told the jurors, were never in the trial to begin with.

Dr. Ross also mentioned that there were twenty-two completed suicides on patients in the treatment arm, as opposed to zero on placebo.

Not only had GSK hidden this information from the public, but they promoted their drug by means of a 1995 paper titled "Reduction of Suicidal Thoughts with Paroxetine with Reference Antidepressants and Placebo."[335] The paper claimed that the risk of suicide on placebo was several times that on paroxetine when in fact the exact opposite was true. All three authors of the paper were SKB consultants or employees.

Dr. Ross told the jurors "I believe this paper should be retracted." When asked if it had been, he replied "Not to the best of my knowledge." Of the nearly seven-fold increase in suicide attempts on Paxil, he stated "This isn't a red flag. It's a claxon."

The following day, Wisner asked Dr. Ross about the FDA instructions to GSK to delete the Paxil-specific language regarding adult suicidality from the prescribing information for that drug. Dr. Ross pointed out that the FDA request pertained only to the Class Labeling section. There was nothing to stop GSK from inserting that information elsewhere, and he showed the jury several places in the label where it would have been appropriate to place this warning.

When asked if GSK should have or could have taken the initiative to change its label to warn prescribers of the increased risk of suicide, Dr. Ross's reply was short and straight to the point:

*I think they absolutely could have, should have, and could have done it without getting prior approval.*

He also informed jurors that to that very day, GSK still had not changed the label to inform prescribers of the risk.

The following day, during cross-examination by defense attorney Andy Bayman, Dr. Ross was asked:

*Other than the 6.7 finding with respect to the secondary analysis of definitive suicidal behavior, you're not aware of anything in GSK's 2006 adult suicidality analysis that would meet the definition of reasonable evidence of an association between the use of Paxil and suicidality that would warrant a label change, correct?*

Dr. Ross replied "That's a bit like saying 'Aside from that, Mrs. Lincoln, how did you enjoy the play?'"

On 27 March, Stewart Dolin's family doctor Marty Sachman took the stand to tell jurors about his relationship with Stewart. They had been friends with each other for thirty-eight years. Their wives were friends with each other, as were their now-grown children. "We were like brothers," Dr. Sachman recalled. "We spent weekends together, travel together. He was my closest friend."

He also stated that if the warning label for Paxil included a warning about the danger of adult suicide, he never would have prescribed the drug to his old friend.

On 11 April, the last witness for the defense, psychiatrist Anthony Rothschild, began his testimony. A quarter of a century earlier, Dr. Rothschild had been one of the first to sound the alarm about SSRI-induced agitation. But now here he was on the witness stand, with the "psychological autopsy" he had prepared for GSK, demonstrating the living Hell Stewart's existence supposedly had become, and testifying that paroxetine had nothing to do with his death.

Dr. Rothschild's testimony lasted two entire days. The day after that, during cross-examination, Rapoport asked Dr. Rothschild how many Paxil-related suicide cases he had testified in. Rothschild replied there had been so many he couldn't remember the exact number.

During his closing statement, defense attorney Andy Bayman asked the jurors "Don't you think if these medicines caused suicide someone would have spoken up?"[336]

The jury didn't buy it, and on 20 April 2017 awarded Wendy Dolin $3 million. This was only the second Paxil suicide case to result in a judgement in favor of the plaintiffs, the first being *Tobin v GlaxoSmithKline*, also litigated by Baum Hedlund.[337]

When I called Dr. Healy to congratulate him on the verdict, he cautioned me "Well, that may not be entirely over yet. I would imagine that GSK probably would appeal it, so let's see what happens."

His words were prescient. On 22 August of the following year, the verdict was overturned by the Seventh US Circuit Court of Appeals. A lawyer for GSK had argued before the court that allowing the verdict to stand would "totally upend the pharmaceutical industry."[338] He may well have been right.

## Be Aware

At the time of writing this, the case is being appealed to the Supreme Court of the United States. Meanwhile, Wendy has not been idle. In memory of her late husband and all the other victims of drug-induced akathisia, she has found the not-for-profit organization MISSD (Medication-Induced Suicide Prevention and Education foundation in memory of Stewart Dolin).

The MISSD website, which can be found at missd.co, emphasizes the organization is not anti-drug: "We are for truth in disclosure, honesty in reporting and legitimate drug trials."[339]

The foundation seeks to raise awareness of drug-induced akathisia and has produced an educational handout, videos, and a one-credit-hour continuing education course on the subject that has been approved by the National Association of Social Workers. In addition, the organization is now working with experts to develop a continuing medical education course for physicians. In 2018, the International Society for Ethical Psychology & Psychiatry presented Wendy with its Humanitarian Award, for raising awareness about akathisia.

Wendy told me:

> *Once we started speaking, all of a sudden people are saying 'Oh my God, this happened to my loved one, and I didn't even know it had a name.' Over the past seven years, we have spoken all over the world. I'm speaking this summer at the Royal College of Psychiatrists in London.*
>
> *With time it just expanded. And we ended up changing our Mission Statement. The original Mission Statement was when you stop, start, or change the dosage of SSRI's or antipsychotics, you need to be aware of symptoms. But then over the course of all the things we do, we started hearing about drugs like Malerone for malaria, Neurontin for pain, Chantix for smoking cessation, some of the anti-emetics for nausea, and all of a sudden we realized this was a broader issue than we even anticipated.*
>
> *So the new mission statement is: when you stop, start, or change the dose of any medication, be aware of side effects such as akathisia.*

Indeed. The organization's website informs readers, "If this could happen to Stewart, it could happen to anyone. MISSD will make a difference."[340]

# CHAPTER 4

# TWO FAMILIES

The stories of David Carmichael and David Crespi have become emblematic of the SSRI era. It was the fate of these two men, so alike in so many ways—both loving husbands and fathers, both highly educated professionals, both respected members of their communities—to become unwitting participants in a giant, uncontrolled experiment.

### A Beautiful Boy

"He was an active, playful, fun-loving beautiful boy."

That's how David Carmichael of Oakville, Ontario, remembers his son Ian.

David Carmichael was a successful physical activity and sports consultant then living in Toronto, Ontario, married with two children—Gillian, age fourteen, and Ian, eleven. At the age of forty-four, life was good. " We had a house where all the neighborhood kids would come," David recalls. "We had lots of stuff for them to play with, and he'd always be out there where the kids were playing, and we had a really close relationship. He was a great little BMX-er. That was his thing that he really enjoyed, and we spent hours at the skate park together."

Although, it is not as if this family was immune to life's vicissitudes. During the recession in 2003, David, like many others, began experiencing financial problems. He began feeling nervous, developed tremors, and had problems getting a sound night's sleep. These sorts of problems are not unknown in middle aged men, but David decided to seek help from his family doctor, who prescribed GSK's blockbuster drug Paxil.[341]

The doctor said nothing to David about suicidality, or any possible side effects of the drug at all. David started on forty milligrams of Paxil, and he felt suicidal the first week on the drug, but after that he started feeling better and was able to procure some new work contracts. In February of the following year, he successfully tapered off the drug.[342]

On 8 July of that same year, he resumed taking Paxil, starting with the prescribed forty-milligram dose. Once again, David felt suicidal, and on 16 July he decided to increase the dose to sixty milligrams, without consulting his doctor. He based this decision, he says, on the *Guide to Drugs in Canada*, published by the Canadian Pharmacists Association, which then listed sixty milligrams as the maximum therapeutic dose. He figured it would be like taking two aspirin tablets for a headache, instead of just one.[343]

David quickly became delusional after increasing the dose of Paxil. In his altered state, the most banal events and conflicts of family life became twisted into terrifying problems requiring extreme solutions. David's son Ian suffered from seizures and a minor learning disability; in David's mind, his son was brain-dead. From time to time, Ian had been teased by his classmates; in David's mind, the boy's existence was a living Hell. Like all siblings, Ian and his sister had squabbled on occasion; in David's mind, the boy was going to murder his sister. At summer camp, Ian had thrown volleyballs at other kids and once pushed another boy into the pool; in David's mind, his son was a danger to other children. And, in David's mind, his wife was on the verge of a nervous breakdown from all these "problems."[344]

David decided his son would be better off in Heaven. On 30 July, the day Ian returned home from summer camp, David told him they were going on an excursion to an indoor BMX park. Excitedly, the boy packed his bag. Just before they departed, David instructed his son to tell his mother he loved her, and he did.[345]

At the hotel, David ordered his son's favorite foods via room service, and together they watched a movie he knew Ian would like. Just after 10:00 PM, David poured a vial of sleep medication into a glass of orange juice and gave it to his son to drink.[346]

The sleep medication did not have the intended effect. Ian remained awake, hallucinating. Father and son stayed up for most of the night, bouncing on the bed, laughing and talking about the hallucinations. Then, at 3:00 AM, David calmly strangled his son to death.[347]

David remained in the hotel for six hours, watching television, and then called the police. He surrendered without any resistance, and was transported to jail and immediately taken off Paxil. Two weeks later, the drug-induced fog that had shrouded his mind lifted, and the enormity of what he had done hit him full force. He cried uncontrollably for three days.[348]

The fact that David had been under the influence of Paxil at the time of the killing played no part in his defense. His attorney advised him that even if they could convince the judge to agree that Paxil played an essential role in what happened, the best he could hope for under those circumstances would be a conviction for manslaughter on the grounds of diminished responsibility. Where these matters are concerned, Canadian law makes no distinction between prescription drugs (such as Paxil) and street drugs. David's attorney advised him to plead not criminally responsible on the grounds that he was suffering from a mental disorder, and the prosecutor agreed to accept the plea.

On 30 September 2005, David was remanded to a medium-security psychiatric facility, and on 4 December 2009, he received an absolute discharge from the Ontario Review Board.[349] In October of 2011, David filed a civil lawsuit against GSK.[350] This lawsuit is still pending.

"Our first court hearing was just January [of 2019]," David told me. "They're trying to get it dismissed based on the statute of limitations. You have a two-year period in terms of the statute of limitations and what we're arguing is I couldn't have possibly filed my civil lawsuit until I received my absolute discharge.

"This is a David versus Goliath battle. You know, even the judge acknowledges that they could drag this on for fifty years if they wanted to. So the whole idea is to use this for educational purposes, to help educate the public."

David summed up matters thusly: "The message is: Know your drugs. I didn't."

Indeed. As David wrote in Dr. Healy's *RxISK* blog: "The tears and pain are still with me, and will be forever."[351]

## Getting Away with Murder

"We had a very good life."

That is how Kim Crespi remembers her marriage to her husband David—before an unspeakable tragedy turned their lives upside down.

Kim and David had known each other back in high school, but they hadn't been childhood sweethearts. But after David's first wife died, he and Kim fell completely in love with each other. She adopted his two children he had by his first wife, Jessica and Dylan. Together David and Kim had three more children, a boy named Joshua and twin girls named Samantha and Tessara. Kim became a full-time homemaker, and David worked as a financial auditor for Wachovia in Charlotte, North Carolina.

"We really liked our house," Kim recalls. "We liked our neighborhood, we were a strong Catholic family." Together they attended Saint Matthew Catholic Church, and David served on the parish financial council.[352]

But David's job could be stressful at times, and over the years he had suffered from anxiety and sleep problems. He went through counseling and tried several different psychotropic medications. None of them seemed to help, and at times made things worse, causing depression and suicidal thoughts which seemed especially bad within four to six weeks after starting the drugs. David kept trying, trusting that the professionals knew best.[353]

In March of 2004, David was diagnosed with testicular cancer. He began treatment for the cancer and at the same time sought help for his anxiety and sleeplessness from a psychiatrist, who prescribed GSK's blockbuster drug Paxil.[354]

The cancer treatment was successful, but meanwhile David had gained over fifty pounds on Paxil, and he tapered off the drug. But the holidays brought renewed stresses, including worries about his job. He also had several health issues, including an infection for which he was prescribed an antibiotic.[355]

David sought the help of a psychiatrist, who prescribed more medication for his problems. David now was on a combination of drugs: clarithromycin for his infection, Ambien for sleeplessness, Trazadone and Prozac for depression. On 19 January 2006, Lunesta was added to the mix.[356]

A 2011 review found that clarithromycin had been found to cause neuropsychiatric effects so severe as to require concomitant medication with neuroleptics or benzodiazepine tranquilizers.[357] Prescribing information for the other four drugs lists the following toxic effects:

> AMBIEN: *abnormal dreams, abnormal thinking, aggressive reaction, delusions, depersonalization, emotional lability, hallucinations, manic reaction*[358]

> LUNESTA: *abnormal dreams, abnormal thinking, agitation, confusion, depersonalization, emotional lability, hallucinations*[359]

> PROZAC: *abnormal dreams, abnormal thinking, agitation, delusions, depersonalization, emotional lability, paranoid reaction*[360]

TRAZADONE: *akathisia, confusion, delusions, hallucinations*[361]

David was taking powerful, brain-altering drugs in a combination that had never been tested.

That same day, David and Kim had attended a therapy session together, and David was preoccupied with dark forebodings—he was going to lose his job, and they would go bankrupt and lose their home. None of this was true, but nobody recognized that David was suffering from delusional thinking.[362]

On 20 January 2006, David was not feeling well and stayed home from work. The twin girls also were sick with colds, and at noon Kim went out to get her hair cut, leaving the girls in the care of their father.[363]

While Kim was out, David stabbed the girls to death, and then called 911 and told the operator "I just killed my two daughters." When the police arrived, David surrendered without any resistance and was charged with capital murder.[364]

A few weeks after the killing, David, who had been plagued with worries about losing his job, learned that Wachovia had just approved his biggest bonus ever.[365]

Prison doctors diagnosed David with bipolar disorder and prescribed medication. The diagnosis was based on his reaction to Prozac, even though he had never shown any symptoms of this condition before starting on Lilly's blockbuster drug.

The family had to rely on the public defender for legal representation. No other lawyer in Charlotte would touch the case. In July of 2006, still in a drugged state, David pleaded guilty to murder, in order to spare his family the trauma of a death penalty trial. He received two consecutive life sentences.

Two years into his sentence, David began experiencing liver and kidney problems and so all of his medications were discontinued. He has remained drug-free ever since. Currently he is housed in a medium-security facility, where he has served as chapel clerk and continues to help his fellow inmates prepare for their GED exams. Kim has remained true to her marriage vows. She also has started a website to warn others about the dangers of psychiatric drugs.[366]

"We have a good relationship" Kim says. "He calls every day. He's a great dad." Kim used to see him weekly, but now she is suffering from Parkinson's disease and has had to curtail the visits. She tells me:

> *I'm hoping to overcome Parkinson's, drug-free. Because I believe the Parkinson's drugs are similar to antidepressants. So I'm just going to stay away from them and I'm just struggling.*
>
> *I think these drugs are poison. They make things worse. At the end of the day, the people who want to give you these drugs, they're not going to be there when all Hell breaks loose. They will be as far away as possible. So, know that you're on your own.*
>
> *It takes a lot of energy to be on this journey. I often wonder why it happened to our family, but we're a family that loves each other so—why not our family? Because it's happening to a lot of people.*
>
> *These drug companies are getting away with murder.*

# CHAPTER 5

# DO ANTIDEPRESSANTS HELP?

## An Open Secret

The Tuesday, May 16 edition of the *Boston Globe* featured a letter to the editor from one Carl N. Brownsberger, M.D., which said in part:

> *Psychiatrists have long understood that Prozac and related drugs can on rare occasions cause terrible restlessness, which, if not treated, can contribute to suicide. The main effect of Prozac is antidepressant, and it prevents suicide.*
>
> *The situation is exactly analogous to aspirin and penicillin. Both can on rare occasions cause sudden death, but they remain good drugs.*[367]

A number of psychiatrists have expressed similar sentiments, especially in the wake of the FDA warnings on the relationship between antidepressants and suicide. Madhukar Trivedi, director of the Mood Disorders Program at the University of Texas Southwestern School of Medicine, told the *New York Times* "The consequences for not treating depression are very high."[368] Psychiatrist Graham Emslie, also of UT Southwestern, told the *NYT* "Limiting doctors' choices in treating depressed kids is not a good thing."[369] And during the September 2004 FDA hearing on the link between antidepressants and youth suicide, Dr. Suzanne Vogel-Sibilia brought her fifteen-year-old son Tony, who implored the panel "Please help me preserve my future. Don't take away my medication."[370]

Are all these commenters right? Are the suicides and murders committed by individuals taking these drugs just collateral damage in service to some greater good?

How much good are these drugs doing, anyway? Irving Kirsch, a Professor of Psychology at the University of Connecticut, wanted to find out.

As a practicing clinical psychologist, Dr. Kirsch had nothing against antidepressants. From time to time, he referred his clients to psychiatrists who prescribed these drugs for them. Sometimes the antidepressants seemed to help, and other times they didn't. Kirsch assumed that the ones who seemed to get better on the antidepressants did so because of the specific effects of the drugs.[371]

But Dr. Kirsch was interested in studying the placebo effect, and he figured that antidepressant trials would be a good place to start.[372] He couldn't have been more right.

Dr. Kirsch and his colleague Guy Sapirstein did a computer search of the relevant literature to find all the published studies that met the following criteria:[373]

1) All the patients had to have a primary diagnosis of major depression

2) Sufficient data had to be reported to calculate within-condition effect sizes

3) Data had to be reported for a placebo group

4) Patients had to randomly assigned to either drug treatment or placebo

5) All patients had to be between the ages of eighteen and seventy-five

6) All patients had to be assessed by means of the Hamilton Rating Scale for Depression, or HAM-D

Drs. Kirsch and Sapirstein found nineteen studies that met all their criteria. These studies looked at a wide variety of antidepressant drugs: tricyclics and tetracyclics, SSRI's, other antidepressants, and even some drugs not normally considered antidepressants: lithium salts (normally prescribed for bipolar disorder, or manic-depressive illness), amylobarbitone (a barbiturate), adinazolam (a benzodiazepine tranquilizer), and synthetic thyroid hormone (the patients in that study did not have a thyroid disorder).[374]

The meta-analysis found that most patients given medication got better—at least in terms of an increased HAM-D score. That's not very surprising. Most patients given placebo also got better. That's not very surprising either—that's the whole reason why most drug trials have a placebo control group.[375]

In fact, seventy-five percent of the improvement seen on the drug could be produced by giving patients a placebo. That was the first surprise. The second surprise was the difference between drug and placebo varied almost not at all. The placebo effect was always between seventy-four and seventy-six percent of the treatment effect, regardless of the type of drug given—even for drugs not considered antidepressants.[376]

What's more, even the small difference between drug and placebo may not have been due to any specific action of the drugs. The dirty little secret of the drug companies (well, one of their many dirty little secrets) is that so-called double-blind trials are anything but. Both patients and clinicians know perfectly well who is getting the active drug and who is getting the placebo, due to presence or absence side effects. Patients who know they are getting the active drug are likely to experience an enhanced sense of hope, which could help lift their depression—after all, what is depression but a loss of hope? Clinicians may be subconsciously biased (or consciously biased, for that matter) and tend to rate patients they know are getting the drug as more improved. This is known as the "active placebo effect." Some drug trials even include an arm in which patients are given a drug which is believed not to have any therapeutic effects on the condition under investigation, but which does produce side effects. Such a preparation is referred to as an "active placebo."[377]

The drugs Drs. Kirsch and Sapirstein looked at had no common mode of action. The only thing they had in common was that they all produced substantial side effects, suggesting that these drugs are nothing more than active placebos for depression.[378]

The whole concept of meta-analysis was still somewhat controversial in 1998, but Kirsch's and Sapirstein's paper, provocatively titled "Listening to Prozac but Hearing Placebo," found a home in the June 1998 issue of *Prevention & Treatment*.[379]

It already had been an open secret that the purported benefits of antidepressants were barely distinguishable from those of placebo. Peter and Ginger Breggin had made the very same point four years earlier in *Talking Back to Prozac*.[380] Nevertheless, Kirsch's and Sapirstein's findings were not welcomed with open arms by everyone concerned. Donald F. Klein, Professor of Psychiatry at Columbia University, wrote in an accompanying commentary, "These conclusions are problematic for those who believe antidepressant medication has made a major contribution to the treatment of the mentally ill." No argument there. He also wrote "The article [by Kirsch and Sapirstein] is criticized because it derives from a miniscule group of unrepresentative, inconsistently and erroneously selected articles…"[381]

He had a point, and Dr. Kirsch, at the prompting of Thomas J. Moore, then at the George Washington University School of Public Health and Health Services, decided to perform another meta-analysis.[382] They filed a Freedom of Information Act request for all trials submitted to the FDA for the approval of six antidepressants: Prozac, Paxil, Zoloft, Effexor, Serzone, and Celexa.[383] These drugs were the six most widely-used "new-generation" antidepressants at the time, although Serzone has since been withdrawn from the market after being linked to cases of liver failure.[384]

Dr. Kirsch and his colleagues reviewed a total of forty-seven studies, but not all of them could be used for the meta-analysis. Four of the Paxil trials, four of the Zoloft trials, and one trial of Celexa had not found significant difference between drug and placebo, and the data had not been reported for these trials.[385]

The left thirty-eight trials for Kirsch et al. to work with. All of the studies had been approved by FDA reviewers who had access to the raw data and evaluated them independently, and their analysis had been approved by an independent advisory panel. Presumably these data were of high quality—high enough to justify the FDA's stamp of approval as "safe and effective."[386]

Again, they found that the placebo replicated approximately eighty percent of the treatment effect seen on the drug. The difference between the drug and placebo was tiny—a mere 1.80 points on the HAM-D. There was no difference between the six antidepressants—all of them were equally effective, or equally ineffective, depending on how you looked at it.[387] For calibration, consider that a two-point reduction in the HAM-D score can be achieved by no longer waking during the night, *or* no longer waking early in the morning, *or* being less fidgety during the interview, *or* by eating better. The patient may still be plagued by the same feelings of guilt, worthlessness, thoughts of suicide, etc.[388]

Moreover, there were no increased benefits at higher doses, indicating that the lack of effectiveness was not due to patients being under-dosed. The difference between the lowest dose and the highest dose was a miniscule four-tenths of a point on the HAM-D scale.[389]

This second meta-analysis was also published in *Prevention & Treatment*, with the equally provocative title "The Emperor's New Drugs"—an allusion to the famous Hans Christian Anderson fable.[390]

In an accompanying commentary, clinical psychologist David Antonuccio and his colleagues argued that these findings most likely overestimated the drug effect of antidepressants. In addition to the aforementioned "active placebo effect," they noted another factor that would tend to minimize the placebo effect: every one of the trials used a placebo washout period, and they asked the readers to imagine if the drug companies would ever consider an "antidepressant washout period" to minimize the drug effect.[391]

Dr. Antonuccio and his colleagues also noted that the studies all relied on clinician ratings (patients themselves usually report smaller changes than treating clinicians do) and that most of the studies allowed co-prescribing of sedative medication—an important point, given that there are at least six items on the HAM-D scale that favor medications with sedative properties.[392]

But again, not everybody concerned received these findings with open arms. Psychiatrist Michael Thase argued that even a small drug effect is better than nothing, in an accompanying commentary whose title constituted a curiously backhanded defense of these drugs: "Antidepressant Effects: The Suit May Be Small, but the Fabric Is Real."[393]

Dr. Thase argued that Kirsch et al. underestimated the public health impact that even small therapeutic effects can have on conditions that affect large number of people. He gave a hypothetical example: suppose an antidepressant increased the rate of remission by ten percent. Multiply that ten percent by millions of people taking these drugs, and you have a real benefit.[394]

But this argument is based on a logical fallacy—treating an incremental variable (HAM-D score) as a categorical variable (like death or pregnancy).[395] Another hypothetical example should make this clear. "Remission" in these studies is usually defined as a HAM-D score at or below some arbitrary cutoff point, usually seven points. Assume the average patient at intake in these studies had a HAM-D score of twenty. That means remission would entail a decrease of thirteen points. But since the average difference between drug and placebo is less than two points, that would mean for every patient in the treatment arm whose score decreases by thirteen points, there should be one in the placebo arm whose score decreases by eleven points. This two-point difference is unlikely to be noticeable by a treating clinician (vide infra).

Dr. Thase and other critics also charged that the studies that formed the basis of the meta-analysis were not reliable. Some claimed that the patients in the trials weren't depressed enough, even though all but one of the trials had been performed on subjects judged "moderately to severely" depressed. Others averred that the trials were too short, the dosages were too small, the clinicians' ratings could not be trusted, and so forth.[396]

This was truly an astonishing argument. These studies reviewed by Dr. Kirsch and his co-authors were the basis on which these medications were approved by the FDA. If the studies were invalid, then the drugs never should have been approved in the first place.

The following year a paper by psychiatrist Maurizio Fava and his colleagues acknowledged Dr. Kirsch's point[397]—that trials bought and paid for by the drugmakers show that the benefits of antidepressants are virtually indistinguishable from those of placebo. Dr. Fava and his colleagues discussed several possible "culprits" for this "problem" and proposed a new experimental design to minimize the placebo effect, making it clear that they considered the placebo effect nothing more than an obstacle to be overcome on the way to getting the drugs to market. Nowhere did they even consider the idea that the placebo effect is a useful signal that the drugs don't work.

Still, there was one criticism of Dr. Kirsch's meta-analysis that needed to be addressed—that Kirsch and his colleagues had not stratified their results according to severity of depression. Perhaps lurking somewhere in this mountain of data was a subset of patients who did benefit substantially from antidepressants.

## The Final Nail in the Coffin

And so Drs. Kirsch and Moore and their colleagues performed yet another meta-analysis. This time they omitted Zoloft and Celexa from their analysis, because the data for all trials submitted to the FDA still were not available. They were able to find the missing data on Paxil, by accessing the website GSK set up in response to Eliot Spitzer's lawsuit, and so that drug was included, along with Prozac, Effexor, and Serzone.[398]

The results were published in the February 2008 edition of *PLoS Medicine*. This time around, the drug-placebo difference was exactly the same as before—a puny 1.80 points on the HAM-D scale. For calibration, in 2004 the National Institute for Health and Clinical Excellence (NICE) in the UK had chosen a three-point improvement in HAM-D scores as the minimum required for a change to be judged "clinically significant."[399]

All but one of the trials had been conducted on patients whose baseline scores qualified them as "very severely depressed," and exclusion of this one trial did not substantially change the results. Only the most severely depressed patients—those with HAM-D scores in excess of twenty-eight on intake—experienced an improvement that exceeded the NICE threshold for clinical significance—and interestingly, in this group of patients, the increased difference between placebo and drug scores was due to a lowering of the placebo effect, not an increase in the drug effect.[400] Dr. Kirsch summarized his findings in a book released the following year, titled *The Emperor's New Drugs: Exploding the Antidepressant Myth.*[401]

Once again, not everybody received these findings with open arms. The Rapid Responses to the paper on the *PLoS Medicine* website included this pearl of wisdom:

> *Dozens of clinical trials plus decades of clinical practice plus millions of content patients can't be that wrong… The use of antidepressants is now deeply rooted and well-established in medical society worldwide, it's safe, it works, and there's no shadow of doubt about it.*[402]

To which Kirsch et al. replied that similar claims could have been in past centuries "about bloodletting, lizard's blood, crocodile dung, pig's teeth, putrid meat, flyspecks, frog sperm, powdered stone, human sweat, worms, spiders, furs, feathers, and all of the other treatments that once were used widely but whose success, if any, is now attributed entirely to the placebo effect."[403]

Another commenter took a more direct approach:

> *I can assure you that antidepressants work very well for all severities of depression and if you stand by the findings of your paper then you are naïve and ignorant.*[404]

Besides abuse and arguments by proclamation, what else did Dr. Kirsch's detractors have? They trotted out the same old argument that the studies on which the meta-analysis was based should not be believed—again ignoring the elephant in the room: if the studies cannot be believed, the drugs should never have been approved in the first place. One commenter re-analyzed the data using different starting assumptions and found the drug-placebo difference was equivalent to 2.69 points on the HAM-D scale—still too puny to meet the NICE minimum threshold for clinical significance. Yet another pointed out that the three-point minimum cutoff is a purely arbitrary standard.[405]

This point is well-taken, but as Dr. Kirsch asked in a 2014 talk, What would a non-arbitrary standard look like?[406]

We have an answer to that question. In a 2013 paper, psychiatrist Stefan Leucht and his colleagues reviewed industry-sponsored antidepressant trials that assessed patients with both the HAM-D scale and the Clinical Global Impression Improvement (CGI-I) scale, a one-to-seven-point assessment of global functioning. They found that a one-point improvement on the CGI-I scale (considered the minimum improvement that would be apparent to a treating clinician) was equivalent to a five- or six-point improvement on the HAM-D scale.[407] The drug-placebo difference Dr. Kirsch and his colleagues found doesn't come anywhere near that. Even the difference from the most severely depressed patients doesn't meet that standard.

There was one more objection that needed to be addressed. Could it be that depression is actually more than one disease, and that each of these different "diseases" responds to a different type of drug? Dr. Kirsch dispatches that objection handily, pointing that when patients fail to respond to one drug, and are switched to another, the same percentage of patients will respond to the second drug, be it another drug from the same class or a drug with a completely different mode of action.[408] All that matters is that the drug produces side effects, so that the patient thinks he is getting something good.[409]

And, as Dr. Kirsch explains, switching placebos can itself be a powerful placebo.[410]

Dr. Kirsch's main conclusion—that so-called "antidepressants" are nothing more than active placebos—was a devastating indictment of the psychopharmaceutical industry. It also was the final nail in the coffin of the chemical imbalance theory of mental illness, for two reasons. In the first place, we never see this degree of placebo effect for conditions such as diabetes, that have a known chemical imbalance.[411] Second, we have already seen that drugs with wildly divergent modes of action can have as much (or as little) effect on depression as serotonin reuptake inhibitors. Indeed, there is a drug called tianeptine (available in France, where it is sold under the trade name Stablon) which *enhances* serotonin reuptake, and which has been shown in trials to have almost exactly the same effect on depressed patients as the SSRI's.[412]

If so-called antidepressants are nothing more than active placebos, what's so bad about that? That's a serious question, and it deserves a serious reply. Dr. Kirsch's answer is that while these drugs may be no more than active placebos, their side effects often are not benign. He reels of a list of toxic effects of Prozac, including sexual dysfunction, headaches, nausea, vomiting, insomnia, drowsiness, diarrhea, sweating, dry mouth, seizures, mania, anxiety, impaired concentration, panic attacks, fatigue, twitching, tremors, dizziness, anorexia, dyspepsia, difficulty swallowing, chills, hallucinations, confusion, agitation, photosensitivity, urinary retention, frequent urination, blurred vision, hair loss, pain in the joints, hypoglycemia, rashes, and serious systemic effects involving the skin, liver, kidneys, and lungs—and that's just the more common ones.[413]

Dr. Kirsch goes on to discuss some nondrug interventions, including psychotherapy, exercise, and bibliotherapy, which have been shown to have as much impact on depression as antidepressants, without any of the toxic effects. Surprisingly, according to Kirsch, effective psychotherapy need not cost any more than antidepressant treatment.[414]

Two years after Dr. Kirsch's book came out, psychiatrist Peter Kramer, author of *Listening to Prozac*, weighed in with an op-ed piece in the *New York Times* titled "In Defense of Antidepressants." Once again, the old argument was trotted out the trials that formed the basis for the approval of antidepressants ("rushed, sloppy trials," in Dr. Kramer's exact words) cannot be believed, once again ignoring the obvious corollary that then the drugs should never have been approved. Kramer also offered this curiously backhanded defense of these nostrums: "Antidepressants work—ordinarily well, on a par with other medications doctors prescribe."[415]

This was cold comfort, given that many of the most lucrative classes of drugs, such as statins, produce no clinical benefits at all for the vast majority of patients who swallow them.[416] And all this was quite a comedown from Dr. Kramer's extravagant promises of nearly twenty years before, of a new "cosmetic psychopharmacology" which had the power to make us "better than well."

In a 2014 paper, Dr. Kirsch suggested that antidepressants be used only as a last resort, when depression is severe and all nondrug interventions have been tried and failed.[417]

None of the nondrug interventions discussed by Dr. Kirsch is a panacea. Perhaps part of the solution is to accept there are no panaceas for this messy, complicated, frustrating business we call Life.

## Casting Doubt on the Active Placebo Hypothesis

A 2017 paper in *Molecular Psychiatry* cast doubt on the active placebo hypothesis.[418] The researchers requested data from all industry-sponsored trials for four antidepressants: fluoxetine, sertraline, paroxetine, and citalopram. Lilly said they couldn't provide these data in electronic format, and Pfizer said they couldn't provide data on the timing of adverse events, so that left two antidepressants for the analysis: paroxetine and citalopram.

The researchers looked at the average reduction for depressed mood, as measured by the first item on the HAM-D scale. The difference between each of the drugs and placebo was was about half a point, on a scale of zero to four. The researchers also found that overall there was no relationship between the presence or absence of adverse events, or their severity, and the drug-placebo difference, and they concluded that the difference between the drug and placebo is unlikely to be due to the active placebo effect.[419]

Elias Eriksson, Professor of Pharmacology at the University of Gothenburg in Sweden and corresponding author for the paper, was quoted in the *Guardian* as saying "I think, once and for all, we've answered the SSRI question. SSRI's work. They may not work for every patient, but they work for most patients. And it's a pity if their use is discouraged because of newspaper reports."[420]

When I asked Dr. Kirsch for his reaction to the Eriksson paper, he began by noting that the authors based their analysis not on total HAM-D scores but rather on a single question from that instrument. "There are a couple of problems with that," he told me. "The biggest problem of course is that while the Hamilton Scale is a very reliable scale, a single item from it will be much less so."

Dr. Kirsch also noted that for one of the two drugs tested, paroxetine, there was a significant difference in depressive mood between patients who had experienced side effects and those who had not, with the former group experiencing a greater reduction. For the other drug, citalopram, there was no significant difference. "That's an indication of a lack of reliability, but also some evidence supporting the contention that others and I have made, that indeed the presence or absence of side effects can make a difference in your results."

More importantly, the main point of Dr. Kirsch and his co-authors—that the average difference between antidepressants and placebo is tiny—remains untouched, regardless of whether any or all of this tiny difference is due to an active placebo effect.

## A Controversy Finally Put to Bed?

On 21 February 2018, a new meta-analysis of antidepressants appeared in the venerable journal *Lancet*.[421] The paper was authored by Andrea Cipriani, Associate Professor of Psychiatry at the University of Oxford, and seventeen of his colleagues, and was greeted with a chorus of praise.

The headline in the equally venerable *BMJ* proclaimed "Large meta-analysis ends doubt about the efficacy of antidepressants."[422] Professor Carmine Pariente of the Royal College of Psychiatrists (who was not involved in the study) told the BBC the study "finally puts to bed the controversy on antidepressants."

Some might say the whole point of science is that nothing is ever "finally put to bed," but never mind that for now. What did the study actually find?

Dr. Cipriani and his colleagues examined 522 trials of twenty-one different antidepressants involving 116,447 participants. Every one of the antidepressants was judged to have outperformed placebo in terms of efficacy, with odds ratios ranging from 1.37 for reboxetine to 2.13 for amitriptyline.[423]

Dr. Cipriani and his co-authors also reported that "Funding by industry was not associated with substantial differences in terms of response or dropout rates"[424]—nicely sidestepping the point that many trials with results unflattering to the companies' products went unpublished. Moreover, as the authors themselves concede, "Non-industry funded trials were few and many trials did not report or disclose any funding."[425]

More importantly, efficacy in this study was defined in terms of response rates, once again committing the logical fallacy of treating an incremental variable (depression rating scores) as a categorical variable. Since the studies involved used several different depression rating scales, it is impossible to calculate the mean absolute difference in depression scores, but the standardized mean difference between antidepressants and placebo was 0.30[426]—actually a tiny bit less than the difference reported by Dr. Kirsch and his colleagues.

In summary, the meta-analysis added nothing to our understanding of the matter. Antidepressants were associated with a small increase in effect compared to placebo, with some unspecified portion of that increase probably due to the active placebo effect, and no evidence that this paltry increase translates into any meaningful benefits in the lives of patients.

Nevertheless, the popular media went to town on this one. "It's Official: Antidepressants Are Not Snake Oil or a Conspiracy—They Work," proclaimed the *Guardian*.[427] "Pop More Happy Pills," screamed the headline in the *Sun*.[428] *Newsweek* weighed in yet again with the headline, "Antidepressants Do Work, and Many More People Should Take Them"[429]—going preposterously beyond the available evidence, since the Cipriani et al. study contained no data about the harms of antidepressants, nor any information about the comparative effectiveness of nondrug interventions.

The annual meeting of the American Society of Clinical Psychopharmacology was held on 28 May—1 June of that year. Marc Stone, Deputy Director of Safety for the Division of Psychiatry Products of the FDA, presented the results of a meta-analysis of all placebo-controlled trials of antidepressants submitted to the FDA for the period 1979-2016 inclusive—a total of 228 trials of twenty-two antidepressants involving 73,178 patients.[430]

But in contrast to Cipriani et al., Dr. Stone and his colleagues analyzed the results in terms of absolute change in HAM-D scores, and obtained the exact same result Dr. Kirsch and his co-authors did, to three significant figures: a drug-placebo difference of 1.80 points on the HAM-D scale.[431]

The response of the news media to this study has been a deafening silence.

## The STAR*D Trial

Mainstream psychiatry now admits that the difference in antidepressant trials between the active drug and placebo are small. Is there any reason to believe antidepressants work any better for patients in actual clinical practice?

In fact, there are ample reasons to believe the reverse is true. A quarter of a century ago, psychiatrists Peter and Ginger Breggin wrote in *Talking Back to Prozac*:

> *Depression is essentially a loss of hope. During clinical trials, participants are given hope that a new medication may finally relieve their suffering, they are given professional attention on at least a weekly basis, and they are monitored for any deterioration of their condition. Thus clinical trials provide the essential elements of any good therapy for depression: hope, professional attention, and close monitoring... Participating in the trial is itself therapeutic, at least during its brief duration.[432]*

Nevertheless, it is still conceivable that dedicated clinicians, tailoring treatment to the individual patient, could achieve results better than the dismal ones obtained in clinical trials. It seems a possibility worth investigating.

The STAR*D trial (Sequenced Treatment Alternatives to Relieve Depression) was designed for just this purpose. The study was funded by the NIMH, not the drug companies. STAR*D was not a placebo-controlled trial. Rather, it was a naturalistic study intended to identify best-practices to maximize remission rates for patients with major depression. It was also both the largest and the longest study ever conducted to study the effects of depression treatment.[433]

The initial study protocol called for all patients to have a diagnosis of major depression, defined as a HAM-D score of at least fourteen points on intake. Otherwise, exclusion criteria were kept to a minimum.[434]

The main study outcome was remission, as defined by a HAM-D score of seven or less. "Response" was defined as reduction in HAM-D scores of at least fifty percent. All patients who entered the trial were started on Celexa, and those who remitted were offered twelve months of "continuing care." (Responders had the choice of either going on to the next step or entering continuing care, although they were encouraged to do the latter.) Those who failed to remit on the second antidepressant were offered a third, and those who failed to remit on the third were offered a fourth.[435]

According to the disclosure statements that accompany these papers, A. John Rush, the principal investigator for the study, has accepted money from Forest Pharmaceuticals, the maker of Celexa. So have several of the study's other core authors, including Madhukar Trivedi, Andrew Nierenberg, and Maurizio Fava.[436] Whether this influenced their choice of Celexa as the first drug given to all patients in the study is not discussed.

The study planners did everything in their power to maximize patient adherence and to give the drugs a chance to work. Patient affiliation with the study was promoted by means of informational brochures, a bi-monthly newsletter, and an informational video emphasizing the public health significance of the trial and the critical role played by the patients themselves. Patients were educated—some might say indoctrinated—in the view that depression is a disease, like diabetes or high blood pressure, and can be treated as effectively as other illnesses.[437]

Outcomes were assessed by means of automated telephone calls, and patients were paid $25.00 for each telephonic research outcome assessment. Physicians met with patients on entry to each new step, with follow-up visits scheduled for weeks two, four, six, nine, and twelve.[438] At each visit, the patient spoke with the clinical research coordinator to discuss the research outcomes assessed in the telephone calls and to resolve any problems.[439]

Patients were reminded by mail of upcoming appointments. Those who missed an appointment were telephoned on the same day to re-schedule the appointment, and the day after that if they missed the first call. If a patient missed the second call, that patient's primary care provider was notified.[440]

Medication dosages were carefully titrated to maximize therapeutic effects and minimize side effects. Clinicians were free to prescribe any of a wide variety of adjunctive medications, either to augment antidepressant therapy or to mitigate the side effects of the antidepressants.[441]

Those who entered continuing care continued to see the treating physician every two months, who was free to prescribe any psychotherapy, dosage change or medication change that was deemed necessary to retain remission status. Extra visits could be scheduled if the patient was judged to be in danger of relapsing, or experiencing intolerable side effects.[442]

This care was made available even to patients who moved out of the area. And all of this was provided free of charge, including the medications—no small point, especially given that one-third of these patients had no health insurance.[443]

And how did all this work out for the patients? The first-step results paper from the study was published in the January 2006 issue of the *American Journal of Psychiatry* and reported that 4,790 patients were screened and 4,041 admitted to the study. Of these, 931 were excluded from the study because either their HAM-D score on intake was less than fourteen points (607 patients) or because their HAM-D scores were missing (324 patients). An additional 234 patients failed to return after taking the HAM-D. That left a total of 2,876 patients.[444]

But, oddly, the 931 patients whose initial HAM-D scores were less than fourteen, or never recorded at all, were included for analysis in subsequent papers. This is an important point. Remember the study protocol defined "relapse" as a HAM-D score of fourteen or more. That meant that patients whose HAM-D score was less than fourteen on intake could not be counted as "relapsing" as long as their scores did not get *worse* under the care of the investigators.[445]

The study authors calculated a "theoretical remission rate" of sixty-seven percent by adding together the percentages of total patients who remitted at each step in the study. But this "theoretical remission rate" *did count not patients who dropped out of the study*. In fact far more patients dropped out than remitted. The authors themselves note that the "theoretical remission rate" assumes that patients who dropped out of the study had the same remission rate as those who stayed in[446]—an absolutely indefensible assumption. These patients were getting state-of-the-art psychiatric help, gratis, by clinicians willing to go the extra mile to help them. Why would they drop out of the trial—unless all that "help" wasn't really helping?

Psychologist H. Edmund Pigott re-analyzed the STAR*D data and found that the actual proportion of patients who remained in the study and achieved sustained remission was 5.8 percent—fewer than one out of seventeen. And even that number is no doubt an overestimate, since the pool of patients included the 931 who did not have a HAM-D score of at least fourteen on intake, and therefore did not qualify for a diagnosis of major depression.[447]

One out of seventeen. That is staggeringly ineffective. And since the study had no placebo controls, there is no way of knowing how much of even that paltry result is due to the placebo effect, or the active placebo effect, or the natural rate of recovery.

How did patients fare before these drugs became available? The answer may surprise you.

### Wales, Then and Now

Psychiatrist David Healy examined hospital records in north-west Wales for the period 1894-1896, before any of the modern psychiatric drugs had been introduced, and compared them to those for the year 1996. North-west Wales was almost ideal for this comparison. Between 1896 and 1996, the population had changed almost not at all in terms of size, age composition, ethnicity, poverty, or rurality. What's more, for both periods there was only one point of access for mental health service users in north-west Wales: Denbigh Hospital in 1894-1896, and District General Hospital in 1996. This is about as close to a controlled experiment as it is possible to get for this sort of thing.[448]

Dr. Healy and his colleagues found that for the period 1894-1896, there were 12.3 admissions per year for depression, while for the year 1996 there were 111—nine times as many. For the period 1894-1896, average number of admissions per depressed patient was 1.1, whereas for the year 1996 the figure was 3.5.[449]

Dr. Healy and his co-authors found the same pattern for other types of serious mental illness, including schizophrenia and bipolar disorder. For the period 1894-1896, most patients had only one admission and then went home and got on with their lives. By contrast, for 1996 there were far more repeat admissions and more total days spent in hospital per patient, and the proportion of patients discharged as "recovered" had dropped from thirty-seven percent to thirty percent.[450] Rather than curing depression and other serious mental illnesses, modern treatments seem to have set up a revolving door of hospitalization-release-rehospitalization.

The picture for 1894-1896 was not all rosy. Thirty percent of patients died within five years of their first admission, more than twice the percentage for 1996. Most of the deaths in the 1894-1896 cohort were from tuberculosis or other respiratory infections, conditions which could easily be controlled by the use of modern-day antibiotics. By contrast, the five-year death rate for 1996 cohort was only fourteen percent, but the majority of those deaths were due to suicide or drug overdose.[451]

In summary, for the period 1894-1896, there were far fewer admissions for depression and other mental illnesses, recovery rates were higher, and patients were far less likely to die as a direct result of their mental illness.

These are astonishing findings. In what other branch of medicine have outcomes gotten worse since the nineteenth century?

## A Devastating Indictment

Around the same time Dr. Healy was analyzing these data, Robert Whitaker, a former reporter for the *Boston Globe*, became interested in these same questions. He reviewed the history of treatment outcomes before and after so-called "antidepressant" drugs were introduced, and the results were shocking. In 1955, at the very dawn of the modern psychotropic era, there were 7,250 first admissions for depression in mental hospitals in the United States—a rate of one for every 4,325 people.[452] But by 2008, fifteen million Americans were said to be diagnosed with major depressive disorder, and of these at least nine million were said to be "severely disabled." A condition that once affected fewer than one out of a thousand people now afflicted nearly one out of twenty.[453]

At the same time, long-term outcomes had gotten worse. Before the antidepressant era, depression was generally a self-limiting condition—sufferers experienced one episode, or at most two, and then got on with their lives.[454] But by the time Whitaker began looking into these matters, depression had turned into a chronic, recurring disorder—a point readily acknowledged by mainstream psychiatry.[455]

Soaring incidence rates, worsening outcomes—this is not what happens when treatments work. And Whitaker found this pattern held not just for depression, but for schizophrenia, anxiety disorder, and bipolar disorder—indeed for every major category of serious mental illness. The proportion of the population disabled by these conditions has skyrocketed.

All this makes no sense at all if you think these drugs are curing mental illness. It makes perfect sense if you think these drugs are causing mental illness.

Whitaker summarized these findings in his 2010 blockbuster work of nonfiction, *Anatomy of an Epidemic*. Without invective, without hyperbole, in methodical, workmanlike fashion, Whitaker laid out a devastating, potentially fatal indictment of biological psychiatry.

This book served to catalyze debate on biological psychiatry and so-called "mental illness" in a way no other book has, before or since, and was named the best investigative reporting book of 2010 by Investigative Reporters and Editors.[456]

Whitaker's opus, along with Kirsch's, were the subjects of a laudatory two-part article in the *New York Review of Books* by Marcia Angell, former Editor-in-Chief of the *New England Journal of Medicine*.[457] The *NYRB* also published responses by four eminently credentialed psychiatrists, none of whom cited any data to refute Whitaker's devastating critique, nor even asserted that such data existed. That issue also featured a reply by Dr. Angell which offered this damning assessment: "I have spent most of my professional life evaluating the quality of clinical research, and I believe it is especially poor in psychiatry."[458]

The four psychiatrists who replied to the *NYRB* article were not alone in their distaste for Whitaker's views. In a 26 April 2015 interview on CBC Radio, former American Psychiatric Association President Jeffrey Lieberman called Whitaker a "menace to society."[459]

Since Whitaker published his devastating indictment, things have only gotten worse. Antidepressant prescriptions have continued to rise, as has the economic burden of depression and the suicide rate.[460]

There is independent evidence that these pills can make things worse in some of the patients who take them. We have already discussed Dr. Healy's study which found that two out of twenty healthy volunteers were thrown into a state of intense suicidal preoccupation after taking sertraline. This alarming finding becomes even more alarming when you realize that more than seventy percent of antidepressant prescriptions are written for patients who have no diagnosis of depression or any other mental illness.[461]

Even for patients who do have a diagnosis of major depressive disorder, these drugs may be making long-term outcome worse. Whitaker himself reels off a long list of studies showing that relapse rates are higher in medicated patients than in non-medicated ones, although as he himself acknowledges, there is an obvious potential confounding factor at work here: perhaps patients who were given antidepressants were more impaired to begin with.[462]

A 2011 meta-analysis found a way to control for this potential confounder. For this analysis, researchers looked at two kinds of studies. One of these was extension studies, in which patients are randomized either to antidepressant medication or placebo, and those who remit are maintained on the same treatment (antidepressant or placebo). The other kind was discontinuation studies, in which all patients are given antidepressant medication, and then randomized either to continued treatment with either antidepressants or placebo.[463]

The researchers compared relapse rates between subjects who remitted on placebo and were maintained on placebo (placebo-placebo), to those who remitted on antidepressants and were switched to placebo (drug—placebo). After controlling for all the potential confounders they could think of, they found the relapse rates were higher among the drug-placebo group than in the placebo-placebo group.[464] Apparently, these drugs are causing changes in the brain that make patients more susceptible to relapse in the future.

Since that time, more evidence has accumulated to support this assertion. A 2017 study looked at long-term outcomes for patients diagnosed with Major Depressive Disorder.[465] Patients were divided into five categories depending on the type of treatment they received: none, "inadequate" without medication; "inadequate" with medication; "adequate" without medication, and "adequate" with medication.

The study authors found that, nine years into the study, patients who were treated with medication fared worse than undrugged patients, and that this difference remained even after controlling for initial severity of depression, along with all the other potential confounders they could think of.

So why do so many people continue to take these drugs? Dr. Healy had an answer to that question, telling me:

> *It's very clear to me that we're giving [antidepressants] to far more people than we should be giving them to, and the reason we are doing that is people are hooked on them.*

# CHAPTER 6

# ARE ANTIDEPRESSANTS ADDICTIVE?

### They Had No Idea What They'd Done to Me

"My life was very, very good."

That's how Michael sums up how things were for him—prior to his suffering from devastating withdrawal effects after discontinuing GSK's blockbuster drug Paxil.

Before that, Michael was an educated, successful professional, financially secure, living life to the fullest. He loved working out at the gym, played competitive sports at a high level, and sang in choirs. He also was meticulous about taking care of his health. He never smoked, drank alcohol, or took drugs of any kind.

Michael's troubles began after he accepted a new position that required him to spend long hours working. He developed arm pain and so sought medical attention for it.

The doctor told him the pain was due to a chemical imbalance, and it was just a matter of finding the right drug for him. So he prescribed, in quick succession, amitriptyline, venlafaxine, nortriptyline, and clonazepam. None of these drugs helped, and he didn't stay on any of them for more than a couple of weeks.

Three months after he stopped the drugs, Michael began experiencing seemingly inexplicable bout of tearfulness and agitation. He says he never had any psychological problems before this. He went back to the doctor and said "There's something wrong with me, but I don't know what it is." Michael's doctor prescribed Paxil.

"I had no idea that [this drug] was the sister of Prozac," Michael told me. "If I had known something like that I would have ran a mile."

Michael asked the doctor, Is it addictive? No, the doctor assured him. Any side effects? You might experience a slight weight gain.

Michael started on Paxil, but the drug left him emotionally numb. After a year, he complained to his doctor, who said "Okay—just don't take it anymore." The doctor did not offer any tapering advice, nor any warning of possible withdrawal effects.

Michael stopped the drug, but three months later he was affected, once again, by seemingly inexplicable bouts of uncharacteristic tearfulness and agitation. He went back to his doctor and pleaded "There's something wrong with me. I don't know what it is. Maybe I need this drug." So the doctor renewed his prescription.

"There was no clinical assessment, no discussion, nothing," Michael recalls.

Michael stayed on Paxil for eight more years. He tried a couple of times to kick the drug but every time he was plagued with withdrawal symptoms. Whenever he went on vacation, he always made sure to take Paxil in his carry-on bag, because even a couple of days without the drug could be debilitating.

Michael finally decided to kick the Paxil for good. He announced his intentions to his doctor, who again offered no advice on tapering off the drug safely. So Michael devised his own tapering plan. Over the course of eight months, he cut the dose down from twenty milligrams to ten to five.

The results were disastrous. For the first time in his life, Michael became suicidal. For hours every morning all he was able to do was to lie in bed in a fetal position, trembling, sweating profusely. He also suffered from vomiting, diarrhea, and uncontrollable crying. He went back to the doctor, pleading "I'm in a very dark place. I don't understand it. Tell me what you know about this drug you've been giving me." The doctor asserted Michael had depression. When he replied, "That's nonsense!" he was then referred to a psychiatrist.

"I didn't want to go," Michael recalls. "It was very obvious to me that I was dealing with people that were very ignorant concerning the pills they were pushing. They had no idea what they'd done to me." But he went anyway to the psychiatrist, who told him it was okay to quit the Paxil cold turkey.

Then things got worse.

### Literally Indescribable

Are antidepressants addictive?

The official answer to that question is No. Both National Institute for Health and Clinical Excellence and the American Psychiatric Association are in agreement on that point. The 2009 NICE guidelines for management of depression in adults informs readers that "antidepressants are not associated with addiction"[466] and urges prescribers to inform patients of "the fact that addiction does not occur with antidepressants."[467] The 152-page APA guidelines for the treatment of patients with major depressive disorder uses the word "addiction" only once: "Common misconceptions about antidepressants (e.g., they are addictive) should be clarified."[468]

Both the NICE guidelines and the APA guidelines do refer to something called "discontinuation syndrome," which includes flu-like symptoms such as nausea, headache, light-headedness, chills, and body aches, as well as neurological symptoms such as paresthesia, insomnia, and electric shock-like phenomena (commonly known as "brain zaps"), but these are characterized as transient and self-limiting:

> *Symptoms are usually mild and self-limiting over about 1 week...* *(NICE 2009).*[469]

*These symptoms typically resolve without specific treatment over 1-2 weeks. (APA 2010).*[470]

Is this correct? John Read, a Professor of Clinical Psychology at the University of East London, along with his colleague James Davies, surveyed the literature in order to determine the prevalence of withdrawal symptoms among users who discontinued antidepressants.[471]

And of course, withdrawal symptoms are defined as those which appeared only after the drug is discontinued. The reappearance of symptoms that were present before the drug was started is not considered withdrawal, but rather the resurgence of the underlying condition.

Drs. Read and Davies found that studies show anywhere from twenty-seven percent to eighty-six percent of those who discontinued antidepressants experienced withdrawal symptoms, and nearly half of those experiencing such effects endorsed the most extreme withdrawal severity rating offered.[472]

What about the claim that withdrawal symptoms typically resolved after one or two weeks? Drs. Read and Davies found ten studies which contained data on the length of withdrawal symptoms. Seven of these found that a significant portion of patients experience withdrawal symptoms for longer than two weeks, and withdrawal periods lasting for several months or more are not uncommon. One study found the mean duration for SSRI withdrawal symptoms was more than ninety weeks.[473]

Drs. Read and Davies filed a Freedom of Information Act request to determine the basis for the current NICE statement on withdrawal—that withdrawal symptoms usually are mild and self-limiting over about one week. NICE replied that the current statement on antidepressant withdrawal was inherited from a 2004 version of the guidelines, which stated:

> *[Withdrawal] symptoms are not uncommon after discontinuing an antidepressant and that they will pass in a few days.[474]*

And what was the basis for this statement? It turns out this earlier statement was based on two pieces of research, neither of which, upon examination, provided any evidence for the one-week claim.[475]

These symptoms may be far from benign. A study of antidepressant withdrawal symptoms reported on the internet forum "Surviving Antidepressants" found a dizzying variety of complaints, including neurological (dizziness, ringing in the ears, burning sensations, sensitivity to light), psychological (suicidality, anger, insomnia, obsessive thoughts, poor concentration and memory, depersonalization, paranoia, terrifying dreams), gastrointestinal (constipation, diarrhea, acid reflux), cardiovascular (palpitations, chest pain, racing heart, skipped beats, high blood pressure), musculoskeletal (muscle weakness, aches and pains), psychosexual/genitourinary (difficulty urinating, erectile dysfunction, "numb penis"), and "other" (recurring infections, bad skin, hives).[476]

Some of these complaints are literally indescribable in standard medical terminology: "vision lagging behind eye movements," "head like cotton balls stuffed in," "brain sloshing."[477]

In September of 2018, the All-Party Parliamentary Group for Prescribed Drug Dependence released its survey of 319 antidepressant users.[478] Among the most startling findings:

- Sixty-four percent of patients claimed not to have received any information from their prescribing doctors on the risks or side effects of antidepressants[479]

- Twenty-five percent were given no advice at all on how to withdraw from antidepressants[480]

- Forty-seven percent experienced withdrawal symptoms that lasted for more than one year[481]

- On a scale of one to ten, the average reported severity of withdrawal symptoms was nine[482]

- Thirty percent reported being out of work indefinitely because of antidepressant withdrawal symptoms[483]

But perhaps even more unsettling were the respondents' personal accounts of what antidepressant withdrawal has done to their lives. A sampling:

> *I am unable to work, communicate, or basically function on any level that makes life worth living.[484]*

> *I exist as a shadow of the person I once was.[485]*

> *I cannot function to do simple tasks like make a cup of tea let alone leave the house to go to work.[486]*

Many respondents claimed that their doctors just denied the very nature of the problem:

> *I was told that 'discontinuation syndrome' could only have lasted a few weeks so I didn't know what I was talking about.[487]*

Others were told they were experiencing a relapse:

> *The psychiatrists simply waived my story out of hand as impossible, saying that 'It was just the old illness coming back' even though I've NEVER experienced ANYTHING even remotely approaching this.[488]*

> *I was told it was just the anxiety and depression coming back but I have never experienced anything even close.[489]*

> *[It was] written off as my 'original condition' returning, and proof that I needed the medication like a diabetic needs insulin.[490]*

Despite being told otherwise, the respondents were adamant that their withdrawal symptoms were different from the original problems which led them to take the drugs in the first place:

*The withdrawal has been far worse than the depression ever was.*[491]

*Depression and despair ten times worse than I ever experienced before commencing on the drug.*[492]

*This is far worse than anything I ever experienced before I went on the drug.*[493]

Many of the respondents reported the withdrawal effects went on for years after discontinuing the drugs:

*It has gotten a little easier with time but even after 5 years of being off venlafaxine I am still not right.*[494]

*It is just over 3 years since I stopped and I don't think I am really over it now... I think my brain and body have been permanently damaged...*[495]

*Seven years on after the last dose of the drug, I am still not the same person I was before starting Seroxat.*[496]

Some of them found themselves unable to kick the drugs, and gave up entirely:

*I can only withdraw for a limited time because the symptoms are too severe to tolerate. I have tried several times to come off unsuccessfully.*[497]

*I don't want to be on these drugs anymore as they have too many side effects and I don't believe they better the quality of my life, but I can't stop.*[498]

So why do the authorities say that antidepressants are not addictive?

## A Semantic Quibble

Let's hit the rewind button and go back to 2002, when BBC's *Panorama* aired the documentary "Secrets of Seroxat." Viewers learned the story of Helen Kelsall, a young woman who began taking Seroxat for anxiety, and experienced terrible withdrawal symptoms when she tried to kick the drug. These symptoms included headaches, muscle pain, sweating, tremors, nausea, balance problems, and "head shocks." She reported that because of these problems, she had missed much of her course work for the last year and was in danger of failing. Viewers were also told that the Maudsley Hospital Medication Helpline had received more reports of problems coming off Seroxat than for any other drug.

In Shelley Jofre's interview with Alistair Benbow, European Head of Clinical Psychiatry for GSK, the following dialogue took place:

> SHELLEY JOFRE: *Your leaflet says: 'Remember, you cannot become addicted to Seroxat.' That's not true, is it?*

> ALISTAIR BENBOW: *Yes, it is true. There is no reliable evidence that Seroxat can cause addiction or dependence, and this has been borne out by a number of independent clinical experts, by regulatory authorities around the world, by the Royal College of Psychiatrists, and a number of other clinical groups.*

> SHELLEY JOFRE: *If people can't stop taking a drug when they want to stop taking it they're addicted, aren't they?*

> ALISTAIR BENBOW: *No, that's not correct. The definition of addiction is not as you describe it. Addiction is characterized by a number of different criteria which includes craving, which includes increasing the dosage of the drug to get the same effect, and a number of other features, and these are not affected by Seroxat.*

SHELLEY JOFRE: *That's not, with respect, what the Oxford English Dictionary says. It says 'Addiction is having a compulsion to take a drug the stopping of which causes withdrawal effects.' Now we've spoken to plenty of people who say they're compelled to take Seroxat because stopping it produces withdrawal symptoms—they're addicted.*

ALISTAIR BENBOW: *If you use that limited definition of addictive, then most prescription medicines could be defined as addictive.*[499]

The second episode in the series, "Emails From the Edge," noted that the words "You cannot become addicted to Seroxat" were approved by the Medicines Control Agency (the forerunner of the MHRA). Yet, the MCA's own rules stated that product information must be conveyed in a language patients can understand.[500]

Shelley Jofre told viewers "What a difference six months and fourteen hundred emails can make"—a reference to the missives *Panorama* received regarding the program, many of which told of severe withdrawal effects after stopping Seroxat. Dr. Benbow appeared on this second episode as well, and told Jofre "It's quite clear that the phrase 'Seroxat is not addictive' was poorly understood by them"—seemingly putting the blame on the patients whose lives were devastated by this drug, rather than on GSK.

Of course, one way of resolving this dispute would be to ask the antidepressant users themselves. Dr. Read and his colleagues did just that. They conducted an online survey of 1,829 antidepressant users in New Zealand, and the results were illuminating.[501]

More than half of respondents reported they had experienced withdrawal effects after stopping antidepressants, and nearly half of those characterized those symptoms as "severe," the most extreme rating category available. A quarter of the respondents considered themselves to be addicted to antidepressants, and 6.2 percent rated themselves as severely addicted (again, the most extreme rating category available).[502]

So why is there even a controversy about this? The argument is all about semantics. The current edition of the *Diagnostic and Statistical Manual, DSM-5*, released in 2013, doesn't even have a category for "addiction," using instead the term "substance use disorder," which is defined by the presence of at least two of a list of eleven symptoms. None of these symptoms—tolerance, craving, withdrawal, and so forth—is by itself either necessary or sufficient for a diagnosis. The authors also proclaim:

> *Symptoms of tolerance and withdrawal occurring during appropriate medical treatment with prescribed medications (e.g., opioid analgesics, sedatives, stimulants) are specifically not counted when diagnosing a substance use disorder.*

In other words, the authors of the DSM-5 have defined this condition in such a way that antidepressants taken as prescribed *by definition* cannot be considered addictive.

But the *DSM* did not always define addiction that way. In the third edition, *DSM-III*, which was published in 1980 and which inaugurated the modern era of biological psychiatry, the corresponding category was called "substance dependence," and a diagnosis of this condition could be made on the basis of withdrawal symptoms alone. In other words, the authors used the same common-sense definition of addiction as it is understood by lay people today.

But this changed when the revised version of *DSM-III, DSM-IIIR*, was released. Now "substance dependence" was defined as cluster of symptoms, as "substance use disorder" continues to be defined today. The revised version of *DSM-III*, with its revamped definition of "substance dependence," was released in 1987.

That was the same year Prozac was approved for the market.

So in answer to the question, "Are antidepressants addictive?" it just depends on what you mean by the word. It is undeniable that a significant fraction, perhaps a majority, of patients who discontinue these drug experience distressing symptoms that they did not have before taking the drug, and which in some cases can be debilitating and/or chronic. This is the meaning of the word addiction, as understood by the world's most trusted English dictionary as well as by the patients themselves.

Admittedly, the most severe withdrawal symptoms are experienced by only a minority of patients, but multiply this by tens of millions of people taking these drugs worldwide and you have a problem. The psychopharmaceutical industry's response to this suffering experienced by actual human beings has been a semantic quibble over the meaning of the word "addiction," which may lead one to wonder whether they really have our best interests at heart.

## Extraordinarily Difficult

On 22 February 2018, the usually sober *Times* of London published an article about the aforementioned Cipriani et al. meta-analysis, titled "More People Should Get Pills to Beat Depression"[503]—even though, as we have already noted, the study contained no data about the hazards of these drugs, nor of the comparative effectiveness of nondrug therapies.

This prompted a letter to the editor, published the following day, by James Davies and some of his professional colleagues from the Council for Evidence-Based Psychotherapy which said in part:

> *The study [by Cipriani et al.] actually supports what is already known, namely that the differences between placebo and antidepressants are so minor that they are clinically insignificant... Lastly, the study does not address the damage caused by long-term prescribing, including the financial burden to the NHS and the disabling withdrawal effects that these drugs cause in many patients, which often last for many years.*[504]

The next day Wendy Burn, President of the Royal College of Psychiatrists, and David Baldwin, Chair of the RCPsych Psychopharmacology Committee, offered this riposte:

> *We know that in the vast majority of patients, any unpleasant symptoms experienced on discontinuing antidepressants have resolved within two weeks of stopping treatment.*[505]

Drs. Read and Davies, along with a number of professional colleagues, wrote to Drs. Burn and Baldwin regarding their statement that antidepressant withdrawal symptoms usually resolve within two weeks. They noted out that the RCPsych's own survey own survey of 800 antidepressant users found that sixty-three percent of them had experienced withdrawal effects and that a quarter or more of these reported anxiety lasting for more than twelve weeks. More disturbingly, as the authors of the letter pointed out, the survey was removed from the RCPsych website less than forty-eight hours after the "two weeks" claim appeared in the *Times*. Read and Davies asked Burn and Baldwin either to provide studies backing up the "two weeks" claim, or else apologize and retract the statement.[506]

Drs. Burn and Baldwin both replied to the letter, but neither one provided any evidence to back up the "two weeks" statement. Baldwin attached two papers to his reply, but neither one was relevant to the question at hand. Burn did not even do that much, and neither one of these eminent doctors said anything at all about the request for retraction.[507]

Accordingly, on 9 March, Drs. Read and Davies and eight of their professional colleagues, along with a number of long-term sufferers of antidepressant withdrawal effects, filed a complaint with the Royal College of Psychiatrists demanding a retraction. The RCPsych dismissed the complaint, without providing any evidence for the "two weeks" claim, other than the one-sentence statement from the 2009 NICE guidelines.[508] Government ministers ordered Public Health England to set up an expert panel to examine the subject of antidepressant withdrawal, with Dr. Baldwin serving as the representative of the RCPsych.[509]

On 4 September, Read's and Davies' systematic review of antidepressant withdrawal effects appeared in the journal *Addictive Behaviors*, and three weeks after that, the *Times* reported that Dr. Baldwin had stepped down from the panel after an online controversy in which bloggers and anonymous commenters on internet threads had called him a "pharma-whore" and a "lying serial rapist worse than Hitler." Dr. Read condemned the online abuse but added "We can't control the anger of people by denial of what these drugs can do." Rosanna O'Connor, Director of Drugs, Alcohol, Tobacco and Justice at PHE expressed regret for any distress Baldwin experienced but promised the review would be published the following year as scheduled.[510]

When I spoke with Dr. Read, he indicated that he actually preferred not to use the term "addiction" in regard to antidepressants, because of the stigma associated with the term, but he also made it clear the semantic argument is not the main issue here. He told me:

> *I think it's a diversion. The issue that we have millions of people, literally millions of people who are trying to come off antidepressants and they can't. Or they are finding it extraordinarily difficult.*
>
> *And at the same time we have the American Psychiatric Association, the Royal College of Psychiatry, and our national guidelines here all lying about this problem, all saying pretty much the same thing—that withdrawal from antidepressants hardly ever lasts longer than one or two weeks, and it's self-limiting.*
>
> *When people tell their doctor that they're experiencing withdrawal effects, the doctor will look up these guidelines and say 'No, no, that's not withdrawal—that's your illness.' So not only do they not get the recognition of the withdrawal, they don't get support for the withdrawal, they're likely to get their drugs actually*

*increased, when they really need a very very slow, supported withdrawal.*

*And this is happening for millions of people around the world. That's why it's important. And that's why whether we call it addiction, dependence, or whatever, the point is that people are having trouble getting off them. And that's why they are reporting, in very large numbers when asked, severe protracted withdrawal effects.*

## A Stunning About-Face

On 29 May 2019, in a stunning about-face, the RCPsych issued a press release stating that "Official guidance on coming off antidepressants needs to reflect the full range of patients' experience…"[511] The statement also noted that many patients experience severe withdrawal symptoms, which can last far longer than existing guidelines acknowledge. In addition, the college called for:

- Routine monitoring of when and why patients are prescribed antidepressants

- Adequate training for all clinicians for best prescribing and managing of antidepressants

- Adequate support services for patients experiencing severe antidepressant withdrawal symptoms

- Expansion of talking therapies

- High-quality research into issues including which antidepressants are likely to work for which individual, and the benefits and harms of long-term antidepressant use

Dr. Read told the *Herald*:

*It seems the minimizing is finally over. [College] members who value research over personal opinions, and who place the public good before the interests of the pharmaceutical industry, have apparently prevailed.*

*This dramatic U-turn may represent a first step towards the RCP regaining the respect of scientists in this field, which will be accelerated by their removing drug company sponsored individuals from senior positions of responsibility.[512]*

The promised review by PHE was released on 10 September,[513] and recommended:

- Increased availability and use of data on the prescribing of medicines that can cause withdrawal

- Enhancing clinical guidance and the likelihood it will be followed

- Improving information for patients and carers on prescribed medicines

- Improved support for patients experiencing withdrawal symptoms

- Further research on the prevention and treatment of dependence and withdrawal

On 18 October 2019, the *BMJ* reported that NICE was updating its guidelines on treating depression to acknowledge that withdrawal effects may be severe and protracted in some patients, and to advise patients to discuss the matter with their health care providers before discontinuing the drugs.[514]

Meanwhile, on this side of the pond, it's still business as usual. And while the changes proposed by PHE most certainly are to be welcomed, it should be borne in mind that the PHE review was not precipitated by any new information on the subject of withdrawal—after all, patients had been telling their psychiatrists about these problems for years. The review was commissioned in response to a Twitter campaign—which may reasonably lead some to question whether psychiatry is capable of effecting meaningful reform of its own excesses.

## Absolute Hell

And what about Michael, whom we met at the beginning of the chapter? After finally kicking the Paxil for good, the years that followed were, in his words, "Absolute Hell." The suicidal feeling became worse. "I wanted to jump in front of buses, I wanted to jump off bridges, cut my wrists, hang myself." Some morning all he could do was to lie in bed, chanting, "I'm not going to kill myself."

"This went on and on and on for months and months and months," he recalls. He had to quit his job and live off his savings.

Now eight years off the Paxil, Michael has begun to put the pieces of his life back together. He has resumed working, part time. But he knows he will never get back the years he has lost. Among the many effects of Paxil withdrawal was a complete loss of sexual functioning, and eight years later he doesn't think that's coming back, either.

"The urge to merge is gone," he laments.

And what about the arm injury that triggered this iatrogenic cascade in the first place? It is still there, but it pales into insignificance in the light of the long lasting, life-altering trauma of psychoactive drug withdrawal.

## The Summing Up

In a 2012 paper titled "Relabeling the Medications We Call Antidepressants,"[515] Dr. Healy, along with clinical psychologist David Antonuccio, proposed a list of criteria for a medication to be called an "antidepressant." In order to be labeled as such, a medication should:

- Be clearly superior to placebo
- Offer a risk/benefit balance that exceeds that of alternative treatments
- Not increase suicidality
- Not increase anxiety and agitation

• Not interfere with sexual functioning

• Not increase depression chronicity

Drs. Healy and Antonuccio reviewed the evidence and concluded that so-called "antidepressants" fall flat on every one of these counts. They suggested, only partly tongue-in-cheek, that instead these drugs be called "antiaphrodisiac medications," "agitation enhancers" "insomnia inducers," "suicidality inducers," "mania stimulators," or "gas busters."[516]

The upshot: These drugs are barely distinguishable from placebo in short-term trials, staggeringly ineffective in a long-term naturalistic study that gave the drugs every chance to work, and capable of causing suicidality in patients who are not depressed and worsening of depressive symptoms in those who are. What's more, discontinuation of these drugs can cause severe and protracted withdrawal effects in a significant proportion of users, leading many of them to take them for years and years. Finally, in a small minority of users, these drugs cause a state of agitation that can lead to violence and suicide.

And yet, some maintain that the FDA black-box warning of 2004 caused an *increase* in youth suicides. That is the matter we shall take up next.

# CHAPTER 7

# DID THE FDA BLACK BOX WARNING INCREASE SUICIDES?

In 2007, a paper appeared in the *American Journal of Psychiatry* by Robert Gibbons of the Center for Health Statistics at the University of Illinois-Chicago, titled "Early Evidence on the Effects of Regulators' Suicidality Warnings on SSRI Prescriptions and Suicide in Children and Adolescents." Dr. Gibbons and his co-authors looked at the rates of both antidepressant prescriptions and suicides in young people, both before and after several FDA warnings of a possible association: the Talk Paper of October 2003, the hearing of February 2004, and the black box warning of October 2004. They found that antidepressant prescriptions for children and adolescents decreased by twenty-two percent, while the youth suicide rate rose fourteen percent.[517]

The authors concluded "If the intent of the pediatric black box warning was to save lives, the warning failed, and in fact it may have had the opposite effect: more children and adolescents have committed suicide since it was introduced."[518]

Predictably, the media had a field day with this one. The *Washington Post* informed readers, "Youth Suicides Increased as Antidepressant Use Fell."[519] The *New York Post* went for the jugular: "Warning May Be Killing Kids,"[520] while the *Chicago Tribune* weighed in with the more restrained "As Youth Suicides Increase, FDA's Label Rule Criticized."[521] Dr. Gibbons told the *Tribune* the FDA black box warning had a "horrible and unintended effect."[522]

There was just one problem: Gibbons and his colleagues looked at antidepressant prescriptions for the years 2004 and 2005, but *they only looked at suicide data for the year 2004*. Examination of Figure 1 of the *AJP* paper shows that antidepressant prescriptions barely budged in 2004, and almost all the decrease in prescriptions occurred in 2005.[523] What happened to suicide rates that year? The paper doesn't say.

But it's easy enough to find out. According to the CDC,[524] in 2005, the first full year after the FDA black box warning, the rate of youth suicides dropped. It dropped again in 2006, and again in 2007. That is exactly what we would expect to find if the FDA black box warning had its intended effect, either by means of decreasing prescriptions for antidepressants, or increased monitoring of pediatric patients for suicidality, or both.

What has happened since 2007? In fact, antidepressant prescriptions for children and adolescents enrolled in Medicare increased every year from 2008 through 2012.[525] So did youth suicide rates. Again, this is exactly what we would expect if the effect of the black-box warning (and the accompanying news coverage) faded with the passage of time.

On 29 August 2018, the online magazine *STAT* published a piece titled "FDA's Continuing Use of 'Black Box' Warning for Antidepressants Ignores the Harms of this Warning." The article featured a full-color picture of a bottle of Paxil along with the caption "Paxil and other antidepressants carry a black-box warning, the most serious type of warning in prescription drug labeling"[526]—as if the source of our problems is that we're not giving Paxil to enough kids.

"All antidepressant prescriptions still contain this frightening black box warning," the authors lamented.[527]

The authors' claimed that since the FDA issued the warning, 1) antidepressant prescriptions for children and adolescents have decreased,

2) psychotherapy visits for children and adolescents declined, and 3) youth suicide attempts and completed suicides have increased.[528]

In regard to the first point: although the piece was published in August of 2018, the authors show no data for antidepressant prescriptions for children beyond September 2005,[529] even though such data is readily available. In fact, as we have seen, after dropping for three years after the warning was issued, the rate has since increased, eventually to exceed what it was before the warning was issued.

The second point—that psychotherapy for children decreased after the warning—does seem a matter for legitimate concern. But one of the principles of epidemiology is that temporality of association is not sufficient to prove causation. The postulated cause-and-effect relationship must be plausible as well,[530] and the authors adduce not a shred of evidence that the warning *caused* the decrease in psychotherapy visits. Even if it did, one possible solution might be to think about ways despondent children and adolescents could access such care without having to be labeled as suffering from a drug-treatable "illness." The authors never consider this point.

The final point—that the black box warning caused an increase in youth suicides—is refuted by the authors' own data. The graph the authors provide clearly shows that the youth suicide dropped every year for the first three full years after the FDA black-box warning has issued[531]—as we have already noted. So how do they justify their conclusion that the warning led to an increase in suicides? By drawing a *trendline* for the years 2005-2016. But there is no logical justification for doing so. We have already seen that antidepressant prescriptions for children increased from 2008 on, and so did youth suicides.

Two days after the *STAT* article appeared, author Bob Whitaker called the authors out on their mendacity in his *Mad in America* blog, but no retraction has been issued.[532]

So let's sum things up: Since 2007, when the Gibbons paper (and the accompanying blizzard of laudatory news stories) appeared, completed suicides for youths aged 5-19 have continued to rise, reaching an all-time high in 2014 (they have appear to have plateaued, dropping slightly for the years 2015 and 2016, the most recent years for which data is available).

Meanwhile, Dr. Gibbons moved on to a plum appointment at the University of Chicago. His curriculum vitae lists over 275 papers, seven books, and seventeen book chapters.

And, as youth suicide rates skyrocketed, a scapegoat had to be found. And the media found her—a little slip of a girl from a small town in Massachusetts named Michelle Carter.

# CHAPTER 8

# THE STORY OF MICHELLE CARTER

The sad tale of Michelle Carter and Conrad Roy unfolded across the public stage like a modern-day morality play. Joe Fitzgerald of the *Boston Herald* summed up the case thusly: "A lovestruck 18-year-old boy who never got to see 19 was just a malleable kid, buried more than three years ago because the heart he wore on his sleeve rendered him totally vulnerable to the lethal instructions of the ruthless Carter."[533] The *New York Post* editorial board called the case "a horrible window on the way we live now."[534] And the *Sun* introduced Michelle Carter to readers as follows: "The 20-year-old from Massachusetts, USA, urged her boyfriend to kill himself by bombarding him with dozens of vile text messages."[535] As she entered the Bristol County Courthouse for her sentencing, one spectator screamed at her on live television: "Kill yourself!"[536]

It's hard to name another defendant in a criminal case in recent history who was vilified more relentlessly than Michelle Carter. Even serial killers or Mafia dons do not usually receive this level of vituperation. And media accounts almost completely ignored the fact that when the tragic denouement of this tale took place, both of these young people were under the influence of the same drug, Celexa.

## There's Lots of Ways

The facts in the case are as follows: at 5:00 PM, 13 July 2014, police found the lifeless body of Conrad Roy in a pickup truck in a parking lot behind the K-Mart in the little town of Fairhaven, Massachusetts. Conrad, who was eighteen years old when he died, had inhaled a lethal dose of carbon monoxide created by a gasoline-powered water pump installed in the vehicle. His death was ruled a suicide.

Conrad's death came as a shock to friends and family. The previous month he had graduated from Old Rochester Regional High School with a 3.8 grade point average, where he was remembered as a well-rounded athlete. He had already earned his Captain's License from the Northeast Maritime Institute and had been accepted into Fitchburg State University for the Fall semester.[537]

When investigators examined Conrad's cell phone, they found that all of his text messages had been deleted except for one thread stretching back a week, which contained a series of messages from Michelle Carter, seventeen, from the nearby town of Plainville.[538] Conrad Roy and Michelle Carter have often been referred to as boyfriend and girlfriend, but they weren't, really. They were texting pals. Although they both lived in small towns less than an hour apart in southern Massachusetts, they had met each other for the first time while both of their families were vacationing in Florida. After that almost all of their relationship had been conducted online, by Facebook and text messages.

When police examined the message thread, they found a disturbing series of missives in which Michelle repeatedly urged Conrad to kill himself. They also found that on the night Conrad died, he had called Michelle twice, and they spoke for forty-three minutes the first time and forty-seven minutes the second. Police surmised that she spoke to him right up until the moment of his death.[539]

Most damning, when they examined Michelle's phone, they discovered a text message Michelle sent two months later to another friend, in which she claimed that Conrad had entertained second thoughts and exited the truck, but she told him to get back in.[540]

Michelle was indicted on 5 February 2015 and arraigned at the New Bedford Juvenile Court the next day. Thomas Quinn, the Bristol County District Attorney, recused himself because he was related to Conrad Roy's family. In a statement, the Bristol County District Attorney's Office said "Instead of attempting to assist him or notify his family or school officials, Ms. Carter is alleged to have strongly influenced him to take his own life, encouraged him to commit suicide, and guided him in the engagement of his own activities which led to his death." Although Massachusetts has no law against assisted suicide, and although Michelle had been in the next town when Conrad died, she was charged with involuntary manslaughter in the death of Conrad Roy.[541]

Michelle's attorney, Joseph Cataldo, asked that the charges be thrown out, but the motion was denied. Cataldo appealed the ruling to the Supreme Judicial Court of Massachusetts, which upheld the lower court's ruling. This was the first time the court had ruled that an indictment for involuntary manslaughter could be upheld on the basis of words alone.[542]

Cataldo waived his client's right to a jury trial,[543] and opening arguments began 7 June 2017.[544] Prosecutors portrayed Michelle as an emotionally needy teen who craved attention, and who simultaneously was relentless in her urging Conrad to kill himself:

> *You're not gonna kill yourself. You say all the time you want to but look, you're still here. You don't wanna die, you don't want the pain to stop.*[545]

> *How bad do you want it? Because if you want it bad you should succeed.*[546]

> *So it didn't work? You said you wanted this bad. I knew you weren't going to try hard. I feel like such an idiot. You didn't ever do anything. You lied about the whole thing. You said you were*

*gonna go to the woods. I thought you really wanted to die. But apparently you don't. I feel played and stupid.*[547]

*Hang yourself, jump off a building, stab yourself idk there's lots of ways.*[548]

She also urged him not to be too concerned for his family:

*Everyone will be sad for a while but they will get over it and move on. They won't be in depression. I won't let that happen. They know how sad you are, and they know that you are doing this to be happy and I think they will understand and accept it. They will always carry you in their hearts.*[549]

Prosecutors portrayed Michelle as basking in the attention generated after Conrad killed himself. She reached out to Conrad's mother and tried to console her in a text message:

*You didn't fail him, not even a little bit. You tried your hardest, I tried my hardest, everyone tried their hardest to save him. But he had his mind set on taking his life.*[550]

Michelle even organized a softball tournament in his memory.[551]

On 12 June, psychiatrist Peter Breggin took the stand as an expert witness. He testified that SSRI's, the class of medications which includes Celexa, target the frontal lobes of the brain, which controls empathy, decision-making, and the ability to feel love and wisdom. He further averred that Michelle was "involuntarily intoxicated" by her medication and in the grip of a grandiose delusion that she alone could help Conrad find his way to Heaven, leaving her to care for his family. [552]

No other expert witness testified to contradict Dr. Breggin's assessment.

Judge Moniz handed down the sentence on 3 August. But first, Conrad's family members were given the opportunity to read their victim impact statements to the courtroom.[553]

Conrad's father, Conrad Jr., told the courtroom "I cannot begin to describe the despair I feel over the loss of my son. I am heartbroken."[554]

Conrad's sister Camdyn stated "Not a day goes by without him being my first thought waking up and my last thought going to bed. I know he loved me more than any big brother ever could."[555]

Conrad's mother Lynn was too distraught to appear in person, but prosecutors read from a written statement from her, which said the Michelle had inflicted "so much pain on myself, his dad, his sisters, and all who loved him deeply."[556]

Then Judge Moniz read his decision. He began by acknowledging that Conrad Roy took significant steps towards ending his own life:

> *His research was extensive. He spoke of it continually. He secured the generator. He secured the water pump. He researched how to fix the generator. He located his vehicle in an unnoticeable area and commenced his attempt by starting the pump.*
>
> *However, he breaks that chain of self-causation. By exiting that vehicle, he takes himself out of the toxic environment that it has become.*

Judge Moniz then dismissed concerns that the case was novel, citing an 1816 case in which a Massachusetts inmate was prosecuted for urging a fellow inmate who had been sentenced to death to hang himself in his cell before his scheduled execution.[557]

This argument seemed a bit odd, given that 200-year-old case ended in acquittal.[558]

Judge Moniz then explained how Michelle's actions constituted "wanton and reckless conduct" which led directly to Conrad's death:

*When Ms. Carter realizes that Mr. Roy has exited the truck, she instructs him to get back into the truck, which, she has reason to know, is or is becoming a toxic environment inconsistent with human life...*

*She admits in a subsequent text that she did nothing. She did not call the police or Mr. Roy's family...*

*She did not notify his mother or his sister.*

*She called no one.*

*And finally, she did not issue a simple additional instruction: 'Get out of the truck.' Consequently this court has found that the Commonwealth has proven, beyond a reasonable doubt, that Ms. Carter's actions and also her failure to act, where she had a self-created duty to Mr. Roy, since she had put him into that toxic environment, constituted, each and all, wanton and reckless conduct.*

Judge Moniz dismissed without explanation Dr. Breggin's argument that Michelle was involuntarily intoxicated at the time she was urging Conrad Roy to end his life, and ruled her guilty of involuntary manslaughter in the death of Conrad Roy.[559]

The Assistant District Attorney demanded that Judge Moniz revoke Michelle's bail immediately, calling her a danger to herself and others. But Moniz, noting that Michelle had always cooperated fully with the long legal process and had never failed to appear in court, allowed her to remain free until sentencing.[560]

That same day, the CBS news magazine *48 Hours* aired "Death by Text: The Case Against Michelle Carter." The piece began with excerpts from a video diary recorded by Conrad, one month before he killed himself. Conrad faced the camera and solemnly intoned:

*It's not realistic what's going on in my head that keeps on piling and piling and piling.*[561]

*I need to be comfortable in my own skin.*[562]

*I need to relax. I really do.*[563]

The announcer goes on to explain "[Conrad's mother] Lynn Roy thought her son was feeling better; he was getting professional help and was on an antidepressant, Celexa." No consideration was given to the possibility that the distress Conrad was experiencing was caused by that drug, even though the prescribing information for Celexa warns of anxiety, agitation, akathisia, and emergent suicidality as possible toxic effects.[564]

Viewers were then shown video clips from the actual trial. But after devoting all of thirty-six seconds to Dr. Breggin's testimony, *48 Hours* brought in psychiatrist Harold Koplewicz (who was not involved in the case) to assure viewers that antidepressants are safe.[565]

Dr. Koplewicz was one of the twenty-two notional authors of GSK's infamous Study 329 of Paxil,[566] which concluded that the drug was safe and effective for treating major depressive disorder in children—even though, as we have already seen, the data showed the exact opposite: the drug was ineffective and caused frighteningly high rates of self-harm and suicidality. Nobody bothered pointing any of this out, let alone asking Dr. Koplewicz if he thought his words (or the words he signed off on) had contributed to any youth suicides.

Sentencing in the case took place on 3 August. The maximum penalty for involuntary manslaughter in Massachusetts is twenty years, and prosecutors had asked for seven to twelve, but Judge Moniz opted for something a good deal less harsh. He sentenced Michelle to two and a half years, with half of that suspended, to be served in the county jail rather than in the state prison.[567]

Judge Moniz also allowed her to remain free pending her appeals, ordered her to undergo mandatory mental health treatment, and forbade her from profiting from telling her side of the story.[568] Courtroom observers predicted the appeals process could drag on for years.[569]

## Another Portrait of Michelle

Dr. Breggin has written extensively about the Michelle Carter case in his blog. The portrait of Michelle that emerges from his writings stands in stark contrast to the one put forth in the courtroom and the news media.

In his first post, published the day the verdict was handed down, Dr. Breggin began by noting that he had served as an expert witness in over one hundred court cases, many of which required him to interview friends, families, and acquaintances of children or adults who have suffered from adverse drug reactions. "At no time have I ever experienced such unanimity of opinion about an individual," he wrote. "Michelle's life story seemed literally too good to be true, and in some ways it was."[570]

At the age of fourteen, Michelle was an outstanding player for her school's softball team, in a community that prided itself on winning softball championships and sending its players to college on athletic scholarships. Michelle's coaches told Dr. Breggin that she was the most caring and helpful teammate they had ever had the pleasure of working with.[571]

Despite being a standout competitor, Michelle was always the first one to step forward and offer reassurance for any teammate who was performing poorly. She also went out of her way in the classroom to help her fellow students and even her teachers.[572]

Dr. Breggin asked the people he interviewed if they knew of anyone in the town of Plainville who had anything bad to say about Michelle. Not one of them did.[573]

"What emerges from the interviews, school, and medical records and texts is a girl whose major intention in life is to love and help people," Dr. Breggin wrote. "Thousands of texts with her friends confirm how much love they shared among themselves, and how her friends in particular saw Michelle as a caring person."[574]

Even after she was charged in the death of Conrad Roy, her school invited her to return for her senior year, and her graduating class voted her the person "Most likely to brighten up your day."[575]

So what went wrong?

## A Troubled Child

Michelle's troubles began when she entered the eighth grade, one month after turning fourteen, when both of her beloved maternal grandparents died in quick succession. Michelle developed anorexia, and within a month had dropped an estimated twenty to thirty pounds. At that point she weighed a mere eighty-five pounds, placing her in the bottom two to three percent for her age and height. Her liver functioning was abnormal and she developed orthostatic hypotension. Michelle was diagnosed with anxiety and depression, and prescribed Prozac.[576]

At first her doctor started her on ten milligrams of the drug, but this was soon increased to twenty—the standard adult dose. But this was not an adult patient—this was an eighty-five-pound girl, with abnormal liver functioning to boot, likely impairing her ability to metabolize the drug. For this child, the standard adult dose was, in Dr. Breggin's words, "a mammoth dose." Then, without any explanation, her doctor increased the dose to thirty milligrams.[577]

Michelle gained weight, as intended, but she was not happy about this and began exercising compulsively. She also developed a strong emotional attachment to another girl and compulsively pursued her friendship until the other girl's mother intervened—adding to Michelle's sense of loss. Michelle's doctor decided to take her off Prozac, and she discontinued the drug, apparently without incident, in October of 2011.[578]

## He Told Me to Kill Them All

Michelle first met Conrad Roy in February of 2012. She was fifteen years old at the time, and he was a year older. They met face-to-face only three times after that, the last time in the summer of 2013, a year before Conrad killed himself. But they kept in touch by means of Facebook and text messages.[579]

In May of 2012, Michelle's mother became concerned about her daughter's anorexia and compulsive exercising. At that point she weighed a scant one hundred pounds—about twenty-five pounds below what was considered normal. Afraid of being viewed as a failure, Michelle was unwilling to see the doctor who had treated her previously, and so her mother took her to another doctor who would remain Michelle's primary care provider all the way through Conrad's death. This new doctor quickly raised Michelle's dose to thirty milligrams, simply because that was the dose she had been prescribed before.[580]

Meanwhile Conrad was having his own problems. On 27 August 2011, his father called the police to their house, claiming his wife had struck him. She was charged with domestic assault and battery, and Conrad's father subsequently obtained a restraining order against her.[581] That same year Conrad tried to commit suicide by overdosing on Tylenol, the first of four attempts before his completed suicide. Notably, this first attempt also involved a girl, who called the police right away and saved his life.[582]

In 2012, Conrad attempted suicide again, was hospitalized, and discharged on antidepressants.[583] Subsequent to this, his messages to Michelle took on a darker tone.

On 10 October 2012, Conrad spent an entire day tormenting her with threats to kill himself. She begged him not to do it, telling him "You're scaring me," but he continued to taunt her, and finally Michelle called a friend and a relative of Conrad's.[584]

Her next message was sent to him five hours later: "Conrad please answer me right now please."[585]

After midnight on 24 November, still on thirty milligrams of Prozac, Michelle sent Conrad a Facebook message, saying she has been having terrible nightmares about the Devil. Conrad responded with an oafish remark about raping her.[586]

The next night Michelle messages Conrad, again telling of seeing the Devil in her nightmares. Conrad tells her he has seen the Devil too, adding "He told me to kill them all."

The following dialogues ensues:[587]

> MICHELLE: *Are you serious?*
>
> CONRAD: *Dead serious.*
>
> MICHELLE: *I'm so sorry baby!*
>
> CONRAD: *He was red and had a black cape.*
>
> MICHELLE: *I learned to fight him and yeah I know I've seen him too. I see him a lot actually*

Michelle confirms that all this takes place in her sleep but adds "To me it seems like real life." Conrad responds "I saw real life." These two young people continued discussing the matter, without gaining any insight as to why they are experiencing these nightmarish visions. Apparently no one ever told them that from the first Prozac Full Prescribing Information to the latest, "abnormal dreams" has always been listed as among the most common adverse reactions.[588]

Sometime after this—the timeline is not exactly clear—Michelle was switched from Prozac to Celexa. She was to remain on this drug until after Conrad killed himself.[589]

Dr. Breggin would later write:

> *These two wounded and distraught adolescents, fifteen and sixteen years old, would develop an on-and-off relationship—mostly without seeing each other, and dominated by Conrad—that would overwhelm the two of them. The mental disturbances caused by their antidepressants, their own emotional vulnerabilities, and the impact upon each other would cut off from other people, devastate their lives, and cause unimaginable suffering to their*

*families and friends. Most of the time both of them would be taking antidepressant drugs, while displaying all of the most serious adverse effects, including an overall worsening of their condition, irritability and hostility, grandiosity, and suicide.[590]*

## A Perfect Storm of Dysfunction

On 19 February 2014, a domestic squabble at the Roy household got out of hand. Conrad's father held his son down and repeatedly punched him in the face. Police were called, and when they arrived Conrad's face was swollen and bloodied. Conrad's father was arrested for assault and battery.[591]

Conrad's texts to Michelle reveal he was also smoking marijuana, although it is not clear how much or how often.[592]

His parent's divorce, his father physically attacking him, his anxiety and depression, and the toxic effects of the drugs (both prescribed and illegal) he was taking, all seemed to be combining to create a perfect storm of dysfunction.[593] Naively, Michelle believed that she loved Conrad and was the only one that could save him,[594] while he was telling her that the only thing that could make him hate her would be if she revealed his suicide plans to anyone else.[595] Michelle, an innocent young girl who saw only the good in people, was not sophisticated enough to recognize an emotional blackmailer when she encountered one, and continued her attempts to help.

And yet, ten days before that ill-fated night in Fairhaven, she changed her tune. For the first time she becomes angry and irritable, and she begins exhorting Conrad to kill himself.[596] What happened?

Reading Michelle's texts, it becomes obvious that she really believed she was helping Conrad. The girl who tried to help everybody was now going to help him end the misery of his earthly existence and go to Heaven.[597] Even more bizarrely, Michelle believed that she herself was capable of consoling his family after his death. If that sounds crazy, that's because it is. It's grandiose and delusional. But where did these delusory ideas come from?

A 2003 paper by a team of Harvard researchers gives us a hint. The researchers reviewed the charts of eighty-two children started on SSRI's and found that twenty-two percent of them suffered psychiatric adverse events, including emotional disorders, behavioral disorders, sleep disorders, and psychotic disorders including obsessions, auditory and visual hallucinations, and delusions. There was no correlation between the adverse events observed and the type of SSRI—all of the drugs were equally bad for kids.[598]

Michelle's medical records, the texts and messages between her and Conrad, as well as other information in the public record, make it clear that both of these young people were suffering from every major category of SSRI-induced mental disorder.[599]

The Harvard study also found that the average duration between initiation of antidepressant therapy and the onset of symptoms was ninety-one days. And when did Michelle begin exhorting Conrad to kill himself? Ninety-one days after her dose of Celexa was doubled, from five milligrams to ten.[600]

Michelle's delusory state continued after Conrad's death. She continued sending him text messages, dozens of them. Here is the text she sent to him on the day of the softball tournament she organized in his memory, two months after Conrad killed himself:

> *Hey babe. I hope your birthday was beautiful and happy yesterday. I was thinking about you the whole day. I wish I was there to celebrate with you. But the tournament went well so well today. I know you were probably looking down with a smile watching the games. I raised over $2300 for you babe! This is the start of my journey to help others. I love you and miss yu so much. Youre forever in my heart. Smile down on me. I hope I made you proud.*[601]

This was the last text message she sent Conrad. Perhaps it finally dawned on her that he was really, truly gone.[602] We don't know. We do know that two days later she sent another friend the message that turned out to be her undoing.

### Did Michelle Really Tell Conrad to "Get Back In?"

In her closing statement, Assistant District Attorney Katie Rayburn read the following text message Michelle sent on 15 September 2014 to her friend Samantha Boardman:

> *Sam his death is my fault honestly I could have stopped him I was on the phone with him and he got out of the car because it was working and he got scared and I fucking told him to get back in Sam because I knew he would do it all over again the next day and I couldn't have him live the way he was living anymore I couldn't do it I wouldn't let him.*[603]

These were the words of a frightened anorectic teenage girl. But they were not read aloud in the courtroom by a frightened anorectic teenage girl. They were read by a forty-something prosecuting attorney who intimidates people for a living. But never mind that for now. The key questions is: Did Michelle really say this?

There is no direct, irrefutable evidence that Michelle ever said these words to Conrad—no text message to him, no voice recording, not even anyone claiming to have overheard these words. And yet, these words became the linchpin of the commonwealth's case against Michelle.[604]

Dr. Breggin points out that the commonwealth portrayed Michelle as an attention-seeking liar who could not be believed. He cites one particularly egregious example: in her cross-examination of Dr. Breggin, the Assistant District Attorney claimed that Michelle had consistently lied in her numerous text messages to friends about cutting herself, citing as proof the "fact" that no one else had ever reported seeing the scars. That night,

Dr. Breggin reviewed all the text messages that were part of the state's case and found two from friends of Michelle who expressed their concern after seeing her scars.[605]

When Dr. Breggin produced these messages during cross examination the next morning, the commonwealth dropped the matter. But they never retracted their claims of the previous day, nor asked the judge to disregard them. They just never brought up the matter again.[606]

The prescribing information for Celexa includes the following toxic effects: amnesia, confusion, depersonalization, psychotic depression, delusion, and psychosis. All of these have to potential to corrupt memories, or creates false ones. Despite this, and despite its characterization of Michelle as someone who could not be trusted, the commonwealth based its case on a single text message, without a shred of corroborating evidence, delivered two months after Conrad killed himself, by a grief-stricken young girl who assumed too much responsibility for other people's woes, and who was still in a drug-induced fog when she sent it.[607]

According to the American Bar Association, the primary duty of the prosecutor is to seek justice, not merely to convict.[608] That doesn't seem to be what was going on in this case.

What was behind this seemingly relentless determination to obtain a conviction at all costs? Dr. Breggin suggests an explanation. As mentioned previously, Bristol County District Attorney Thomas Quinn recused himself because of a familial relationship to Conrad Roy—specifically, he was the first cousin of Roy's grandmother. But Michelle's attorney Joseph Cataldo argued that the case should not be prosecuted by attorneys who owed their jobs to Conrad Roy's cousin, and asked that it be turned over to another county attorney's office, or to a special prosecutor, or to the US Attorney. His request was denied.[609]

The day the verdict was handed down, Dr. Breggin published his first blog post about the case. Eight days later, Judge Moniz presided over an emergency hearing requested by the Bristol County District Attorney's

Office in which Assistant District Attorney Katie Rayburn demanded that Dr. Breggin be enjoined from writing anything about the case. This is called Prior Restraint, and normally it is invoked only in matters pertaining to national security.[610]

Dr. Breggin was not at the hearing, and was not even aware that it has happened until the news media began calling him and asking about it. Michelle's attorneys were not at the hearing either, having been given less than twenty-four hours advance notice.[611]

Dr. Breggin would later explain his reasons for writing about the case:

> *Michelle was not only convicted unjustly, two or more years before the trial the DA began subjecting her to excoriating public criticism calculated to make her look like a monster. Michelle deserves to have her story told by someone who is not out to harm her.*[612]

He went on to discuss numerous cases in which he has served as an expert witness, in which men, women, and children had committed atrocious acts of violence, adding:

> *In not one of these cases did the DA's office stir up as much hatred against the offender as the Bristol County DA's office in Massachusetts has stirred up against Michelle Carter... The DA refuses to let go of its need to control what the world thinks of Michelle Carter.*[613]

Dr. Breggin reassured Judge Moniz that he was not revealing any information from Conrad's medical records, which had been embargoed, and that he had Michelle Carter's permission to use information from her medical records.[614] On 1 September, Judge Moniz refused to impose a gag order on Dr. Breggin. He could go on writing about the case.[615]

Meanwhile, the day after the verdict was announced, Conrad's mother Lynn Roy filed a $4.2 million wrongful death lawsuit against Michelle in Norfolk Superior Court.[616] On the last day of August, Cataldo filed notice to appeal her conviction.[617] And on 4 October, former Assistant District Attorney Katie Rayburn's nomination for a District Court Judgeship was unanimously approved by the Governor's Council. An article in the *Sun Chronicle* noted admiringly "She was one of the two prosecutors who won a manslaughter conviction against [Michelle] Carter in a controversial case that went all the way to the state Supreme Judicial Court…"[618]

## A Society Drugging Its Children

One month after Judge Moniz handed down his verdict, I called Dr. Breggin to get his take on matters. We talked about his inquiry into the world of Conrad and Michelle, a world of children seemingly lacking any kind of meaningful adult guidance, and trying without much success to help each other with their depression and anxiety and eating disorders.

"And the major helper was Michelle," he told me. "And she was also extremely needy. And unable, despite her friends wanting her to, to break off from the abusive Conrad."

I ask Dr. Breggin if he blames the death of Conrad Roy on anybody besides Michelle or Conrad himself. He says:

> *I think there is a broad circle here that includes the doctors that gave her as a child Prozac and Celexa, the doctors who gave him antidepressants, the drug companies and the leaders of American psychiatry that have been pushing antidepressants on children.*
>
> *I think we have the estrangement from adults in the lives of children that's being now reinforced by texting and other means of communications.*
>
> *Conrad was a young man, he was nineteen at the time, she was seventeen, both were very young and very immature and very needy and weren't provided the services they really needed. Instead their young brains were doused in neurotoxins.*

*In my practice, I treat children who I have great affection for, who have done horrible things under the influence of drugs, like assault their parents in terrible ways, and who are transformed when I got them off the drugs, and they've done it with the help of at least one devoted parent, usually two.*

*Let me sum up. It's a terrible tragedy. I wouldn't want to blame even Conrad's parents, nor Conrad, who was very abusive to Michelle. Michelle herself was a lovely child, she seemed to have very loving parents. This is a social phenomenon. A society drugging its children, not providing them services, and not taking seriously enough how the children are being thrown into each other's arms, texting without adult supervision, I think that's really in many ways the core here.*

## Aftermath

On Wednesday 6 February 2019, the Supreme Judicial Court of Massachusetts upheld Michelle's conviction and prison sentence.[619] Her lawyers asked the sentence be stayed while they appealed the case to the Supreme Court of the United States, but on Monday, 11 February, she was ordered to begin serving her sentence immediately.[620]

On Tuesday 9 April, the wrongful death suit filed against Michelle Carter by Lynn Roy was dismissed by the Norfolk Superior Court "with prejudice," meaning the case could not be re-opened. Attorneys for both sides declined to comment.[621]

On Monday 22 July, Senator Barry Feingold and Representative Natalie Higgins of the Massachusetts Legislature introduced a bill to criminalize "suicide coercion." Dubbed "Conrad's Law," the proposed measure would establish a penalty of up to five years in state prison for coercing or encouraging another person to commit suicide, or providing the knowledge or means for doing so. The bill specifically exempted doctor-assisted suicide, although doctor-assisted suicide is not even legal in Massachusetts.[622]

# CHAPTER 9

# ANTIDEPRESSANTS
# AND RAMPAGE KILLINGS

## I Love You, Mom

On 20 July 2012, clad in tactical combat gear and carrying a Smith and Wesson M&P 15 semiautomatic rifle, a Remington Model 870 pump action shotgun, and a Glock .22 semiautomatic pistol, twenty-seven-year-old James Eagan Holmes entered Theater 9 of the Century 16 Megaplex in Aurora, Colorado, during a midnight screening of *Batman Returns*. Holmes threw two tear gas grenades and then opened fire into the crowd, killing twelve persons and wounding seventy more. After his gun jammed, Holmes walked out of the theater and surrendered to police.[623]

During interrogation, when asked to spell his surname, Holmes haughtily replied "Like Sherlock." Investigators later found that he had rigged up home-made bombs (which, fortunately, never detonated) inside his home to divert emergency responders during the attack.[624]

During the trial, the victims' surviving family member told tales of lives permanently shattered by the massacre—of holidays, weddings, and graduations that never will be celebrated as well as depression, night terrors, and survivors' guilt.[625]

Ashley Moser had just told her daughter Veronica to expect a baby brother or sister. Six-year-old Veronica was cut down by Holmes' bullets, as was Ashley's unborn baby. "I don't know who I am anymore," Ashley told the court. "I was a mom when I was 18, and that's all I knew how to be. And now I'm not a mom."[626]

Amanda Medek told of the loss of her younger sister Micayla, who was twenty-three when she was murdered. "She never fell in love," Amanda said of her. "She never got to have a family. She had big plans and she never got to do that."[627]

Matthew McQuinn, twenty-seven years old (the exact same age as Holmes), died protecting his fiancée from a hail of bullets. "He was always smiling and his eyes just had mischief in them," his mother, Jerri Jackson, recalled. In her last conversation with her son, he told her he was going to the midnight show and she admonished him to be careful and he replied, "Oh, nothing's going to happen. I love you, Mom."[628]

A jury found Holmes guilty of twelve counts of capital murder and numerous other counts as well, and on 26 August 2015 a judge sentenced him to twelve life terms in prison, to be served consecutively, plus 3,318 years. He was not eligible for parole. He currently is being held in solitary confinement in a maximum-security prison in an undisclosed state, which is how he will spend the rest of his days.[629]

Who is James Holmes, and what could have been the cause of his rage?

## A Gifted Student

James Holmes grew up in a stable churchgoing middle-class household. His father Bob was a statistician, his mother Arlene a nurse. She remembers her son as a boy who always did his homework and his chores. According to Arlene, the boy never showed any signs of violence, nor any interest in drinking or drugs.[630]

A gifted student, James enrolled in the doctoral program in Neuroscience at the University of Colorado in the autumn of 2011. His fellow students remember him as introverted, a bit socially awkward, but this description could apply to a lot of graduate students.[631]

James sailed academically through the first semester of his studies, but then he hit a bit of a rough patch. Over Christmas break he was diagnosed with glandular fever, and he returned to his studies, but his schoolwork suffered. He had always been a bit shy, and he had difficulties giving presentations in class.[632]

At this time he also underwent the end of his first serious romantic relationship. James himself described the breakup as "cordial," and in fact it was his ex-girlfriend who, no doubt with the best of intentions, urged him to seek help at the campus student wellness center. There on 21 March 2012, James had his first appointment with psychiatrist Lynn Fenton.[633]

James confessed to Dr. Fenton that he had thoughts of killing people, three and four times a day. Fenton was not alarmed by these revelations, and perhaps there is no good reason to believe she should have been. Such thoughts are not exactly unheard of, especially among young, introverted loners.[634]

It was on this day that Dr. Fenton prescribed fifty milligrams of Zoloft to James for his social anxiety.[635]

Subsequently, James' fleeting thought or fantasies about killing people began coalescing into concrete plans. In an online chat with his ex-girlfriend, four days after starting Zoloft, James revealed to her his bizarre new theory that killing people would help him increase his "human capital." At first she assumed he was just kidding, but as the conversation continued she realized he really meant it.[636]

Two days later, Holmes went to see Dr. Fenton again. He didn't mention his theory of "human capital" to her, but he did tell her that the obsessional thoughts had not stopped. Fenton doubled the dose of Zoloft from fifty to one hundred milligrams.[637]

James's condition continued to deteriorate. During his fourth appointment with Dr. Fenton, he still did not tell her about his "human capital" delusion, although he did reveal that his homicidal ideation had increased.[638]

"Psychotic level thinking," Dr. Fenton recorded in her notes for that session. "Guarded, paranoid, hostile thoughts he won't elaborate on." It was at this meeting that Fenton increased the dose of Zoloft again, to 150 milligrams.[639]

James continued to go downhill. His final class presentation was a disaster, and he failed his exams. He was offered the chance to take them again, but instead he dropped out. At his last appointment with Dr. Fenton, she was so alarmed at the decline in his condition she offered to keep seeing him gratis, but he refused.[640]

It was sometime after that—we don't know exactly when—that James stopped taking Zoloft. We do know that his last prescription ran out on 26 June, less than one month before the massacre of 21 July.[641]

## Aftermath

Holmes was arrested and confined to a psychiatric hospital facility, where he became disturbed and was prescribed tranquilizers. In December he was given another SSRI antidepressant, for the first time since he discontinued the Zoloft in June, and he tried to kill himself.[642]

Psychiatrist David Healy was retained as an expert witness for the defense and met with Holmes. Later he would tell an interviewer that had he been called to the witness stand, he would have told the jury "These killings would never have happened had it not been for the medication James Holmes had been prescribed."[643]

But Dr. Healy was never asked to testify. The public defender did argue that Holmes was not guilty due to reasons of insanity, but the concept of involuntary intoxication played no role in the defense.[644]

The sad story of James Holmes was the subject of yet another *Panorama* documentary presented by the inimitable Shelley Jofre, titled "A Prescription for Murder?" which premiered on 26 July 2017. The program also revealed that antidepressants had been linked to twenty-eight reports of homicide submitted to the UK medicines regulator, as well as thirty-two reports of homicidal ideation.[645]

The denunciations began before the program had even aired.

"There still is a huge stigma around taking medication for mental health," an essay in the *Daily Metro* lamented, the day before the episode was broadcast:

> *When do we hear the stories of antidepressants going brilliantly? Where are the documentaries around people whose lives have been saved by antidepressants? Where are the shows around people who've found love because their medication helps them to socialize?*[646]

*Newsweek* weighed in yet again, also before the program aired, quoting Professor Carmine Pariente of the Royal College of Psychiatrists:

> *There is no good evidence that antidepressants increase the risk of violent behavior, and the extremely rare (and tragic) cases that are cited in support of this theory could be explained by chance: antidepressants are prescribed relatively widely, and so by chance some on antidepressants will commit a violent act. Moreover, people on antidepressants may be suffering from some forms of mental disorder or distress that may, albeit very occasionally, increase the risk of reacting impulsively or violently.*[647]

The day after the program aired, the *Times* printed a letter from Wendy Burn, President of the Royal College of Psychiatrists, titled "Stop This Dangerous Scaremongering Over Antidepressants," in which she proclaimed "There is absolutely no evidence to suggest a causal relationship between these drugs and murder."[648] Author Peter Hitchens offered this rejoinder: "Has anyone actually established a link, one might justly ask, between 'antidepressants' and the benefits they are alleged to provide?"[649]

The next day, a piece appeared in *Lancet* in which Dr. Pariente blamed rising suicide rates not on antidepressants but on the FDA black box warning:

> *When the rates of SSRI prescriptions for children and adolescents decreased after US and European regulatory agencies issued warnings about a possible suicide risk with antidepressant use in paediatric patients, this decrease was associated with an increase in suicide rates.[650]*

As evidence for this proposition, Dr. Pariente cited Robert Gibbons' 2007 paper in the *American Journal of Psychiatry*—a paper whose conclusions have since been completely debunked by author Robert Whitaker.[651]

### Your Client Is Going to Die

When I discussed the case with Dr. Healy, he made it clear that Pfizer knew a long time ago that some people can have bad reactions to its blockbuster drug:

> *When healthy volunteers take the drug, it makes them restless, it makes them suicidal. They become suicidal on the drug. It's not that all people do. You give it to twenty healthy volunteers, and maybe only one has a reaction. In the early eighties, Pfizer knew.*
>
> *They didn't publish the trial. They didn't publish any of the healthy volunteer data. In the clinical trials done where people are depressed, you can see the same thing. But in those cases they can argue it away, that's it's caused by the illness. You can't argue that point with healthy volunteer studies.*
>
> *So, quite aside from what the clinical trials show, and the fact that was well-known—that these drugs can make you quite*

*restless, can make you suicidal—even if one could ignore this, forget all that—if you're trying to analyze the Holmes case, you have to look at all the facts on the record, and ask What happened? Why did this happen? There just isn't a mental illness there that would have led this to happen.*

*There is the fact that he did get put on a serotonin-reuptake-inhibiting antihistamine some years before this, and he had a very bad reaction to it. There is the fact that he got put on the drug and he tried to warn his doctor that he shouldn't be on this drug, and she just increased the dose. And there is the fact that both of the parents—not knowing that he had been on the drug—after the event, months later, both of them got put on SSRI's, both of them. And had very bad reactions.*

*There is the fact that three months after the event, when he had been in a drug-free state, and he had been—and I forget the details of how he was, but he was kind of agitated and some doctor figured that it might be a good idea if he would be put on an SSRI—and he attempted suicide.*

*So there's a strong case that can be made that even if there were no clinical trial evidence, no healthy volunteer evidence, if you first look just at the case, and ask what caused this to happen, you can claim that the drug may have played a part—and if you then try to look at the healthy volunteer evidence, the clinical trial evidence that shows that the drug can make people this way—you know you're in the ballpark of Well, it's the likeliest way to explain what happened. It's not one hundred percent sure, but it's by far the likeliest explanation to make.*

I then asked Dr. Healy why he believed the involuntary intoxication defense was not used in the Holmes case. This was his reply:

*My hunch is a deal was made. The prosecutor said we won't execute this guy if you don't bring up this. It's going to look bad if you have this guy Healy come in and claim all the literature is ghostwritten, there's no access to data—it's going to be one of those things that is going to shake public confidence in the regulation of drugs. Well, if you're going to argue this, well, we're going to fight and you might lose and your client is going to die.*

## More Rampage Killings

The Aurora Theater massacre was just one in a series of high-profile antidepressant-associated rampage killings. In addition to that one and the Standard Gravure shooting (already discussed in the Preface and in Chapter 2), a sampling of such events follows. Only incidents in which two or more persons were killed in a public place, and in which antidepressants specifically were implicated, are included. No claim is made for the completeness of this list:

21 APRIL 1999: *Eric Harris, seventeen, and Dylan Klebold, eighteen, of Columbine, Colorado, shot and killed twelve of their fellow students and a teacher at Columbine High School before killing themselves in the school library. An additional sixteen victims were hospitalized for injuries. Witnesses recalled the pair were laughing as they carried out the massacre.[652] Eric was taking the antidepressant Luvox at the time of his death and before that had been prescribed Zoloft.[653] Dylan had been taking Saint John's Wort,[654] a herbal preparation that is sold in Germany as an antidepressant and which is similar in its mode of action to SSRI's.[655]*

21 MARCH 2005: *Sixteen-year-old Jeffrey Weise of Red Lake, Minnesota, shot and killed his grandfather (a tribal police officer at the Red Lake Indian reservation) and his grandfather's companion*

172

*before driving his grandfather's squad car to Red Lake Senior High School. There he shot and killed an unarmed security guard before entering the school and killing a teacher and five students. Witnesses described him as smiling during the attack.[656] Jeffrey had been taking sixty milligrams of Prozac, three times the normal adult dose.[657]*

7 NOVEMBER 2007: *Pekka-Eric Auvinen, eighteen, a student at the Upper Jokela Secondary School in Finland, entered the school and opened fire, killing six students along with the school nurse and the head teacher before turning the gun on himself and ending his own life. He had begun taking SSRI antidepressants in April of the previous year, but apparently discontinued them some time in the autumn of 2007, shortly before the massacre took place.[658]*

14 FEBRUARY 2008: *Steven Kazmierczak, a twenty-seven-year-old former graduate student at Northern Illinois University, walked into a classroom on the NIU campus and opened fire, killing five and wounding at least sixteen more before turning the gun on himself and ending his own life. Kazmierczak's girlfriend told CNN had had been taking Prozac, Ambien, and Xanax, and had discontinued the Prozac three weeks before the shooting.[659]*

23 SEPTEMBER 2008: *Maati Saari, a twenty-two-year-old culinary student at the Seinäjoki University of Applied Science in Finland, entered the school and opened fire, killing ten, as well as setting several fires, before using the gun to end his own life. Witnesses later described him as "calmly" dispatching his victims one by one.[660] An investigation determined he had been taking an antidepressant as well as a benzodiazepine tranquilizer, alprazolam.[661]*

29 MARCH 2009: *Forty-five-year-old Robert Stewart entered Pinelake Health and Rehab, a 120-bed nursing home facility where his estranged wife worked, and opened fire, killing seven elderly patients and a nurse. He was shot and wounded by police and subsequently taken into custody.[662] Two days before the shooting Stewart had been prescribed Lexapro and Xanax. A blood test showed he also had twelve times the therapeutic level of Ambien, a sleep aid he had been taking to counter the agitation induced by the antidepressants. At the trial, Stewart's attorney claimed that Stewart had no memory of the incident.[663] Stewart was convicted on multiple counts and sentenced to 179 years in prison.[664]*

16 SEPTEMBER 2013: *Aaron Alexis, a thirty-four-year-old naval veteran and civilian contractor entered the Washington Navy Yard and opened fire, killing twelve and wounding three more before being gunned down by police.[665] The previous month Alexis had been prescribed Trazadone for his insomnia.[666]*

24 MARCH 2015: *Twenty-eight-year-old First Officer Andreas Lubitz of Germanwings Flight 9525 waited until he was alone in the cockpit, then locked himself in and aimed the plane at the ground. All of the passengers and crew, including Lubitz, were killed—150 lives lost in all. Lubitz's treating physicians and family members all refused to be interviewed by investigators. The toxicology report revealed that Lubitz had the antidepressants citalopram and mirtazapine in his system, as well as the sleep aid zopiclone, at the time of the crash. A few days before, Lubitz had also received prescriptions for the antidepressant escitalopram, the antipsychotic Dominal, and the sleep aid zolpidem. In an email to his psychiatrist, Lubitz stated he had been taking the tranquilizer lorazepam.[667]*

In the wake of the Germanwings crash, an article in the *New York Times* warned readers not about the dangers of antidepressants, but about the dangers of public discussions of the possible role of antidepressants in rampage killings. "The stigma is enormous,"[668] lamented William Hurt Sledge, Professor of Psychiatry at Yale.

Ron Honberg, Director of Policy and Legal Affairs for the National Alliance on Mental Illness (an organization that receives massive funding from drugmakers),[669] concurred:

> *These kind of stories reinforce the anxiety, the doubts, the concerns that people have that 'I have to keep my symptoms concealed at all costs,' and that doesn't benefit anyone.*[670]

## Precursors to Suicidality and Violence

Tales of antidepressant-associated rampage killings, however horrifying, are still just anecdotes. Are there any data—as opposed to anecdotes—that show antidepressants increase violence? There are. We have already noted the 2010 review by Thomas Moore and his colleagues which showed there were eight times as many violence case reports associated with antidepressants than there would be if these reports were distributed randomly.[671]

In January of 2016, less than a year after the Germanwings crash took place, Peter Gøtzsche and his colleagues at the Nordic Cochrane Collaboration reviewed the clinical study reports for industry-sponsored RCT's of five antidepressants—Cymbalta, Prozac, Paxil, Zoloft, and Effexor. They found these drugs more than doubled the risk of akathisia and suicidality in children and adolescents and nearly tripled the risk of aggressive behavior.[672]

Serious events included homicidal threat, homicidal ideation, assault, sexual molestation, and a threat to take a gun to school (all in patients taking Cymbalta), damage to property, punching household items, aggressive assault, verbal abuse, and aggressive threats (Paxil), and belligerence (Prozac).[673]

The following October, Dr. Gøtzsche and his colleagues reviewed the incidence of harms related to suicidality and violence in thirteen studies in which antidepressants were given to healthy volunteers.[674] The five categories of harms the researchers looked at were violence, suicidality, psychotic events, emotional disturbances, and "activation events" (a catch-all term encompassing aggression, agitation, akathisia, and similar types of events). Antidepressants nearly doubled the rate of harms related to suicidality and violence in healthy volunteers, and, as Gøtzsche and his co-authors note, that figure is no doubt an underestimate, since for eleven of the thirteen trials only published journal articles were available—and we have already seen that these articles systematically under-report the actual rate of harms in the trials.

We know these drugs blunt feelings of empathy, in some of the people who take them.[675] We know they can cause hostility and aggression, in some of the people who take them. We know that in rare cases, they can cause a psychotic break in some of the people who take them. What happens when you get all these effects in the same individual? Sounds like a recipe for mass violence.

It seems premature, at best, to conclude antidepressants cannot be playing a role in rampage killings. Given the other well-documented harms and the meager benefits provided by these drugs, a little more critical scrutiny seems in order.

Meanwhile, who know how many more rampage killings have occurred in which the link to antidepressants has not been reported by the media?

In July of 2019, the United States Secret Service National Threat Assessment Center released a report titled "Mass Attacks in Public Spaces—2018." Twenty-seven such events in which at least three persons were harmed took place that year, and twelve of the attackers had a known history of "mental health" diagnosis and/or treatment, and yet the report contained not a word about what drugs these perpetrators had been prescribed.[676]

§

On 14 December 2012, Adam Peter Lanza, twenty, shot his mother four times in the head with a Savage Mark II .22 caliber bolt-action rifle, and then drove to nearby Sandy Hook Elementary School which he had attended as a child, carrying with him a Sig Sauer P226 semi-automatic 9mm pistol, a Glock 20 semi-automatic 10mm pistol, and a Bushmaster Model XM 15-E2S semi-automatic rifle. He entered the building at approximately 9:30 AM, appearing calm, and proceeded to massacre twenty children and six school employees before killing himself with a single shot to the head with the Glock.[677]

Able Child, a non-profit organization for parents, caregivers, and children's rights, filed a Freedom of Information Act request for the release of Adam Lanza's medical records. Patrick B. Kwanashie, Assistant Attorney General for the State of Connecticut, argued against the request at a hearing, claiming that the release of such information could "cause a lot of people to stop taking their medications."[678]

Who could argue with that?

# CHAPTER 10

# CONCLUSIONS

On Tuesday 5 March 2019, the FDA approved Janssen's new drug Spravato, or esketamine in nasal spray form, for "treatment-resistant depression".[679] (Interestingly, psychiatrist Michael Thase, Dr. Kirsch's main antagonist in the "Emperor's New Drugs" controversy, was the Principal Site Investigator for the clinical trials, while Kim Witczak, who had spoken so movingly about her husband's Zoloft-induced suicide at the 2006 FDA hearings, was the only member of the FDA panel who voted not to approve the drug.) The recommended course of treatment for this drug, which is to be administered only in a doctor's office, is twice-weekly for one month, followed by weekly or biweekly treatments thereafter.[680]

A quick explanation is in order here. Many drugs come in two molecular forms, called optical isomers, which are mirror-images of each other. Often, only one of the two isomers is active. Esketamine is one of the two isomers of the club drug ketamine, known colloquially as "Special K." Separating this isomer and dispensing it in pure form enables Janssen to patent a drug which has already been available for decades and vend it at premium prices.

As we have already noted, normally, before a drug can be approved, the FDA requires two positive clinical trials showing the drug outperforms placebo. There can be any number of negative trials, which just don't count. The FDA had to bend even these modest requirements for

Janssen. A single four-week trial showed a four-point improvement on the sixty-point Montgomery-Åsberg Rating Scale for Depression—which is likely too paltry to be detectable in a face-to-face assessment of global functioning by a treating clinician.[681]

The results of two other placebo-controlled trials were *negative*. The only way Spravato could be approved was for the FDA to count the results of a relapse study, which essentially showed that patients who did well on the drug, did well on the drug. This was an unprecedented move on the part of the agency.[682]

Spravato comes with a price tag of $4,720 to $6,785 for the first month of treatment and $2,360 to $3,450 per month thereafter,[683] which means the cost of a year's treatment could be as much as $44,825. And this is the same stuff (admittedly in purer form) you can buy in a nightclub bathroom for a good deal less.

Janssen is no stranger to controversy. On 4 November 2013, the United States Department of Justice announced that Janssen's parent corporation, Johnson and Johnson, agreed to pay $2.2 billion to settle claims of illegal marketing of its products, including allegations that Janssen had illegally marketed the antipsychotic drug Risperdal for children.[684] On 1 July 2016, a jury awarded $70 million to a young boy who grew breasts after being given Risperdal.[685]

None of the laudatory news stories made this clear, nor did they mention there were three suicides in the trials, all occurring in the treatment arm. This alarming finding becomes even more alarming in light of the fact that actively suicidal patients were excluded from these trials.[686]

Nonetheless, the announcement was heralded as a breakthrough. The *New York Times* proclaimed the new product "could help millions."[687] Not to be outdone, the *Washington Post* touted "the biggest advance for depression in years."[688]

So-called "antidepressants" have been on the market for more than six decades. One out of eight Americans aged twelve or older have taken them within the last twelve months, including a staggering one out of four prime-age women.[689] Sixty-eight percent of those consuming antidepressants had been taking them for two years or more.[690] Worldwide spending on these drugs topped $14 billion in 2014 and is expected to reach nearly $17 billion by 2020.[691] Our rivers contain not just measurable amounts of Prozac but enough to alter the behavior of fish living in these waters.[692]

Once upon a time, children were taught religious parables and national myths that placed their lives in a larger context of meaning, as well as stories that underscored the value of hard work (*The Little Red Hen*), foresight (*The Three Little Pigs*) and perseverance (*The Little Engine That Could*). They learned about the young Teddy Roosevelt overcoming his childhood asthma through strenuous exercise, and the young Abe Lincoln reading by the firelight and then walking miles to return books he had borrowed. Today tomes such as *Brandon and the Bipolar Bear*, *Turbo Max*, and *My Bipolar Roller Coaster Feelings Book* teach the little ones the importance of psychotropic medication compliance.

Every cog in this machine is greased with drug company money:

- The *DSM* Task Force members on the payrolls of the drug companies[693]

- The university departments and the CRO's which test the drug companies' wares[694]

- The ghostwriters who spin the results to maximize the marketability of those wares

- The journals which rely on drug company advertising and reprint orders for much of their revenue stream[695]

- The mainstream media outlets which also are heavily dependent on drug company advertising[696]

- The Key Opinion Leaders on the payrolls of the drug companies who tout those companies' wares at professional meetings

- The "continuing education" courses underwritten by the drug companies[697]

- The advocacy organizations like the National Alliance on Mental Illness and the National Council for Behavioral Health,[698] which receive massive funding from the drug companies

- The professional organizations like the American Academy of Child and Adolescent Psychiatry and the American Psychiatric Association,[699] which also receive massive funding from the drug companies

- The FDA which in a large measure is financed by drug company "user fees" and whose officials (like Dr. Laughren) often go on to lucrative positions with the drug companies[700]

- Congress, in which both sides of the aisle are bought and paid for by the drug companies[701]

And, as prescriptions for antidepressants have skyrocketed, outcomes have gotten worse. What was once a rare and usually self-limiting condition has become chronic, debilitating, and frighteningly common.[702] Depression is now the leading cause of disability worldwide.[703]

In the United States alone, the economic cost of depression rose from $83 billion in 2000 to $173 billion in 2005 to $210 billion in 2010. That figure includes $27 billion in direct medical costs, $53 billion in workplace costs, and $5.4 billion in suicide-related costs.[704] The suicide rate has also soared, and by 2017 was higher than it had been at any time since the Second World War.[705]

The bad news regarding antidepressant drugs just keeps piling up. A paper published in the March 2019 issue of the *European Journal of Clinical Pharmacology* reported that the risk of violent suicide more than triples during the first twenty-eight days of SSRI antidepressant treatment. The authors cautioned readers "Ongoing treatment should not be discontinued, nor initiation of treatment delayed, based on the outcomes of this study, since the hazards of undertreatment outweigh the risks of therapy."[706]

On Monday 8 April 2019, a paper published in *JAMA Pediatrics* reported that emergency room visits for suicidal ideation or suicide attempts in children and adolescents nearly doubled during the period 2007-2015. There was no significant increase in total emergency room visits for youths during this time frame.[707]

On Monday 24 June, a meta-analysis of randomized controlled trials of fourteen different antidepressants concluded that these drugs caused a doubling of suicide attempts and a near tripling of the rate of completed suicides.[708] Both the *Sun*[709] and the *Daily Mail*[710] reported these findings, but none of the American papers did.

On Friday 26 July Dr. Gøtzsche and two of his colleagues at the Nordic Cochrane Collaboration published a meta-analysis of all randomized controlled trials of antidepressants with a follow-up period of at least twenty-four weeks (there were only twenty-two papers that met these criteria).[711] Only two of the studies reported any functional outcomes at all from after the randomization phase—one reported on school attendance and one on the number of heavy drinking days. None of the papers provided data on relapse rates, withdrawal effects, all serious adverse events, or deaths. Gøtzsche and his colleagues concluded "The randomised trials currently available cannot be used to investigate persistent harms of antidepressants."

On 3 and 4 August, two mass shootings took place within thirteen hours of each other—one in El Paso, Texas, in which twenty-two were killed,[712] and the other in Dayton, Ohio, in which ten died.[713] On 9 September, an article in the *Washington Post* reported that former NBC president and Trump associate Bob Wright unveiled a proposal to explore ways of predicting incidents of mass violence through use of advanced technology such as smartphones and advanced watches.[714] The possible role of antidepressants in rampage killings was not mentioned.

On 25 September, a narrative review on the benefits and harms of antidepressants by Janus Jakobsen and two of his colleagues appeared in *BMJ Open*. Dr. Jakobsen and his co-authors noted:

> *Although the available evidence (based on the available assessment scales) shows that the **average** effect on depressive symptoms is minimal, theoretically and in clinical practice some patients might benefit significantly from antidepressants. Nevertheless, if the **averaged** effect is minimal and close to zero effect and some patients benefit significantly from antidepressants, then there has to be a comparable proportion of patients who are significantly harmed by antidepressants—otherwise the averaged effect would not be close to zero effect. (Emphasis in the original)[715]*

Dr. Jakobsen and his co-authors also noted that SSRI antidepressants significantly increased the rate of all serious adverse events in trials.[716]

A "medicine" that creates more problems than it solves is not a medicine at all—it's a poison.

On 17 October, the CDC announced that the suicide rate for persons aged 10-24, after remaining stable from the years 2000 through 2007, had risen every year after that—the same year Dr. Gibbons published his paper purporting to show that antidepressants did not cause youth suicides. The rate went up from 6.8 suicides per 100,000 youths in 2007 to 10.6 per 100,000 in 2017.[717] Even more ominously, the rate of increase had also gone up sharply, beginning in the year 2013. An article in the *Washington Post* mentioned several possible explanations but did not even consider the possible role of antidepressants.[718]

On 27 October, an article appeared in the *Herald* which discussed skyrocketing rates of antidepressant prescriptions which quoted Aileen Blower, Vice Chair of the Child and Adolescent Faculty in Scotland for the Royal College of Psychiatrists, who informed readers that antidepressants "definitely reduce suicide risk."[719] No evidence was cited in support of this assertion.

One week later, the *Herald* published a letter from Dr. Read and two of his colleagues who demanded the statement be retracted, adding:

> *It is no longer acceptable for senior health professionals to make public statements on serious public health issues based on anything other than scientific evidence.*
>
> *Perhaps such unquestioning acceptance of drug company marketing, by psychiatrists and others, has contributed to the overuse of psychiatric drugs on our children, and the rest of us, in the first place?*[720]

On 31 October, an article by psychiatrists Caleb Gardner and Arthur Kleinman appeared in the *New England Journal of Medicine*. Titled "Medicine and the Mind—The Consequences of Psychiatry's Identity Crisis,"[721] the essay recited a familiar litany of complaints—there are no biological tests for any of the conditions commonly treated by psychiatrists, no coherent theoretical understanding of "mental illness," and an overreliance on overlapping symptom checklists and hurried "medication management" visits.

But psychiatry has been writhing in the throes of this identity crisis for forty-five years now. Is it time to consider the possibility that the entire field is a failed enterprise, a wrong turn in human history?

As if all this were not enough, now doctor-assisted suicide is being touted as a remedy for "treatment-resistant" depression.[722] This is already being done in the Netherlands, Belgium, and Switzerland, and Canada is considering legalizing the practice as well.[723]

Recently, a couple of lengthy feature stories have appeared in the news media, detailing the last days of despondent young women who have made this final exit,[724] but nobody seems very interested in learning how they got to the point where this looked like their best option. No one ever considered the possible role of the psychiatric profession in creating these patients' despair, despite the large and growing body linking antidepressants to worsening depression and suicidality. Rather, these forlorn young women were portrayed as victims of some inexorable disease process— even though there is not a shred of credible evidence for this supposition.

This is not what happens when treatments work.

I asked every one of the experts I interviewed for this book these questions: How did we get to this point? And where do we go from here? Dr. Doshi declined to comment. As for the rest of them, here are their answers.

John Read, Professor of Clinical Psychology at the University of East London:

> *We got to this point in two ways. One, by the very effective marketing by the drug companies of the chemical imbalance mantra. And which they've never found. They've never found the chemical imbalance, and most psychiatrists are beginning to acknowledge they never will. It isn't there.*
>
> *So it's a very effective marketing of a simplistic biogenetic model of human distress, coupled with an abnegation of responsibility, largely by psychiatry but to some extent by GP's, who about twenty years ago forgot what the professional and ethical boundary between a medical discipline and a profit-making organization looks like.*
>
> *The bottom line is 'follow the money.' That's how we got here.*
>
> *As to where we go from here: we're having a fairly positive year, inasmuch that we are confident that the Public Health England review will come out with a clear set of conclusions that dependence is frequent, and can be severe and protracted, and will make recommendations that NHS start providing proper services for people to come off these drugs. We are one hundred percent sure*

*that these guidelines will be re-written by the end of December, to be evidence-based for the first time in twenty years.*

*So I think we are moving in the right direction, painfully and slowly, against a lot of opposition from the organizations that ought to be leading the change, namely the College of Psychiatrists and the College of GP's. That allowed, we are producing some significant change.*

*I'm less optimistic for your side of the Atlantic, I'm afraid. The major drug companies, as you know, are very powerful in America. I wouldn't call psychiatry in America a scientific or medical profession. I'm afraid American psychiatry has shamelessly abandoned any pretense of being an evidence-based profession a long time ago.*

Irving Kirsch, Associate Director of the Program in Placebo Studies at the Harvard Medical School and the Beth Israel Deaconess Medical Center, and author of *The Emperor's New Drugs*:

*The way we got here was people mistaking a statistically significant difference for a clinically meaningful one. We got here with drug companies promoting their products and hiding some of the negative data for a long time.*

*The way we need to go from here is, first of all, not to do any more first-time prescribing. Don't prescribe antidepressants to someone who has never taken them. The risks are not worth the benefits that you get with them.*

*The good news is that whatever response you can get from antidepressants you can get fully, to the same degree, with a number of other, safer treatment options. Psychotherapy, exercise, and meditation produce the same response you get from the drugs.*

David Healy, Professor of Family Medicine at McMaster University and author of *Pharmageddon*:

*If the greatest concentration of Fake News on the planet centers on the medicines doctors hand out, and this news hypes the benefits of treatment to the point of portraying negative trials of a drug as positive, and hides the hazards to the point of denying that any exist, and if in addition in the case of the antidepressants these are difficult get off, to the extent that there are more reports to FDA of drug withdrawal syndrome for paroxetine and duloxetine than for oxycodone and fentanyl combined—wouldn't you expect us to be awash in antidepressants?*

*The antidepressants constitute one of the greatest public health hazards we now face—certainly one of the greatest unmentioned hazards. They are a major contributor to current polypharmacy, and this in turn likely plays a part in falling life expectancy. If doctors don't wake up to the need to recognize the hazards these medicines pose—they risk going out of business. If medicines work wonderfully well and are free of hazards, nurses and pharmacists will be used as cheaper prescribers than doctors.*

Peter Breggin, psychiatrist and author of *Medication Madness*[725] and *Guilt, Shame, and Anxiety*[726]:

*It's almost impossible to prove that antidepressants work. The studies that are done are all very short-term, they are highly manipulated, and yet despite every effort of the drug companies, it is practically impossible to show there's any advantage in helping people with depression.*

*We know these drugs cause depression, and we know they worsen the overall condition of people, we know they cause suicidality, all of that is explained in detail in the full prescribing information for every single antidepressant. We're getting more extensive warnings about worsening depression, extensive warnings about agitation, irritability, anxiety, hostility, aggression. So we're in a situation where we're giving neurotoxins to people that make them worse, and we're giving them to depressed people and making them even more depressed, so it's no surprise that the use of antidepressants is paralleled with overall an increase in suicidality, and not a decrease.*

*There's no epidemiological evidence that antidepressants are helping people. The most reliable indicator that a medical treatment is useful is a decline in the frequency of the disease, and you don't see that with any psychiatric treatment, because none of them have been helpful, especially in the long run. If antidepressants were working, we would expect a decline in the number of depressed people, a decline in the number of suicides, and we don't see it.*

*Where do we go from here? Well, I don't think there's any doubt that in a sane society we wouldn't be giving out antidepressants. They don't work.*

*What is needed is for physicians to stop prescribing these drugs, for patients to get supervised withdrawal from these drugs, and for doctors to learn how to do supervised withdrawal from them.*

*Then we need better approaches. Marriage and family counseling and psychotherapy, training in how to parent, and other efforts to strengthen the family are key to helping everyone in the family, including the children and young people. Moderate exercise can help, meditation can help, religion can help, the enthusiastic encouragement of a coach can help, and time can heal. A sound diet based on whole foods and especially on plants can transform overall health and hence mental health. A myriad of things help depression. All of life helps depression.*

*So what we need to do is to encourage people to employ a variety of alternative approaches, without ever taking neurotoxic drugs.*

# References

*48 Hours.* "Death by Text: The Case Against Michelle Carter." Narr. Erin Moriarty. CBS. August 16, 2017.

Able Child. "CT AAG Nervous About Releasing Adam Lanza's Medical Records: Disclosure 'Can Cause a Lot of People to Stop Taking Their Medications.'" September 1, 2013. http://ablechild.org/2013/09/01/ ct-aag-nervous-about-releasing-adam-lanzas-medical-records-disclosure-can-cause-a-lot-of-people-to-stop-taking-their-medications/

Albert and Mary Lasker Foundation. "1964 Albert Lasker Clinical Medical Research Award: Iproniazid for the Treatment of Severe Depression." 2018. http://www.laskerfoundation.org/awards/show/iproniazid-for-the-treatment-of-severe-depression/

All-Party Parliamentary Group for Prescribed Drug Dependence. "Antidepressant Withdrawal: A Survey of Patients' Experience by the All-Party Parliamentary Group for Prescribed Drug Dependence." September 2018. http://prescribeddrug.org/wp-content/uploads/2018/10/ APPG-PDD-Survey-of-antidepressant-withdrawal-experiences.pdf

Alliance for Human Research Protection. "FDA Issues Public Health Advisory." October 27, 2003. http://ahrp.org/fda-issues-public-health-advisory-entitled-reports-of-suicidality-in-pediatric/

Altonn, Helen. "Prozac's Role in Maui Deaths Going to Court." *Honolulu Star-Bulletin,* January 9, 1998. http://archives.starbulletin.com/98/01/09/news/story2.htm

American College of Neuropsychopharmacology. "Executive Summary: Preliminary Report of the Task Force on SSRIs and Suicidal

Behavior in Youth." January 21, 2004. https://acnp.org/wp-content/uploads/2017/10/Task-Force-Report-on-SSRIs-and-Suicide-in-Youth-Exec-Summary.pdf

American Psychiatric Association. "Practice Guidelines for the Treatment of Patients With Major Depressive Disorder, Third Edition." October 2010. https://psychiatryonline.org/pb/assets/raw/sitewide/practice_guidelines/guidelines/mdd.pdf

Anderson, Travis, and Martin Finucane. "Judge Orders Michelle Carter to Begin Serving Sentence." *Boston Globe*, February 11, 2019. https://www.bostonglobe.com/metro/2019/02/11/sjc-rejects-michelle-carter-bid-stay-sentence/mXl9rpxOwNxSoMVLS7zDHM/story.html

Andrews, Paul W., Susan G. Kornstein, Lisa J. Halberstadt, Charles O. Gardner, and Michael C. Neale. "Blue Again: Perturbational Effects of Antidepressants Suggest Monoaminergic Homeostasis in Major Depression." *Frontiers in Psychology* 2, (July 7, 2011): 1-24. https://doi.org/10.3389/fpsyg.2011.00159

Angell, Marcia. "The Epidemic of Mental Illness: Why?" *New York Review of Books*, June 23, 2011. https://www.nybooks.com/articles/2011/06/23/epidemic-mental-illness-why/

Angell, Marcia. "The Illusions of Psychiatry." *New York Review of Books*, July 14, 2011. https://www.nybooks.com/articles/2011/07/14/illusions-of-psychiatry/

Angier, Natalie. "New Antidepressant Is Acclaimed but Not Perfect." *New York Times*, March 29, 1990.

Antonuccio, David O., David D. Burns, and William G. Danton. "Antidepressants: A Triumph of Marketing Over Science?" *Prevention & Treatment* 5, (July 15, 2002): Article 25.

Applebaum, Paul S. "Should Mental Disorders Be a Basis for Physician-Assisted Death?" *Psychiatric Services* 68, no. 4 (April 2017): 315-317. https://doi.org/10.1176/appi.ps.201700013

Associated Press. "Warning Label on Antidepressant is Opposed." *New York Times*, September 21, 1991.

Avery, David, and George Winokur. "Suicides, Attempted Suicides, and Relapse Rates in Depression." *Archives of General Psychiatry* 35, (June 1978): 749-753.

Axelrod, Julius. "An Unexpected Life in Research." *Annual Review of Pharmacology and Toxicology* 28, (1988): 1-23.

Bachmann, Christian J., Lise Aagaard, Mehmet Burcu, Gerd Glaeske, Luuk J. Kalverdijk, Irene Peterson, Catharina C.M. Schuiling-Veninga, et al. "Trends and Patterns of Antidepressant Use in Children and Adolescents From Five Western Countries, 2005-2012." *European Neuropsychopharmacology* 26, (2016): 411-419. https://dx.doi/10.1016/j.euroneuro.2016.02.001

Baldwin, David, and Wendy Burn. "Pills for Depression." *Times*, February 24, 2018. https://www.thetimes.co.uk/article/86afb2fc-18c7-11e8-a427-78e8af199a96

Bandettini di Poggio, M., S. Anfosso, D. Audenino, and A. Primavera. "Clarithromycin-Induced Neurotoxicity in Adults." *Journal of Clinical Neuroscience* 18, no. 3 (March 2011): 313-318. https://doi.org.10.1016/j.jocn.2010.08.014

Basken, Paul. "Landmark Analysis of an Infamous Medical Study Points out the Challenges of Research Oversight." *Chronicle of Higher Education*, September 17, 2015. chronicle.com/article/Landmark-Analysis-of-an/233179

Bass, Alison. "State Paid School $218,000 on Falsely Billed DMH Study." *Boston Globe*, January 7, 1996.

Bass, Alison. "Brown Researcher Faced Billing Questions in the Past." *Boston Globe*, January 21, 1996.

Bass, Alison. "5 Ex-Employees Allege Harassment by Brown." *Boston Globe*, June 24, 1996.

Bass, Alison. "Drug Companies Enrich Brown Professor." *Boston Globe*, October 4, 1999.

Bass, Alison. *Side Effects: A Prosecutor, a Whistleblower, and a Best-Selling Antidepressant on Trial*. Chapel Hill: Algonquin Press, 2008.

Baum, Hedlund, Aristei, & Goldman, PC. "Damning Testimony from Former GlaxoSmithKline CEO Jean-Pierre Garnier in Paxil Suicide Case." March 17, 2017. https://www.youtube.com/watch?v=EZlzzNAQ2fQ

Beasley, Charles H., Bruce E. Dornseif, Janet C. Bosomworth, Mary E. Sayler, Alvin H. Rampey, John H. Heiligenstein, Vicki L. Thompson,

David J. Murphy, and Daniel N. Masica. "Fluoxetine and Suicide: A Meta-Analysis of Controlled Trials of Treatment for Depression." *BMJ* 303, (September 21, 1991): 685-692.

Begley, Sharon, and Debra Rosenberg. "One Pill Makes You Larger, and One Pill Makes You Small." *Newsweek*, February 7, 1994.

Bellon, Tina. "US Appeals Court Says GSK Cannot Be Sued Over Generic Drug Verdict." Reuters, August 22, 2018. https://www.reuters.com/article/us-gsk-lawsuit/u-s-appeals-court-says-gsk-cannot-be-sued-over-generic-drug-suicide-idUSKCN1L72D1

Bielefeldt, Andreas Ø., Pia A. Danborg, and Peter C. Gøtzsche. "Precursors to Suicidality and Violence on Antidepressants: Systematic Review of Trials in Adult Healthy Volunteers." *Journal of the Royal Society of Medicine* 109, no. 10 (October 2016): 381-392. https://doi.org/10.1177/0141076816666805

Blazer, Natalie. "Federal Court Allows Claims Against Branded Drug Maker for Injuries Caused by Generic Pill." *Product Liability Monitor*, March 10, 2014. https://product-liability.weil.com/pharma-medical-devices/federal-court-allows-claims-against-branded-drug-maker-for-injuries-caused-by-generic-pill/

Bloomberg News. "British Drug Shares Get a Lift." *New York Times*, January 1, 1993.

Boseley, Sarah. "Bitter Pill." *Guardian*, May 7, 2001. https://www.theguardian.com/education/2001/may/07/medicalscience.highereducation

*Boston Globe* Staff. "Read the Texts at the Center of the Massachusetts Teen Suicide Case." *Boston Globe*, June 6, 2017. https://www.google.com/url?q=https://www.bostonglobe.com/metro/2017/06/05/read-texts-center-massachusetts-teen-suicide-case/YIjOPc1K0I-CLoyUx97uwLL/story.html&sa=U&ved=0ahUKEwjDhq6ltuTfAhUBneAKHfBWCMEQFggFMAA&client=internal-uds-cse&cx=006376928391721581342:dttdzxtrxse&usg=AOvVaw1qlpNR0_cFAjAxaaf6sdAz

*Boston Globe* Staff. ""When Are You Doing It?' Read the Carter Case Texts." *Boston Globe*, June 8, 2017. https://www.bostonglobe.com/metro/2017/06/08/when-are-you-doing-read-latest-texts-michelle-carter-case/Ei7L2NXVxXozc6T7MU29BJ/story.html

Boudreau, Abbie, and Scott Zamost. "Girlfriend: Shooter Was Taking Cocktail of 3 Drugs." *CNN*, February 20, 2008. http://www.cnn.com/2008/CRIME/02/20/shooter.girlfriend/index.html

Breggin, Peter R. *Toxic Psychiatry: Why Therapy, Empathy, and Love Must Replace the Drugs, Electroshock, and Biochemical Theories of the "New Psychiatry."* New York: Saint Martin's Griffin, 1991.

Breggin, Peter R. "How GlaxoSmithKline Suppressed Data on Paxil-Induced Akathisia: Implications for Suicidality and Violence." *Ethical Human Psychology and Psychiatry* 8, no. 2 (Summer 2006): 91-100. http://dx.doi.org/10.1891/ehpp.8.2.91

Breggin, Peter R. *Guilt, Shame, and Anxiety: Understanding and Overcoming Negative Emotions.* New York: Prometheus Books, 2014.

Breggin, Peter R. "Michelle Carter: Did She Text Her Boyfriend to Death?" August 3, 2017. https://www.madinamerica.com/2017/08/michelle-carter-text-boyfriend-death/

Breggin, Peter R. "Michelle Starts Prozac and Sees the Devil." August 7, 2017. https://www.madinamerica.com/2017/08/michelle-carter-starts-prozac-sees-devil/

Breggin, Peter R. "DA Goes After Her Expert Witness to Stop His Blog." August 30, 2017. https://www.madinamerica.com/2017/08/michelle-carter-expert-witness-stop-blog/

Breggin, Peter R. "Did She Tell Conrad to Get Back in the Truck?" September 6, 2017. https://www.madinamerica.com/2017/09/michelle-carter-part-iv-did-she-tell-conrad-get-back-in-the-truck/

Breggin, Peter R. "The Michelle Carter Texting Case Becomes a Witch Hunt." September 13, 2017. https://www.madinamerica.com/2017/09/part-v-michelle-carter-texting-trial-witch-hunt/

Breggin, Peter R. "How Adult Society Betrayed Michelle Carter and Conrad Roy." September 20, 2017. https://www.madinamerica.com/2017/09/part-vi-adult-society-betrayed-michelle-carter-conrad-roy/

Breggin, Peter R., and Ginger R. Breggin. *Talking Back to Prozac: What Doctors Aren't Telling You About Prozac and the New Antidepressants.* New York: Saint Martin's Press, 1994.

Brown, Mark. "Antidepressants Work, so Why Do We Shame People for Taking Them?" *Guardian*, September 1, 2017. https://www.theguardian.com/commentisfree/2017/sep/01/antidepressants-work-shame-people-ssri

Brown, Mick. "Nick Drake: The Fragile Genius." *Telegraph*, November 25, 2014. https://www.telegraph.co.uk/culture/music/worldfolkand-jazz/11250728/Nick-Drake-the-fragile-genius.html

Brownsberger, Carl N. "Yes, Prozac Has Risks—So Do All Drugs." *Boston Globe*, May 16, 2000.

Bureau d'Enquêtes et d'Analyses pour la Sécurité de l'Aviation Civile. "Final Report." March 2016. https://www.madinamerica.com/wp-content/uploads/2016/04/Germanwings-crash-final-BEA-report-2015-0125.en-LR.pdf

Burn, Wendy. "Stop This Dangerous Scaremongering Over Antidepressants." *Times*, July 27, 2017. Opinion and Editorial 28.

Burnstein, Brett, Holly Agostino, and Brian Greenfield. "Suicidal Attempts and Ideation Among Children and Adolescents in US Emergency Departments, 2007-2015." *JAMA Pediatrics* https://doi.org/10.1001/jamapediatrics.2019.0464 [Epub ahead of print].

CBC Radio. "Listener Mail—Dr. Jeffrey Lieberman." May 1, 2015. https://www.cbc.ca/radio/thesundayedition/men-will-be-boys-the-refugee-problem-christiana-pflug-ve-day-1.3055705/listener-mail-dr-jeffrey-lieberman-1.3057807

CDC. "Fatal Injury Reports: National, Regional, and State 1981-2016." Page last updated February 19, 2017. https://webappa.cdc.gov/sasweb/ncipc/mortrate.html

CDC. "Antidepressant Use Among Persons Aged 12 and Over: United States, 2011-2014." August 2017. https://www.cdc.gov/nchs/data/databriefs/db283.pdf

CDC. "Death Rates Due to Suicide and Homicide Among Persons Aged 10-24: United States, 2000-2017." October 17, 2019. https://www.cdc.gov/nchs/data/databriefs/db352-h.pdf

Campbell, Clark. "Top Scientists Allege U of T Academic Chill." *Globe and Mail Canada*, September 6, 2001. https://www.theglobeandmail.com/news/national/top-scientists-allege-u-of-t-academic-chill/article4152673/

Canadian Association of University Teachers. "'A Complete Vindication' for David Healy." May 2002. https://bulletin-archives.caut.ca/bulletin/articles/2002/05/'a-complete-vindication'-for-david-healy

Carey, Benedict. "Panel to Weigh Expansion of Antidepressant Warnings." *New York Times*, December 13, 2006.

Carey, Benedict. "Panel Wants Broader Antidepressant Labeling." *New York Times*, December 14, 2006.

Carey, Benedict. "Nasal Spray, a Quick-Acting Treatment for Depression, Is Approved by the FDA." *New York Times*, March 5, 2019.

Carlsson, Arvid. "Rationale and Design of a Selective Inhibitor of 5-HT Re-uptake." *British Journal of Clinical Practice: A Symposium* 19, (1982): 19-22.

Carmichael, David. "Three Weeks to Prescripticide." May 12, 2016. https://rxisk.org/three-weeks-to-prescripticide/

Carmichael, David. "Calm, Organized, Homicidal Behaviour: My Connection to School Shooters." March 27, 2018. https://www.madinamerica.com/2018/03/calm-organized-homicidal-behaviour-connection-school-shooters/

Carmichael, David. "David Carmichael." Accessed May 14, 2019. www.davidcarmichael.com

Cassidy, Simon, and John Henry. "Fatal Toxicity of Antidepressant Drugs in Overdose." *British Medical Journal* 295, no. 6605 (October 24, 1987): 1021-1024.

Cheifetz, Irving, Claude Paulin, Hulusi Tuatay, and Eli H. Rubin. "Iproniazid in Pulmonary Tuberculosis." *Diseases of the Chest* 25, no. 4 (April 1954): 390-396. https://doi.org/10.1378/chest.25.4.390

Cipriani, Andrea, Toshi Furukawa, Georgia Salanti, Anna Chaimani, Lauren Atkinson, Yusuke Ogawa, Stefan Leucht, et al. "Comparative Efficacy and Acceptability of 21 Antidepressant Drugs for the Acute Treatment of Adults With Major Depressive Disorder: A Systematic Review and Meta-Analysis." *Lancet* 391, no. 10128 (April 7, 2018): 1357-1366. https://doi.org/10.1016/S0140-6736(17)32802-7

Cole, Paul. "The Last 10 Days of Singer-Songwriter Nick Drake's Life Are Revealed in His Father's Heartbreaking Diary." *Birmingham Mail*,

November 22, 2014. https://www.birminghammail.co.uk/news/midlands-news/last-10-days-singer-songwriter-nick-8153684

Cornwell, John. *The Power to Harm.* New York: Viking, 1996.

Cowley, Geoffrey. "The Promise of Prozac." *Newsweek*, March 26, 1990.

Crane, George. "The Psychiatric Side Effects of Iproniazid." *American Journal of Psychiatry* 12, no. 7 (January 1956): 494-501.

Creaney, W., I. Murray, and David Healy. "Antidepressant Induced Suicidal Ideation." *Human Psychopharmacology* 6, (August 1991): 329-332.

Crespi, Kim. "Crespi Family Hope." 2012.
http://www.crespifamilyhope.org/about-us/

Cullen, Dave. *Columbine.* Grand Central Publishing, 2009. https://books.google.com/books?id=ZQONT3jE1-sC&printsec=frontcover&d-q=Columbine&hl=en&sa=X&ved=0ahUKEwi84fiQoP3fAhWIGt-8KHa9mAsYQ6AEIKjAA#v=snippet&q=Luvox&f=false

Cullen, Kevin. "Three Little Words Sunk Michelle Carter." *Boston Globe*, June 16, 2017. https://www.bostonglobe.com/metro/2017/06/16/three-lit-tle-words-sunk-michelle-carter/7MgZibLEgQ7As6zvNOaDJI/story.html

Danborg, P.B., M. Valdersdorf, and Peter C. Gøtzsche. "Long-Term Harms from Previous Use of Selective Serotonin Reuptake Inhibitors: A Systematic Review." *International Journal of Risk and Safety in Medicine* 30, no. 2 (July 26, 2019): 59-71. https://doi.org/10.3233/JRS-180046

Davies, James, Joanna Moncrieff, Peter Kinderman, and Viscount Hinch-ingbrooke. "Stigma and Efficacy of Taking Antidepressants." *Times*, February 23, 2018. https://www.thetimes.co.uk/article/stigma-and-effi-cacy-of-taking-antidepressants-0zvsg560x

Davies, James, and John Read. "A Systematic Review into the Incidence, Severity, and Duration of Antidepressant Withdrawal Effects: Are Guidelines Evidence-Based?" *Addictive Behaviors*, September 4, 2018. https://doi.org/10.1016/j.addbeh.2018.08.027 [Epub ahead of print].

Dolin, Wendy. "About MISSD." 2019. https://missd.co

Dolin, Wendy. "Akathisia." 2019. https://missd.co

Doshi, Peter. "No Correction, No Retraction, No Apology, No Comment: Parox-etine Trial Reanalysis Raises Questions About Institutional Responsi-

bility." *BMJ* 351, (September 16, 2015): h4629. https://doi.org.10.1136/
bmj.h4629

Doshi, Peter, Kay Dickersin, David Healy, S. Swaroop Vedula, and Tom
Jefferson. "Restoring Invisible and Abandoned Trials: A Call for People
to Publish the Findings." *BMJ* 346, (June 13, 2013): f2865. https://doi.
org.10.1136/bmj.f2865

*Economist*. "24 & Ready to Die." November 10, 2015.
https://www.youtube.com/watch?v=SWWkUzkfJ4M

Ellement, John R., and Travis Andersen. "Mass. High Court Upholds Carter
Ruling." *Boston Globe*, February 6, 2019. https://www.bostonglobe.
com/metro/2019/02/06/sjc-rule-case-michelle-carter-convicted-in-
voluntary-manslaughter-death-year-old-man/jmOuFii7iTZFKrnEX-
PzzAM/story.html

Ember, Sydney. "Longtime Psychiatry Chair Resigns." *Brown Daily Herald*, April
7, 2009. http://www.browndailyherald.com/2009/04/07/longtime-psy-
chiatry-chair-resigns/

FDA. "Psychopharmacological Drugs Advisory Committee, Friday,
September 20, 1991." https://upload.wikimedia.org/wikipedia/
commons/7/7a/1991_FDA_Psychopharmacological_Drugs_Advisory_
Committee.pdf

FDA. "Psychopharmacologic Drugs Advisory Committee, Monday, February
2, 2004." http://psychrights.org/research/digest/AntiDepressants/
FDA2-2-2004Hearing.htm

FDA. "Psychopharmacologic Drugs Advisory Committee, Tuesday, December
13, 2006." https://breggin.com/antidepressant-drugs-resources/FDA-
2006-drug-companies-allowed-to-hide-adult-suicide-data.pdf

FDA. "Ambien (zolpidem tartrate)." February 2008.
https://www.accessdata.fda.gov/drugsatfda_docs/
label/2008/019908s027lbl.pdf

FDA. "Celexa (citalopram hydrobromide) Tablets/Oral Solution." Revised
January 2009. https://www.accessdata.fda.gov/drugsatfda_docs/label/20
09/020822s037,021046s015lbl.pdf

FDA. "Prozac (fluoxetine hydrochloride)." 2011. https://www.accessdata.fda.gov/
drugsatfda_docs/label/2011/018936s091lbl.pdf

FDA. "Lunesta (eszoplicone)." May 2014. https://www.accessdata.fda.gov/drugsatfda_docs/label/2014/021476s030lbl.pdf

FDA. "Desyryl (trazadone hydrochloride)." June 17, 2017. https://www.accessdata.fda.gov/drugsatfda_docs/label/2017/018207s032lbl.pdf

FDA. "FDA Briefing Document: Psychopharmacologic Drugs Advisory Committee (PDAC) and Drug Safety and Risk Management (DRaRM) Advisory Committee Meeting February 12, 2019." https://www.fda.gov/downloads/AdvisoryCommittees/CommitteesMeetingMaterials/Drugs/PsychopharmacologicDrugsAdvisoryCommittee/UCM630970.pdf

Fava, Maurizio, A. Eden Evins, David J. Dorer, and David A. Schoenfeld. "The Problem of the Placebo Response in Clinical Trials for Psychiatric Disorders: Culprits, Possible Remedies, and a Novel Study Design Approach." *Psychotherapy and Psychosomatics* 72, (2003): 115-127. https://doi.org/10.1159/000069738

Fitzgerald, Joe. "Knox Seeks Sympathy Where None Deserved." *Boston Herald*, November 18, 2017. https://www.bostonherald.com/2017/08/05/fitzgerald-knox-seeks-sympathy-where-none-deserved/

Forsman, Jonas, Thomas Masterman, Johan Ahlner, Göran Isaacsson, and Anna Karin Hedström. "Selective Serotonin Re-uptake Inhibitors and the Risk of Violent Suicide: A Nationwide Postmortem Study." *European Journal of Clinical Pharmacology* 75, no. 3 (March 2019): 393-400. https://doi.org/10.1007/s00228-018-2586-2

Friedlander, Henry. *The Origins of Nazi Genocide*. Chapel Hill: University of North Carolina Press, 1995.

Friedman, Richard A., and Andrew C. Leon. "Expanding the Black Box—Depression, Antidepressants, and the Risk of Suicide." *New England Journal of Medicine* 356, no. 23 (June 7, 2007): 2343-2346. https://doi.org.10.1056/NEJMp078015

Friesen, Joe. "Man Not Criminally Responsible in Son's Death." *Globe and Mail Canada*, October 1, 2005. https://www.theglobeandmail.com/news/national/man-not-criminally-responsible-in-sons-death/article987568/

Gardner, Caleb, and Arthur Kleinman. "Medicine and the Mind—The Consequences of Psychiatry's Identity Crisis." *New England Journal of*

*Medicine* 381, (October 31, 2019):697-699. https://doi.org/ 10.1056/ NEJMp1910603

Gibbons, Robert, C. Hendricks Brown, Kwan Hur, Sue H. Marcus, Dulal K. Bhaumik, Joëlle A. Erkins, Ron M.C. Herings, and J. John Mann. "Early Evidence on the Effects of Regulators' Suicidality Warnings on SSRI Prescriptions and Suicide in Children and Adolescents." *American Journal of Psychiatry* 164, no. 9 (September 2007): 1356-1363. https://doi.org/10.1176/appi.ajp.2007.07030454

Gibeaut, John. "Mood-Altering Verdict: Judge Suspects Prozac Settlement Though Case Went to Jury." *ABA Journal* 82, 8 (August 1994): 18.

GlaxoSmithKline. "Annual Report for the Year Ended 31st December 2000." April 12, 2001. https://www.gsk.com/media/4698/annual-report-2000.pdf

GlaxoSmithKline. "Annual Report for the Year Ended 31st December 2001." March 28, 2002. https://www.gsk.com/media/2659/annual-report-2001.pdf

GlaxoSmithKline. "Annual Report for the Year Ended 31st December 2002." March 28, 2003. https://www.gsk.com/media/2663/annual-report-2002.pdf

Goldacre, Ben. *Bad Pharma*. London: Fourth Estate, 2012.

Goode, Erica. "Role of Illness in Germanwings Crash Raises Worry About Stigma." *New York Times*, March 30, 2015.

Gorman, Christine. "Prozac's Worst Enemy." *Time*, October 10, 1994. http://content.time.com/time/magazine/article/0,9171,981579,00.html

Graham, Judith. "As Youth Suicides Rise, FDA's Label Rule Criticized." *Chicago Tribune*, September 7, 2007. https://www.chicagotribune.com/news/ct-xpm-2007-09-07-0709061231-story.html

Greenberg, Paul E., A.A. Fournier, T. Sisitsky, C.T. Pike, and R.C. Kessler. "The Economic Burden of Adults With Major Depressive Disorder in the United States (2005 and 2010)." *Journal of Clinical Psychiatry* 76, no. 2 (February 2015): 155-162. https://doi.org/10.4088//JCP.14m09298

Grunberg, E., and R.J. Schnitzer. "Studies on the Activity of Hydrazine Derivatives of Isonicotinic Acid in the Experimental Tuberculosis of Mice." *Quarterly Bulletin of Sea View Hospital* 13, no. 1 (January 1952): 3-11.

Haga, Chuck. "Relatives: Could Meds Play a Role?" *Minneapolis Star-Tribune*, March 25, 2005.

Hahn, Patrick D. "Drug Companies Prey on Children." *Baltimore Sun*, December 25, 2016.

Halsey, Ashley, Peter Herman, and Clarence Williams. "D.C. Navy Yard Attack Kills 12, Injures 8; Alleged Shooter Dead, Is ID'd as Aaron Alexis." *Washington Post*, September 13, 2013. https://www.washingtonpost. com/local/dc-navy-yard-rampage-leaves-14-dead-alleged-shooter-killed-idd-as-aaron-alexis/2013/09/16/d084842e-1ef9-11e3-94a2-6c66b668ea55_story.html?utm_term=.ce7d67e6142c

Hammad, Tarak, Thomas Laughren, and Judith Racoosin. "Suicidality in Pediatric Patients Treated With Antidepressant Drugs." *Archives of General Psychiatry* 63, no. 3 (March 2006): 332-339. https://doi. org.1001.archpsych.63.3.332

Harris, Gardiner. "Regulators Want Antidepressants to List Warning." *New York Times*, March 23, 2004.

Harris, Gardiner. "Spitzer Sues a Drug Maker, Saying it Hid Negative Data." *New York Times*, June 30, 2004.

Harris, Gardiner. "Antidepressant Study Seen to Back Expert." *New York Times*, August 20, 2004.

Harris, Gardiner. "FDA Links Drugs to Being Suicidal." *New York Times*, September 14, 2004.

Harris, Gardiner. "FDA Panel Urges Stronger Warning on Antidepressants." *New York Times*, September 15, 2004.

Harris, Gardiner. "Warning Called Likely on Drug Risk for Suicide." *New York Times*, September 24, 2004.

Harris, Gardiner. "Top Psychiatrist Didn't Report Drug Makers' Pay." *New York Times*, October 3, 2008.

Harris, Gardiner. "Drug Makers Are Advocacy Group's Biggest Donors." *New York Times*, October 21, 2009.

Harrison, Emma. "TB Drug is Tried In Mental Cases: Use of Iproniazid at Rockland Indicates Energizing Effect in Cases of Depression." *New York Times*, April 7, 1957.

Healy, David. "The Structure of Psychopharmacological Revolutions." *Psychiatric Development* 4, (1987): 349-376.

Healy, David. "A Failure to Warn." *International Journal of Risk and Safety in Medicine* 12, (1999): 151-156.

Healy, David. "The Three Faces of Antidepressants: A Critical Commentary on the Clinical Economic Context of Diagnosis." *Journal of Nervous and Mental Disease* 187, no. 3 (1999): 174-180.

Healy, David. *The Antidepressant Era*. Cambridge: Harvard University Press, 1999.

Healy, David. "Emergence of Antidepressant Induced Suicidality." *Primary Care Psychiatry* 6, no. 1 (2000): 23-28.

Healy, David. "Good Science or Good Business?" *Hastings Center Report* 30, no. 2 (March April 2000): 19-22. https://doi.org/10.2307/3528308

Healy, David. "Psychopharmacology and the Government of the Self." Talk given at the University of Toronto, November 30, 2000. Accessed November 19, 2018. https://www.pharmapolitics.com/feb2healy.html

Healy, David. "Conflicting Interests in Toronto: Anatomy of a Controversy at the Interface of Academia and Industry." *Perspectives in Biology and Medicine* 45, no. 2 (Spring 2002): 250-263.

Healy, David. "Lines of Evidence on the Risks of Selective Serotonin Reuptake Inhibitors." *Psychotherapy and Psychosomatics* 72, (2003): 71-79.

Healy, David. *Let Them Eat Prozac*. New York: New York University Press, 2004.

Healy, David. *Mania: A Short History of Bipolar Disorder*. Baltimore: Johns Hopkins University Press, 2008.

Healy, David. "Science, Rhetoric, and the Causality of Adverse Effects." *International Journal of Risk and Safety in Medicine* 24, (2011): 1-14. https://doi.10.3233/JRS-2011-534

Healy, David. *Pharmageddon*. Berkeley: University of California Press, 2012.

Healy, David. "Study 329.org: Science With a Conscience." September 3, 2015. https://davidhealy.org/study329-org-science-with-a-conscience/

Healy, David. "Response." Accessed April 17, 2019. https://study329.org/responses-keller-et-al/

Healy, David. "Prescription for Murder." RxISK.org, July 26, 2017. https://rxisk.org/prescription-for-murder/

Healy, David. "One Side of the Background to an Academic Freedom Dispute." Academy for the Psychoanalytic Arts. Accessed December 7, 2018. http://www.academyanalyticarts.org/healy-academic-freedom-dispute

Healy, David. "Study 329." Accessed December 9, 2018. https://study329.org/wpcontent/uploads/2014/12/Famous-Grouse-Lecture-Transcript.pdf

Healy, David, and David O. Antonuccio. "Relabeling the Medications We Call Antidepressants." *Scientifica*, 2012, 6 pages, Article ID 965908. http://dx.doi.org/10.6064/2012/965908

Healy, David, Margaret Harris, Pamela Michael, Dinah Cattell, Marie Savage, Padmaja Chalasani, and David Hirst. "Service Utilization in 1896 and 1996: Morbidity and Mortality Data From North Wales." *History of Psychiatry* 16, no. 1 (2005): 27-41. https://doi.org.10/1177/0957/154X05044604

Healy, David, Joanna Le Noury, and Julie Wood. *Children of the Cure: Missing Data, Lost Lives and Antidepressants.* Samizdat Health Writers' Co-operative Inc., Kindle.

Heck, Isobel. "Controversial Paxil Paper Still Under Fire 13 Years Later." *Brown Daily Herald*, April 2, 2014. http://www.browndailyherald.com/2014/04/02/controversial-paxil-paper-still-fire-13-years-later/

Hengartner, Michael, and Martin Plöderl. "Newer-Generation Antidepressants and Suicide Risk in Randomized Controlled Trials: A Re-Analysis of the FDA Database." *Psychotherapy and Psychosomatics*, June 24, 2019. https://doi.org/10.1159/000501215 [Epub ahead of print].

Hieronymous, F. A. Lisinski, S. Nilsson, and E. Eriksson. "Efficacy of Selective Serotonin Reuptake Inhibitors in the Absence of Side Effects: A Mega-Analysis of Citalopram and Paroxetine in Adult Depression." *Molecular Psychiatry* 23, (2018): 1731-1736. https://doi.org.10.1038/mp2017.147

Hignett, Katherine. "Antidepressants Do Work, and Many More People Should Take Them." *Newsweek*, February 22, 2018. https://www.newsweek.com/antidepressants-major-depressive-disorder-study-815415

Hill, Austin Bradford. "The Environment or Disease: Association or Causation?" *Proceedings of the Royal Society of Medicine* 58, no. 5 (May 1965): 295-300.

Hirschfeld, Robert M.A. "Suicide and Antidepressant Treatment." *Archives of General Psychiatry* 57, (April 2000): 325-326.

Hitchens, Peter. "How to Be a Scaremonger—Reflections on BBC *Panorama's* Study of the Aurora Mass Murders." July 27, 2017. https://hitchens-blog.mailonsunday.co.uk/2017/07/how-to-be-a-scaremonger-reflections-o-bbc-panoramas-study-of-the-aurora-mass-murders-.html

Hollister, Leo E. "Drugs in Emotional Disorders: Past and Present." *Annals of Internal Medicine* 51, no. 5 (November 1959): 1032-1047.

Hollon, Steven D. "The Emperor's New Drugs: Effect Size and Moderation Effects." *Prevention & Treatment* 5, (July 15, 2002): Article 28.

Howe, Peter J. and Alison Bass. "Probe of Brown Mental Health Contract Handed Over to AG." *Boston Globe*, March 29, 1996.

Huber, Peter. "Junk Science in the Courtroom." *Forbes*, July 8, 1991.

Hughes, Shannon, David Cohen, and Rachel Jaggi. "Differences in Reporting Serious Adverse Events in Industry Sponsored Clinical Trial Registries and Journal Articles on Antidepressant and Antipsychotic Drugs: A Cross-Sectional Study." *BMJ Open* 2014;4:e005535

Iacobucci, Gareth. "NICE Updates Antidepressant Guidelines to Reflect Severity and Length of Withdrawal Symptoms." *BMJ* 2019 Oct 18;367:l6103. https://doi.org/10.1136/bmj.l6103

*Independent* staff. "Antidepressants Linked to 28 Murders in Three Decades, BBC Investigation Finds." *Independent*, July 25, 2017. https://www.independent.co.uk/life-style/health-and-families/health-news/antidepressants-ssris-muders-suicide-panorama-depression-anxiety-side-effects-a7859876.html

Investigative Reporters and Editors. "2010 IRE Awards Winners." Accessed January 3, 2019. https://www.ire.org/awards/ire-awards/winners/2010-ire-awards-winners/#book

Jakobsen, Janus Christian, Christian Gluud, and Irving Kirsch. "Should Antidepressants be Used for Major Depressive Disorder?" *BMJ Evidence-Based*

*Medicine* Published Online First: 25 September 2019. https://doi. org/10.1136/bmjebm-2019-111238

Janssen. "Prescribing Information for SPRAVATO." March 2019. http://www.janssenlabels.com/package-insert/product-monograph/ prescribing-information/SPRAVATO-pi.pdf

Janssen. "Janssen Announces US FDA Approval of SPRAVATO™ (esketamine) CIII Nasal Spray for Adults With Treatment-Resistant Depression (TRD) Who Have Cycled Through Multiple Treatments Without Relief." March 5, 2019. https://www.janssen.com/janssen-announc- es-us-fda-approval-spravato-esketamine-ciii-nasal-spray-adults-treat- ment-resistant

Jick, Susan S., Alan D. Dean, and Herschel Jick. "Antidepressants and Suicide." *BMJ* 310, no. 6974 (January 28, 1995): 215-218.

Jofre, Shelley. "A Prescription for Murder?" *BBC News*, July 26, 2017. https://www.bbc.co.uk/news/resources/idt-sh/aurora_shooting

Johnson, Carolyn Y., and Laurie McGinley. "In Biggest Advance for Depres- sion in Years, FDA Approves Novel Treatment for Hardest Cases." *Washington Post*, March 5, 2019. https://www.washingtonpost. com/health/2019/03/06/biggest-advance-depression-years-fda-ap- proves-novel-treatment-hardest-cases/?noredirect=on&utm_term=. c3e6e8f4a09a

Julious, Steven. "Efficacy and Risk for Antidepressants in Paediatric and Adoles- cent Patients." *Statistical Methods in Mental Health Research* 22, no. 2 (2013): 190-218. https://doi.org.10.1177.0962280211432210

Jureidini, Jon N., Leemon B. McHenry, and Peter R. Mansfield. "Clinical Trials and Drug Promotion: Selective Reporting of Study 329." *International Journal of Risk and Safety in Medicine* 20, (2008): 73-81. https://doi. org.10.3233/JRS-2008-0426

Jureidini, Jon N., David Healy, Mickey Nardo, Melissa Raven, Elia Abi Jaoude, Catalin Tufanaru, and Joanna LeNoury. "Re: Restoring Study 329: Response to Keller and Selected Colleagues." February 3, 2016. https://www.bmj.com/content/351/bmj.h4320/rr-29

Jureidini, Jon N., and Anne Tonkin. "Paroxetine in Major Depression." *Journal of the American Academy of Child and Adolescent Psychiatry* 42, no. 5 (May 2002): 514.

Kamman, Gordon, John G. Freeman, and Rubel Lucero. "The Effect of 1-Isonic-otinyl 2-Isopropyl Hydrazide (IIH) on the Behavior of Long-Term Mental Patients." *Journal of Nervous and Mental Diseases* 118, no. 5 (November 1953): 391-407.

Keller, Martin B., Boris Birmaher, Gabrielle A. Carlson, Gregory N. Clarke, Graham J. Eslie, Harold Koplewicz, Stan Kutcher, Neal Ryan, William H. Sack, and Michael Strober. "Re: Restoring Study 329: Efficacy and Harms of Paroxetine in Treatment of Major Depression in Adolescence. Response from the Authors of the Original Study 329." January 18, 2016. https://www.bmj.com/content/351/bmj.h4320/rr-27

Keller, Martin B., Boris Birmaher, Gregory N. Clarke, Graham J. Emslie, Harold Koplewicz, Stan Kutcher, Neal Ryan, William Sack, and Michael Strober. "Letter From Keller et al." Accessed December 16, 2018. https://study329.org/responses-keller-et-al/

Keller, Martin B., Neal D. Ryan, Michael Strober, Rachel G. Klein, Stan P. Kutcher, Boris Birmaher, Owen R. Hagino, et al. "Efficacy of Paroxetine in the Treatment of Adolescent Major Depression: A Randomized, Controlled Trial." *Journal of the American Academy of Child and Adolescent Psychiatry* 40, no. 7 (July 2001): 762-772. https://doi.org/10.1097/00004583-200107000-00010

Keller, Martin B., Neal D. Ryan, Michael Strober, Elizabeth B. Weller, James P. McCafferty, Owen R. Hagino, Boris Birmaher, and Karen D. Wagner. "Paroxetine in Major Depression." *Journal of the American Academy of Child and Adolescent Psychiatry* 42, no. 5 (May 2002): 514-515.

Keller, Martin B., Neal D. Ryan, and Karen Dineen Wagner. "Paroxetine in Adolescent Major Depression." *Journal of the American Academy of Child and Adolescent Psychiatry* 41, no. 4 (April 2002): 364.

Kelly, Ryan. "Slayings Suspect is One of Dead." *Wyoming Tribune Eagle*, February 6, 1998, A1.

Khan, Arif, Heather A. Warner, and Walter A. Brown. "Symptom Reduction and Suicide Risk in Patients Treated With Placebo in Antidepressant Clinical Trials." *Archives of General Psychiatry* 57, (April 2000): 311-317.

King, Robert A., Mark A. Riddle, Phillip B. Chappell, Maureen T. Hardin, George M. Anderson, Paul Lombroso, and Larry Scahill. "Emergence of Self-Destructive Phenomena in Children and Adolescents During

Fluoxetine Treatment." *Journal of the American Academy of Child and Adolescent Psychiatry* 30, no. 2 (March 1991): 179-185. https://doi.org/10.1097/00004583-199103000-00003

Kirsch, Irving. *The Emperor's New Drugs: Exploding the Antidepressant Myth*. New York: Basic Books, 2010.

Kirsch, Irving. "Antidepressants and the Placebo Effect." *Zeitschrift für Psychologie* 222, no. 3 (2014): 128-134. https://doi.org.1027/2151-2604/a00176

Kirsch, Irving. "Dr. Irving Kirsch: The Emperor's New Drugs: Exploding the Antidepressant Myth." Accessed December 31, 2018. https://www.youtube.com/watch?v=UC5RZRG7-QQ

Kirsch, Irving, Brett J. Deacon, Tania B. Huedo-Medina, Alan Scoboria, Thomas J. Moore, and Blair T. Johnson. "Initial Severity and Antidepressant Benefits: A Meta-Analysis of Data Submitted to the Food and Drug Administration." *PLoS Medicine* 5, no. 2 (February 2008): 260-268. https://journals.plos.org/plosmedicine/article/file?id=10.1371/journal.pmed.0050045&type=printable

Kirsch, Irving, and Joanna Moncrieff. "Clinical Trials and the Response Rate Illusion." *Contemporary Clinical Trials* 28, no. 4 (July 2007): 348-351. https://doi.org.10.1016/j.cct.2006.10.012

Kirsch, Irving, Thomas J. Moore, Alan Scoboria, and Sarah S. Nicholls. "The Emperor's New Drugs: An Analysis of Antidepressant Medication Data Submitted to the U.S. Food and Drug Administration." *Prevention & Treatment* 5, (July 15, 2002): Article 23.

Kirsch, Irving and Guy Sapirstein. "Listening to Prozac but Hearing Placebo: A Meta-Analysis of Antidepressant Medication." *Prevention & Treatment* 1, no. 2 (June 1998): ArtID: 2a.

Klebold, Susan. "I Will Never Know Why." *Oprah Magazine*, November 2009. https://www.oprah.com/omagazine/susan-klebolds-o-magazine-essay-i-will-never-know-why/all

Klein, Donald F. "Listening to Meta-Analysis but Hearing Bias." *Prevention & Treatment* 1, no. 2 (June 1998): ArtID: 6c.

Kline, Nathan S. "Monoamine Oxidase Inhibitors: An Unfinished Picaresque Tale." In *Discoveries in Biological Psychiatry*, edited by F.J. Ayd and B. Blackwell, 194-204. Philadelphia: Lippincott, 1970.

Knox, Patrick. "Texts on Trial: Who Is Michelle Carter, What Happened to Conrad Roy, and Why Did She Encourage Her Boyfriend to Kill Himself?" *Sun*, August 4, 2017. https://www.thesun.co.uk/news/3741960/michelle-carter-guilty-encouraging-conrad-roy-boyfriend-suicide/

Kondro, Wayne, and Barbara Sibbald. "Drug Company Experts Advised Staff to Withhold Data About SSRI Use in Children." *Canada Medical Association Journal* 170, no. 5 (March 2, 2004): 783.

Konner, Melvin. "Good Health: Out of the Darkness." *New York Times Magazine*, October 2, 1994.

Koplewicz, Harold S. *It's Nobody's Fault: New Hope and Help for Difficult Children*. New York: Random House, 1996.

Kramer, Peter D. *Listening to Prozac: A Psychiatrist Explores Antidepressant Drugs and the Remaking of the Self*. New York: Penguin Books, 1993.

Kramer, Peter D. "In Defense of Antidepressants." *New York Times*, July 9, 2011.

Kreifels, Susan. "Family Hopes Prozac Case Leads to Awareness: They Lost Their Lawsuit, but Still Believe the Drug Caused Their Parents' Deaths." *Honolulu Star-Bulletin*, April 1, 1999.

Krieder, George. "Suicides, Drugs, and the Open Hospital." *Hospital and Community Psychiatry* 17, no. 7 (July 1966): 20-23.

Kuhn, Roland. "The Imipramine Story." In *Discoveries in Biological Psychiatry*, edited by Frank J. Ayd and Barry Blackwell, 205-217. Philadelphia: Lippincott, 1970.

Kvaale, Erlend P., Nick Haslam, and William H. Gottdeiner. "The 'Side Effects' of Medicalization: A Meta-Analytic Review of How Biogenetic Explanations Affect Stigma." *Clinical Psychology Review*, 33, no. 6 (August 2013): 782-794. https://doi.org/10.1016/j.cpr.2013.06.002

Lacasse, Jeffrey R., and Jonathan Leo. "Serotonin and Depression: A Disconnect Between Advertisements and the Scientific Literature." *PLoS Medicine* 2, no. 12 (November 8, 2005): e92, https://doi.org/10.1371/journal.pmed.0020392

*Lancet* Editorial Staff. "Is GSK Guilty of Fraud?" *Lancet* 363, no. 9425 (July 12, 2004): 1919. https://doi.org/10.1016/S0140-6736(04)16435-0

Langreth, Robert, and Roberta Ruiz. "The Forgotten Patients." *Forbes*, September 13, 2010.

Lannan, Katie. "Bill Calls for Coercion to be a Crime." *Lowell Sun*, July 25, 2019. http://www.lowellsun.com/todaysheadlines/ci_32747521/bill-calls-coercion-be-crime

Law360. "Widow's Trial Against GSK Wraps With $39M Damages Plea." April 21, 2017. https://www.law360.com/articles/914039/widow-s-trial-against-gsk-wraps-with-39m-damages-plea

Lennard, Jeremy. "Ten Dead in US School Shooting." *Guardian*, May 22, 2005. https://www.theguardian.com/world/2005/mar/22/usgunviolence.usa

LeNoury, Joanna, John M. Nardo, David Healy, Jon Jureidini, Melissa Raven, Catalin Tufanaru, and Elia Abi Jaoude. "Restoring Study 329: Efficacy and Harms of Paroxetine and Imipramine in Treatment of Major Depression in Adolescence." *BMJ* 351, (September 16, 2015): h4320. https://doi.org.10.1136/bmj.h4320

Leslie, Laurel K., Thomas B. Newman, P. Joan Chesney, and James M. Perrin. "The Food and Drug Administration's Deliberations on Antidepressant Use in Pediatric Patients." *Pediatrics* 11, no. 6 (July 2005): 195-204. https://doi.org.10.1542/peds.2005-0074

Leucht, Stefan, Hein Fennema, Rolf Engel, Marion Kaspers-Janssen, Peter Lepping, and Armin Szegedi. "What Does the HAMD Mean?" *Journal of Affective Disorders* 148, (2013): 243-248. https://doi.org/10.1016/j.jad.2012.12.001

Linde, Klaus, M.M. Berner, and L. Kriston. "Saint John's Wort for Major Depression." *Cochrane Database of Systematic Reviews*. October 8, 2008. https://doi.org/10.1002/14651858.CD000448.pub3

Linton, David. "Prosecutor in Texting-Suicide Case Involving Plainville Woman Gets Judgeship." *Sun-Chronicle*, October 5, 2017. https://www.thesunchronicle.com/news/local_news/prosecutor-in-texting-suicide-case-involving-plainville-woman-gets-judgeship/article_deab9ec9-090b-5080-aff1-536c616da215.html

Lite, Jordan. "Warning May Be Killing Kids." *New York Post*, September 7, 2007.

Loomer, H.P., J.C. Saunders, and Nathan S. Kline. "Iproniazid, an Amine Oxidase Inhibitor as an Example of a Psychic Energizer." *Hearings Before the Subcommittee of the Committee on Appropriations*. United

States Senate, 85th Congress, First Session on HR 6287, pp. 1382-1390. Washington DC, US Government Printing Office 1957.

López-Muñoz, Francisco, Ronaldo Ucha-Udabe, and Cecilia Alamo. "The History of Barbiturates a Century After Their Clinical Introduction." *Neuropsychiatric Disease and Treatment* 1, no. 4 (December 2005): 329-343.

Lynch, Terry. *The Depression Delusion: The Myth of the Brain Chemical Imbalance Volume 1*. Mental Health Publishing, 2015.

Makand, Prakash, Sanjay Gupta, and Mantosh Dewan. "Suicidal Ideation Related to Fluoxetine Treatment." *New England Journal of Medicine* 324, no. 6 (February 7 1991): 420.

Market Research Store. "Global Depression Drug Market Poised to Surge from USD \$14.51 Billion in 2014 to USD \$16.80 Billion by 2020." May 10, 2016. https://globenewswire.com/news-release/2016/05/10/838292/0/en/Global-Depression-Drug-Market-Poised-to-Surge-from-USD-14-51-Billion-in-2014-to-USD-16-80-Billion-by-2020-MarketResearch-Store-Com.html

Maxouris, Christina, Nicole Chavez, Eric Levenson, and Amir Vera. "El Paso Vigils Bring Together a City in Mourning After Mass Shooting." *CNN*, August 5, 2019. https://www.cnn.com/2019/08/05/us/el-paso-shooting-monday/index.html

McArdle, Helen. "U-turn as Psychiatrists Say Patients Should be Warned of Antidepressant Withdrawal Risk." *Herald*, May 30, 2019. https://www.heraldscotland.com/news/17673220.antidepressants-u-turn-as-psychiatrists-say-patients-should-be-warned-of-withdrawal-risk/

McArdle, Helen. "Mental Health Prescriptions Rising Fastest in 10-to-14 Year Old Scots: Sedatives Up 700% and Antidepressants Up 180%." *Herald*, October 27, 2019. https://www.heraldscotland.com/news/17994753.mental-health-prescriptions-rising-fastest-10-14-year-old-scots/?ref=fbshr&fbclid=IwAR28GngjBCLgFBerLXaY1XP08gDNxVONaDD8RaeX2NL4m3xnR9JUgYmbVjM

McCabe, Cathy. "Mass. Woman Must Stand Trial in Teen Friend's Suicide." *Boston Globe*, July 1, 2016. https://www.bostonglobe.com/metro/2016/07/01/sjc-rules-teen-charged-with-cajoling-friend-commit-suicide-must-stand-trial/J6bZdTPL6MNIaJ4iTlNLAJ/story.html

McDonald, Danny. "Michelle Carter's Attorney Files Notice to Appeal Her Conviction." *Boston Globe*, September 1, 2017. https://www.boston-globe.com/metro/2017/08/31/michelle-carter-attorney-files-notice-ap-peal-her-conviction/DdjdfV4RZSHCWzhYlEB8fP/story.html

McGinley, Laurie. "Former FDA Head Gottlieb Joins Pfizer Board." *Washington Post*, June 28, 2019.

Melander, Hans, Jane Alqvist-Rastad, Gertie Meijer, and Björn Beerman. "Evidence-B(i)ased Medicine—Selective Reporting From Studies Sponsored by Pharmaceutical Industry: Review of Studies in New Drug Applications." *BMJ* 326, May 31, 2003. https://doi.org.10/1136/bmj.326.7400.1171

Meier, Barry. "Glaxo Plans Public Listing of Drug Trials on Web Site." *New York Times*, June 19, 2004.

Meier, Barry. "Glaxo to Begin Posting Drug Trial Results." *New York Times*, September 1, 2004.

Ministry of Justice, Finland. "Jokela Secondary School Shooting: Report of the Investigation Commission." February 26, 2009. https://turvallisuustut-kinta.fi/material/attachments/otkes/tutkintaselostukset/fi/poikkeuk-sellisettapahtumat/SbmrFqAo3/Jokela_School_Shooting_on_7_November_2007.pdf

Ministry of Justice, Finland. "Kauhajoki School Shooting on September 23 2008: Report of the Investigation Commission." February 17, 2010. https://schoolshooters.info/sites/default/files/Kauhajoki%20School%20Shooting.pdf

Mitchell, Stephen. *Gilgamesh: A New English Version*. New York: Free Press, 2006.

*MOJO* Staff. "The 20 Most Important Artists of the Last 20 Years." *MOJO*, January 10, 2014. https://www.mojo4music.com/articles/10647/the-20-most-important-music-artists-of-the-last-20-years

Mojtabai, Ramin, and Mark Olfson. "Proportion of Antidepressants Prescribed Without a Psychiatric Diagnosis is Growing." *Health Affairs* 30, no. 8 (August 2011): 1434-1442. https://doi.org/10.1377/hlthaff.2010.1024

Mondics, Chris. "Philadelphia Jury Pins $70m Verdict on Janssen for Its Risperdal Drug." *Inquirer*, July 1, 2016. https://www.philly.com/

philly/business/20160702_Philadelphia_jury_pins__70m_verdict_on_
Janssen_for_its_Risperdal_drug.html

Montgomery, S.A., D.L. Dunner, and G.C. Dunbar. "Reduction in Suicidal
Thoughts With Paroxetine in Comparison with Reference Antidepressants and Placebo." *European Neuropsychopharmacology* 5, no. 1 (March
1995): 5-13.

Moore, Thomas J., Joseph Glenmullen, and Curt D. Furberg. "Prescription
Drugs Associated With Reports of Violence Towards Others." *PLoS
One* 5, no. 12 (December 2010): e15337. https://doi.org.1371/journal.
pone.0015337

Mullin, Gemma. "'Rare but Serious' Risk of Suicide for Patients on Antidepressants, New Findings Reveal." *Sun*, June 25, 2019. https://www.thesun.
co.uk/news/9367136/antidepressants-rare-serious-risk-suicide/

Murphy, Paul P., Konstantin Toropin, Drew Griffin, Scott Bronstein, and Eric
Levenson. "Dayton Shooter Had an Obsession With Violence and
Mass Shootings, Police Say." *CNN*, August 7, 2019. https://www.cnn.
com/2019/08/05/us/connor-betts-dayton-shooting-profile/index.html

NNT. "Statins in Persons at Low Risk of Cardiovascular Disease." Accessed
December 31, 2018. http://www.thennt.com/nnt/statins-per-
sons-low-risk-cardiovascular-disease/

National Institute for Health and Clinical Excellence. "Depression in Adults:
Recognition and Treatment." October 28, 2009. https://www.nice.org.
uk/guidance/cg90

National Institute of Mental Health. "Sequenced Treatment Alternatives to
Relieve Depression Study." Accessed January 5, 2019. https://www.
nimh.nih.gov/funding/clinical-research/practical/stard/index.shtml

*New York Post* Editorial Board. "The Michelle Carter Case: A Horrible Window
on the Way We Live Now." *New York Post*, June 16, 2017. https://
nypost.com/2017/06/16/the-michelle-carter-case-a-horrible-window-
on-the-way-we-live-now/

*News and Current Affairs.* "Hard to Swallow." Narr. Peter Mansfield. CBC, June
12, 2001.

Newspapers.ink: Newspapers in PDF. Accessed January 1, 2019. https://newspa-
pers.ink/sun-22February-2018/

North Carolina Department of Public Safety Offender Public Information. "Robert K. Stewart." 2012. https://webapps.doc.state.nc.us/opi/viewoffender. do?method=view&offenderID=1142611&searchLast-Name=Stewart&searchFirstName=Robert&searchGender=M&searchRace=1&searchDOB=09/23/1963&searchDOBRange=2&listurl=pagelistoffendersearchresults&listpage=1

Oldham, John, Daniel Carlat, Richard Friedman, and Andrew Nierenberg, and Marcia Angell. "'The Illusions of Psychiatry': An Exchange." *New York Review of Books*, August 18, 2011. https://www.nybooks.com/articles/2011/08/18/illusions-psychiatry-exchange/

O'Neal, Brandi L., and Melanie Biggs. "Sequenced Treatment Alternatives to Relieve Depression: Patient Education Manual, February 1, 2001." Accessed January 5, 2019. https://www.madinamerica.com/wp-content/uploads/2011/12/STAR_D%20Patient%20Education%20Plan%20Manual.pdf

O'Neill, Ann. "Victims: James Holmes' Bullets Tore Huge Holes in Their Lives." *CNN*, August 11, 2015. https://www.cnn.com/2015/08/26/us/james-holmes-aurora-massacre-sentencing/index.html

O'Neill, Ann. "Theater Shooter Holmes Gets 12 Life Sentences Plus 3,318 Years." *CNN*, August 27, 2015. https://www.cnn.com/2015/08/26/us/james-holmes-aurora-massacre-sentencing/index.html

Orr, Becky. "Anti-Depressant Lawsuit Begins in Cheyenne." *Wyoming Tribune-Eagle*, May 22, 2001.

Orr, Becky. "Paxil Verdict: $6.4 million." *Wyoming Tribune-Eagle*, June 7, 2001.

Osborne, Hannah. "BBC, SSRIs, and 'A Prescription for Murder': Experts Slam *Panorama* Documentary on Antidepressants." *Newsweek*, July 26, 2017. https://www.newsweek.com/bbc-panorama-antidepressants-murder-james-holmes-642068

Otto, Michael W., and Andrew A. Nierenberg. "Assay Sensitivity, Failed Clinical Trials, and the Conduct of Science." *Psychotherapy and Psychosomatics* 71, (2002): 241-243. https://www.karger.com/Article/Pdf/64813

*PLoS*. "Responses to Article." Accessed December 31, 2018. archive.li/t0yH0

Painter, M.M., M.A. Buerkley, M.L. Julius, A.M. Vajda, D.O. Norris, L.B. Barber, E.T. Furlong, M.M. Schulz, and H.L. Schoenfuss. "Antidepressants at Environmentally Relevant Concentrations Affect Predator

Avoidance Behavior of Larval Fathead Minnows (*Pimephales promelas*)." *Environmental Toxicology and Chemistry* 28, no. 12 (December 2009): 2677-2684. https://www.doi.org10.1897/08-556.1

*Panorama.* "Secrets of Seroxat." Narr. Shelley Jofre. BBC. October 13, 2002.

*Panorama.* "Seroxat: Emails From the Edge." Narr. Shelley Jofre. BBC. May 11, 2003.

*Panorama.* "Taken on Trust." Narr. Shelley Jofre. BBC. September 21, 2004.

*Panorama.* "Secrets of the Drug Trials." Narr. Shelley Jofre. BBC. January 29, 2007.

Paphides, Peter. "Stranger to the World." *Guardian*, April 24, 2004. https://www.theguardian.com/music/2004/apr/25/folk

Pariente, Carmine. "*Panorama's* Prescription." *Lancet* 4, July 28, 2017, e21. https://doi.org.10.1016/S2215-0366(17)30312-7

Park, Hana. "U. Professors Among 'Most Influential Minds.'" *Brown Daily Herald*, March 11, 2016. http://www.browndailyherald.com/2016/03/11/u-professors-among-most-influential-scientific-minds/

Parsons, Mitch. "Paroxetine in Adolescent Major Depression." *Journal of the American Academy of Child and Adolescent Psychiatry* 41, no. 4 (April 2002): 364.

Paskey, Janice. "Psychiatrist and University of Toronto Settle Dispute." *Chronicle of Higher Education*, May 17, 2002. https://www.chronicle.com/article/PsychiatristUniversity-of/15145

Pear, Robert. "Drug Industry, Having Long Smiled on Republican, Now Splits Donations Equally." *New York Times*, October 14, 2008.

Pfizer. "Scott Gottlieb Elected to Pfizer's Board of Directors." June 27, 2019. https://investors.pfizer.com/investor-news/press-release-details/2019/Scott-Gottlieb-Elected-to-Pfizers-Board-of-Directors/default.aspx

Pigott, Edmund H., Allan M. Leventhal, Gregory S. Alter, and John J. Boren. "Efficacy and Effectiveness of Antidepressants: Current Status of Research." *Psychotherapy and Psychosomatics* 79, (July 9, 2010): 267-279. https://doi.org/10.1159/000318293

Pressley, Linda. "The Troubled 29-Year-Old Helped to Die by Dutch Doctors." *BBC News*. August 9, 2018. https://www.bbc.com/news/stories-45117163

Preston, Robert, and Cynthia Pfeifer. "Garnier Hits Back at Spitzer Over Allegations of Fraud at GSK." *Sunday Telegraph*, June 6, 2004. https://www.telegraph.co.uk/finance/2887277/Garnier-hits-back-at-Spitzer-over-allegations-of-fraud-at-GSK.html

Public Health England. "Prescribed Medicines Review: Summary." September 10, 2019. https://www.gov.uk/government/publications/prescribed-medicines-review-report/prescribed-medicines-review-summary

Rabin, Roni Caryn. "A Suicide Leaves Tough Questions." *New York Times*, September 11, 2017.

Ramachandrai, Chaitra T., Narayana Subramanyam, and Vikram K. Yergani. "Antidepressants: From MAOIs to SSRIs and More." *Indian Journal of Psychiatry* 53, no. 2 (2011): 180-182. https://www.doi:10.4103/0019-5545.82567

Ransom, Jan. "Michelle Carter 'Involuntarily Intoxicated' by Prescription Before Friend's Suicide, Psychiatrist Testifies." *Boston Globe*, June 12, 2017. https://www.bostonglobe.com/metro/2017/06/12/michelle-carter-ssri-hampered-her-ability-feel-empathy-make-good-decisions-psychiatrist-says/zCrOp77pYoDNZldPlT7TSI/story.html

Ransom, Jan. "Mother of Conrad Roy III Seeks $4.2 Million in Wrongful Death Suit Against Michelle Carter." *Boston Globe*, August 4, 2017. https://www.bostonglobe.com/metro/2017/08/04/mother-conrad-roy-iii-seeks-wrongful-death-suit-against-michelle-carter/me1NraKa2N-qdyZb5HECC8I/story.html?event=event12

Ransom, Jan, and Travis Anderson. "Michelle Carter Receives 15 Months in Jail; Will Remain Free Pending Appeal." *Boston Globe*, August 3, 2017. https://www.bostonglobe.com/metro/2017/08/03/will-michelle-carter-sentenced-prison-maybe-not/iAB02N4H3jMojUi5DnxMQO/story.html

Ransom, Jan, and John R. Ellement. "Texting Suicide Came After 'Sick Game of Life and Death.'" *Boston Globe*, June 6, 2017. https://www.bostonglobe.com/metro/2017/06/06/woman-charged-with-cajoling-friend-commit-suicide-faces-involuntary-manslaughter-trial/8yl-BhZifsAYU2ix71ZFQTJ/story.html

Ransom, Jan, and John R. Ellement. "I Love You. Kill Yourself." *Boston Globe*, June 9, 2017. https://www.bostonglobe.com/metro/2017/06/09/michelle-carter-texting-trial-resume/kadMPvxS3sjEPK60EEWhKP/story.html

Rayner, Gordon. "Finnish School Shooting: How Killer 'Calmly' Picked off His Victims." *Telegraph*, September 23, 2008. https://www.telegraph.co.uk/news/worldnews/europe/finland/3068671/Finnish-school-shooting-how-killer-calmly-picked-off-his-victims.html

Read, John, and Nick Argyle. "Hallucinations, Delusions, and Thought Disorder Among Adult Psychiatric Patients With a History of Child Abuse." *Psychiatric Services*, 50, no. 11 (November 1999): 1467-1472. https://doi.org/10.1176/ps.50.11.1467

Read, John, Claire Ashby-James, Mary Boyle, Pat Bracken, Steven Coles, James Davies, Duncan Double, et al. to the Royal College of Psychiatrists. March 9, 2018. http://cepuk.org/wp-content/uploads/2018/03/Complaint-to-RCPsych.pdf

Read, John, Claire Ashby-James, Mary Boyle, Pat Bracken, Steven Coles, James Davies, Duncan Double, et al. to the Royal College of Psychiatrists. May 1, 2018. https://www.madinamerica.com/2018/05/royal-college-dismisses-complaint/

Read, John, Richard P. Bentall, and Roar Fosse. "Time to Abandon the Bio-Bio-Bio Model of Psychosis: Exploring the Epigenetic and Psychological Mechanisms by Which Adverse Life Events Lead to Psychotic Symptoms." *Epidemiologia e Psychiatria Sociale* 18, no. 4 (2009): 299-310.

Read, John, Claire Cartwright, and Kerry Gibson. "Adverse Emotional Effects Reported by 1829 New Zealanders While Taking Antidepressants." *Psychiatry Research* 216, (2014): 67-73. http://dx.doi.org/10.1016/j.psychres.2014.01.042

Read, John, Paul Jay Fink, Thom Rudegair, Vincent Felitti, and Charles L. Whitfield. "Child Maltreatment and Psychosis: A Return to a Genuinely Integrated Bio-Psycho-Social Model." *Clinical Schizophrenia and Related Psychoses* 2, no. 3 (October 2008): 235-254. https://doi.org/10.3371/CSRP.2.3.5

Read, John, Nick Haslam, and Lorenza Magliano. "Prejudice, Stigma, and 'Schizophrenia': The Role of Bio-Genetic Ideology." In *Models of Madness: Psychological, Social, and Biological Approaches to Schizophrenia*, edited by John Read and Jacqui Dillon, 157-177. Abingdon: Routledge, 2013.

Read, John, Nick Haslam, L. Sayce, and E. Davies. "Prejudice and Schizophrenia: A Review of the 'Mental Illness is an Illness Like Any Other' Approach." *Acta Psychiatrica Scandinavica* 114, no. 5 (November 2006): 303-318. https://doi.org/10.1111/j.1600-0447.2006.00824.x

Read, John, Beverly Thorpe, and Marion Brown. "Dangerous Opinions." *Herald*, November 3, 2019. https://www.heraldscotland.com/opinion/18011286.herald-sunday-letters-readers-talking-week/

Read, John, Jim van Os, Anthony P. Morrison, and C.A. Ross. "Childhood Trauma, Psychosis and Schizophrenia: A Literature Review With Theoretical and Clinical Implication." *Acta Psychiatrica Scandinavica* 112, no. 5 (October 2005): 330-350. https://doi.org/10.1111/j.1600-0447.2005.00634.x

Reiss, Jaclyn, and Jan Ransom. "How the Testimony Unfolded on the First Day of the Texting Suicide Case." *Boston Globe*, June 7, 2017. https://www.bostonglobe.com/metro/2017/06/06/how-testimony-unfolded-first-day-texting-suicide-case/YeIFSnLft0BPhSgrKiYtDI/story.html

Reuters. "Warning on Suicide in Prozac Use is Sought." *New York Times*, May 24, 1991.

Rice-Oxley, Mark. "It's Official: Antidepressants Are Not Snake Oil or a Conspiracy—They Work." *Guardian*, February 21, 2018. https://www.theguardian.com/society/2018/feb/21/its-official-antidepressants-are-not-snake-oil-or-a-conspiracy-they-work

Riley, Charles, and Emily Jane Fox. "GlaxoSmithKline in $3 Billion Fraud Settlement." *CNNMoney*, July 2, 2012. https://money.cnn.com/2012/07/02/news/companies/GlaxoSmithKline-settlement-index.htm

Rimmer, Abi. "Large Meta-Analysis Ends Doubts About Efficacy of Antidepressants." *BMJ* 360, (February 22, 2018). https://doi.org.10/10.1136/bmj.k847

Robitzek, Edward H., Irving J. Selikoff, and George G. Ornstein. "Chemotherapy of Human Tuberculosis With Hydrazine Derivatives of Isonicotinic Acid." *Quarterly Bulletin of Sea View Hospital* 13, no. 1 (January 1952): 27-51.

Rochelau, Matt. "Appeal in Michelle Carter Case May Take Years to Resolve." *Boston Globe*, August 3, 2017. https://www.bostonglobe.com/metro/2017/08/03/appeal-michelle-carter-case-may-take-years-resolve-experts-say/GaXXZYfvCRSXpzJG9j5raI/story.html

Rothschild, Anthony J., and Carol A. Locke. "Reexposure to Fluoxetine After Serious Suicide Attempts by Three Patients: The Role of Akathisia." *Journal of Clinical Psychiatry* 52, no. 12 (December 1991): 491-493.

Royal College of Psychiatrists. "RCPsych Calls Upon NICE to Update its Antidepressant Withdrawal Advice." May 29, 2019. https://www.rcpsych.ac.uk/news-and-features/latest-news/detail/2019/05/29/rcpsych-calls-on-nice-to-update-its-antidepressant-withdrawal-advice

Ruoff, Alex. "AbbVie, Bristol-Myers Among Patient Advocacy Groups' Big Backers." Bloomberg Government, October 8, 2019. https://about.bgov.com/news/abbvie-bristol-myers-among-patient-advocacy-groups-big-backers/?fbclid=IwAR3A_1rf8Q0UsgHUhoxBh1pQtn-Fe3sfnlyMME0tBc7j6odzY1yup8vgtloA

Rush, John A., Madhukar H. Trivedi, Stephen R. Wisniewski, Andrew A. Nierenberg, Jonathan W. Stewart, Diane Warden, George Niederehe, et al. "Acute and Longer-Term Outcomes in Depressed Outpatients Requiring One or Several Treatment Steps: A STAR*D Report." *American Journal of Psychiatry* 163, no. 11 (November 2006): 1905-1917. https://doi.org/10.1176/ajp.2006.163.11.1905

Rütgen, Markus, Carolina Plenti, Martin Tik, Daniela Melitta Pfabigan, Ronald Sladky, Manfred Klöbel, Michael Woletz, et al. "Antidepressant Treatment, Not Depression, Leads to Reductions in Behavioral and Neural Responses to Pain Empathy." *Translational Psychiatry* 9, Article 164 (2019). https://doi.org/10.1038/s41398-019-0496-4

Sachdev, Ameet. "Stewart Dolin 1952-2010." *Chicago Tribune*, July 18, 2010. https://www.chicagotribune.com/living/ct-xpm-2010-07-18-ct-met-dolin-obit-0718-20100718-story.html

Sandler, Martin. "Monoamine Oxidase Inhibitors in Depression: History and Mythology." *Journal of Psychopharmacology* 4, no. 3 (1990): 136-139. https://doi.org/10.1177/026988119000400307

Sandy Hook Advisory Commission. "Final Report of the Sandy Hook Advisory Commission." March 6, 2015. http://www.shac.ct.gov/SHAC_Final_Report_3-6-2015.pdf

Scanlon, Leslie, and Todd Murphy. "Wesbecker Rampage Not Linked to Prozac." *Courier Journal*, December 13, 1994.

Schafer, A. "Biomedical Conflicts of Interest: A Defence of the Sequestration Thesis—Learning from the Cases of Nancy Olivieri and David Healy." *Journal of Medical Ethics* 30, no. 1 (February 2004): 8-24. http://dx.doi.org/10.1136/jme.2003.005702

Schulenk, Udo, and Suzanne van de Vathorst. "Treatment-Resistant Major Depressive Disorder and Assisted Dying." *Journal of Medical Ethics* 41, no. 8 (2015): 577-583. http://dx.doi.org/10.1136/medethics-2014-102458

Schumer, Fran. "Bye-Bye Blues: The New Wonder Drug for Depression." *New York*, December 18, 1989.

Schworm, Peter. "Plainville Teen Accused of Urging Friend to Kill Himself." *Boston Globe*, February 27, 2015. https://www.bostonglobe.com/metro/2015/02/27/plainville-teen-charged-with-manslaughter-friend-suicide/WM5yHKA5IpobG2WXEWHLFM/story.html

Scott, Ellen. "Can We Please Stop Demonising Antidepressants?" *Metro News*, July 25, 2017. https://metro.co.uk/2017/07/25/can-we-please-stop-demonising-antidepressants-6804436/

Selikoff, Irving J., Edward H. Robitzek, and George G. Ornstein. "Toxicity of Hydrazine Derivatives of Isonicotinic Acid in the Chemotherapy of Human Tuberculosis." *Quarterly Bulletin of Sea View Hospital* 13, no. 1 (January 1952): 17-26.

Selikoff, Irving J., Edward H. Robitzek, and George G. Ornstein. "Treatment of Pulmonary Tuberculosis With Hydrazide Derivatives of Isonicotinic Acid." *JAMA* 150, no. 10 (November 8, 1952): 973-980.

SFGate. "Police Suspect Murder-Suicide in Deaths of Father and 2 Kids." May 1, 1997. https://www.sfgate.com/news/article/Police-Suspect-Murder-Suicide-In-Deaths-of-Father-2841957.php

Sharma, Tarang, Louise Schow Guski, Nanna Freund, and Peter C. Gøtzsche. "Suicidality and Aggression During Antidepressant Treatment: Systematic Review and Meta-Analysis Based on Clinical Study Reports." *BMJ* 2016; 352:165 http://dx.doi.10.1136/bmj/i65

Silversides, Ann. "Hospital Denies That Withdrawal of MD's Job Offer Was Related to Drug Company Funding." *Canada Medical Association Journal* 164, no. 13 (June 26, 2001): 1879.

Smith, Jackson A. "The Use of the Isopropyl Derivative of Isonicotinylhydrazine (Marsilid) in the Treatment of Mental Disease: A Preliminary Report." *American Practitioner and Digest of Treatment* 4, no. 8 (August 1953): 19-20.

Smyth, Chris. "More People Should Get Pills to Beat Depression." *Times*, February 22, 2018. https://www.thetimes.co.uk/article/more-people-should-get-pills-to-beat-depression-sv5vhczss

Smyth, Chris. "Drugs Adviser David Baldwin Quits After Being Branded 'Worse Than Hitler' in Online Abuse Row." *Times*, September 25, 2018. https://www.thetimes.co.uk/article/drugs-adviser-david-baldwin-quits-after-being-branded-worse-than-hitler-in-online-abuse-row-srtqltmfs

Soumeri, Stephen, and Ross Koppel. "FDA's Continuing Use of 'Black Box' Warning for Antidepressants Ignores the Harms of this Warning." *STAT*, August 29, 2018. https://www.statnews.com/2018/08/29/fda-antidepressants-black-box-warnings-harms/?utm_source=*STAT*+Newsletters&utm_campaign=f6cc09a85d-MR_COPY_08&utm_medium=email&utm_term=0_8cab1d7961-f6cc09a85d-143355333

Spencer, Ben. "New Health Alert over Antidepressants as Study Finds a 'Rare but Serious Risk' of Suicide for Patients on Pills." *Daily Mail*, June 24, 2019. https://www.dailymail.co.uk/news/article-7176689/New-study-finds-rare-risk-suicide-patients-antidepressants.html

Stockman, Tom, Dolapo Odegbaro, Sami Timmi, and Joanna Moncrieff. "SSRI and SNRI Withdrawal Symptoms Reported on an Internet Forum." *International Journal of Risk and Safety in Medicine* 29, no. 3-4 (2018): 175-180. https://doi.org/10.3233/JRS-180018

Stone, Marc, Shamir Kalaria, Kyle Richardville, and Brian Miller. "Components and Trends in Treatment Effects in Randomized Placebo-Controlled Trials in Major Depressive Disorder from 1979-2016." Poster presented at the American Society of Clinical Psychopharmacology, Miami, May 28-June 1, 2018.

Suk, Jeannie. "ABA Criminal Justice Standards." August 15, 2017. https://h2o.law.harvard.edu/text_blocks/30177

Sulzberger, A.G., and Mark Binker. "Gunman Kills 8 at N. Carolina Nursing Home." *New York Times*, March 29, 2009, A16.

*Sun-Times* Media Wire. "Drug Firm to Pay $3 M to Widow of Man Who Jumped In Front of Train." *Chicago Sun-Times*, April 21, 2017. https://chicago.suntimes.com/health/gsk-must-pay-3m-to-widow-of-man-who-jumped-in-front-of-cta-train/

Szaniszlo, Marie. "Wrongful Death Suit Against Michelle Carter 'Resolved.'" *Boston Herald*, April 9, 2019. https://www.bostonherald.com/2019/04/09/wrongful-death-suit-against-michelle-carter-re-solved/

Tager, Jack. "'Murder by Counseling': The 1816 Case of George Bowen (Northampton)." *Historical Journal of Massachusetts* 38, no. 2 (Fall 2010): 103-119.

Teicher, Martin H., Carol Glod, and Jonathan O. Cole. "Emergence of Intense Suicidal Preoccupation During Fluoxetine Treatment." *American Journal of Psychiatry* 147, no. 2 (February 1990): 207-210. https://doi10.1176/ajp.147.2.207

Thase, Michael E. "Antidepressant Effects: The Suit May Be Small, but the Fabric Is Real." *Prevention & Treatment* 5, (July 15, 2002): Article 32.

Thomas, Katie, and Michael S. Schmidt. "Glaxo Agrees to Pay $3 Billion in Fraud Settlement." *New York Times*, July 2, 2012.

Tighe, Lori. "Decision in Family's Lawsuit Against Prozac Rests With Jury." *Honolulu Star-Bulletin*, January 9, 1998. http://archives.starbulletin.com/98/01/09/news/story2.html

Trivedi, Madhukar, A. John Rush, Stephen R. Wisniewski, Andrew A. Nierenberg, Diane Warden, Louise Ritz, Grayson Norquist, et al. "Evaluation of Outcomes With Citalopram for Depression Using Measurement-Based Care in STAR*D: Implications for Clinical Practice."

*American Journal of Psychiatry* 163, no. 1 (January 2006): 28-40. https://doi.org/10.1176/appi.ajp.163.1.28

Turkoz, I., L. Alphs, P. Lim, A. DiBernardino, M. Shawi, and D. Hough. "Demonstration of the Relationships Among Clinical Global Impression of Severity of Depression Scale and Montgomery-Åsberg Depression Rating, Patient Health Questionnaire-9, and Sheehan Disability Scales." Poster presented at the 14th Annual Meeting of the International Society of CNS Clinical Trials and Methodology, February 20-22, 2018. https://isctm.org/public_access/Feb2018/PDFs/Turkoz-poster.pdf

United States Department of Justice. "Complaint Ex 1." Accessed December 15, 2018. https://www.justice.gov/usao-ma/file/872511/download

United States Department of Justice. "GlaxoSmithKline to Plead Guilty and Pay $3 Billion to Resolve Fraud Allegations and Failure to Report Safety Data: Largest Health Care Fraud Settlement in U.S. History." July 2, 2012. https://www.justice.gov/opa/pr/glaxosmithkline-plead-guilty-and-pay-3-billion-resolve-fraud-allegations-and-failure-report

United States Department of Justice. "Johnson & Johnson to Pay More Than $2.2 Billion to Resolve Criminal and Civil Investigations: Allegations Include Illegal Marketing and Kickback to Doctors and Pharmacists." November 4, 2013. https://www.justice.gov/opa/pr/johnson-johnson-pay-more-22-billion-resolve-criminal-and-civil-investigations

United States Secret Service National Threat Assessment Center. "Mass Attacks in Public Spaces—2018." July 2019. https://www.secretservice.gov/data/press/reports/USSS_FY2019_MAPS.pdf

Urbinato, David. "Jury Rules Prozac Maker Not Liable for Man's Deadly Rampage." Associated Press, December 13, 1994. https://www.apnews.com/9350e89fb1d872b5c876fbfce4138aa8

Valenstein, Eliot S. *Blaming the Brain: The Truth About Drugs and Mental Health*. New York: Free Press, 1998.

Valuck, Robert J., Heather D. Orton, and Anne Libby. "Antidepressant Discontinuation and Risk of Suicide Attempt: A Retrospective, Nested Case-Control Study." *Journal of Clinical Psychiatry* 70, no. 8 (August 2009): 1069-1077. https://doi.org/10.4088/JCP.08m04943

Van Erp, Theo, Esther Walton, Derrek P. Hibar, Lianne Schmaal, Wenhao Jiang, David C. Glahn, Godfrey D. Pearlson, et al. "Cortical Brain Abnormalities in 4474 Individuals With Schizophrenia and 5098 Control Subjects via the Enhanced Neuro Imaging Genetics Through Meta Analysis (ENIGMA) Consortium." *Biological Psychiatry*, May 14, 2018. https:doi.org.10.1016/j.biopsych.2018.04.023 [Epub ahead of print].

Vendantam, Shankar. "Youth Suicide Rates Increased as Antidepressant Use Fell." *Washington Post*, September 6, 2007. http://www.washingtonpost.com/wp-dyn/content/article/2007/09/05/AR2007090502303.html

Verhovek, Sam Howe. "15 Bodies Are Removed From School in Colorado." *New York Times*, April 22, 1999.

Vittengl, Jeffrey R. "Poorer Long-Term Outcomes Among Persons With Major Depressive Disorder Treated with Medication." *Psychotherapy and Psychosomatics* 86, (2017): 302-304. https://doi.org/10.1159/000479162

Vogel, Steve, Sari Horwitz, and David A. Fahrenthold. "Navy Yard Gunman Aaron Alexis Told VA Doctors He Was Not Thinking of Harming Others." *Washington Post*, September 18, 2013. https://www.washingtonpost.com/politics/2013/09/18/aee01b22-20a6-11e3-b73c-aab60bf735d0_story.html?utm_term=.aad4c67556b1

WRAL. "Defense: Defendant Doesn't Remember Nursing Home Shooting." August 1, 2011. https://www.wral.com/news/local/story/9936931/

Wan, William. "White House Weighs Controversial Plan on Mental Illness and Mass Shootings." *Washington Post* September 9, 2019. https://beta.washingtonpost.com/health/white-house-considers-controversial-plan-on-mental-illness-and-mass-shooting/2019/09/09/eb58b6f6-ce72-11e9-87fa-8501a456c003_story.html

Wan, William. "Teen Suicides are Increasing at an Alarming Pace, Outstripping All Other Age Groups, a New Report Says." *Washington Post*, October 17, 2019. https://www.washingtonpost.com/health/teen-suicides-increasing-at-alarming-pace-outstripping-all-other-age-groups/2019/10/16/e24194c6-f04a-11e9-8693-f487e46784aa_story.html

Waters, Rob. "Drug Report Barred by FDA/Scientist Links Antidepressants to Suicide in Kids." *San Francisco Chronicle*, February 1, 2004. https://

www.sfgate.com/health/article/Drug-report-barred-by-FDA-Scientist-links-2825996.php

Waters, Rob. "Lawmakers Open Probe of FDA/Agency Accused of Barring Safety Data on Antidepressants." *San Francisco Chronicle*, March 31, 2004. https://www.sfgate.com/health/article/Lawmakers-open-probe-of-FDA-Agency-accused-of-2773090.php

Waters, Rob. "FDA Was Urged to Limit Kids' Antidepressants/Advice Citing Risk of Suicide Rejected." *San Francisco Chronicle*, April 16, 2004. https://www.sfgate.com/health/article/FDA-was-urged-to-limit-kids-antidepressants-2767075.php

West, E.A. "FDA's Support of Prozac a Milestone in a 'Sordid Controversy.'" *Saint Petersburg Times*, August 8, 1991.

Whitaker, Robert. *Anatomy of an Epidemic: Magic Bullets, Psychiatric Drugs, and the Astonishing Rise of Mental Illness in America*. New York: Broadway Books, 2010.

Whitaker, Robert. "Adolescent Suicide and the Black Box Warning: *STAT* Gets it All Wrong." August 31, 2018. https://www.madinamerica.com/2018/08/adolescent-suicide-and-the-black-box-warning-stat-gets-it-all-wrong/

Whitaker, Robert, and Lisa Cosgrove. *Psychiatry Under the Influence: Institutional Corruption, Social Injury, and Prescriptions for Reform*. New York: Palgrave Macmillan, 2015.

Whyte, Chelsea. "US Suicide Rate at its Highest Since the End of the Second World War." *New Scientist*, June 19, 2019. https://www.newscientist.com/article/2207007-us-suicide-rate-at-its-highest-since-the-end-of-the-second-world-war/

Wilens, Timothy, Joseph Biederman, Anne Kwon, Rhea Chase, Laura Greenberg, Eric Mick, and Thomas J. Spencer. "A Systematic Chart Review of the Nature of Psychiatric Adverse Events in Children and Adults Treated With Selective Serotonin Reuptake Inhibitors." *Journal of Child and Adolescent Psychopharmacology* 13, no. 2 (2003): 143-152. https://doi.org/10.1089/104454603322163862

Wingert, Pat. "Young and Depressed." *Newsweek*, October 6, 2002. https://www.newsweek.com/young-and-depressed-146623.

Wirshing, William C., Theodore van Putten, James Rosenberg, Stephen Marder, Donna Ames, and Tara Hicks-Grey. "Fluoxetine, Akathisia, and Suicidality: Is There a Causal Connection?" *Archives of General Psychiatry* 49, no. 7 (July 1992): 580-581. https:doi/org/10.1001/archpsyc.1992.01820070074012

Wolfson, Andrew. "Prozac Maker Secretly Paid Millions to Secure Favorable Verdict in Mass Shooting Lawsuit." *Courier-Journal*, September 11, 2019. https://www.courierjournal.com/story/news/investigations/2019/09/11/standard-gravure-shooting-drugmakers-secret-payment-revealed-mass-shooting-lawsuit/2263776001/

Wong, David T., Frank P. Bymaster, and Eric A. Engleman. "Prozac (Fluoxetine, Lilly 11040), the First Selective Serotonin Uptake Inhibitor as an Antidepressant Drug: Twenty Years Since Its First Publication." *Life Sciences* 57, no. 5 (1995): 411-441.

World Health Organization. "Depression." March 22, 2018. https://www.who.int/newsroom/fact-sheets/detail/depression

Wright, Gary L. "Crespi to Plead Guilty to Murder: Father Expected to Serve Life in Prison for Killing Twin Daughters." *Charlotte Observer*, July 16, 2006.

XE: The World's Trusted Currency Authority. Accessed December 26, 2018. https://www.xe.com/

YouTube. "Peter Breggin Antidepressant Testimony." January 12, 2012. https://www.youtube.com/watch?v=zjHtBAkncgk.

YouTube. "David Healy Antidepressant Testimony." January 18, 2012. https://www.youtube.com/watch?v=VjXDDMK-Awg

Zeller, E.A., Barsky, J.R. Fouts, W.F. Kirscheimer, and L.S. van Orden. "Influence of Isonicotinic Acid Hydrazide (INH) and 1-Isconicotinyl-2-Isopropyl Hydrazide (IIH) on Bacterial and Mammalian Enzymes." *Experientia* 8, no. 9 (September 1952): 349-350.

Zitrin, Richard, and Carol M. Langford. *The Moral Compass of the American Lawyer*. New York: Ballantine Books, 1999.

# *Index*

## A

Akathisia, 18, 41, 43, 70, 76, 88, 89, 94, 95, 101, 153, 175, 176

Amitriptyline, 8, 10, 11, 115, 126

## B

Breggin, Peter, vii, 18, 23, 28, 29, 30, 31, 32, 36, 38, 41, 70, 74, 88, 106, 117, 150, 152, 153, 154, 155, 157, 160, 161, 162, 163, 187

## C

Carmichael, David, 96, 195, 253, 254

Carter, Michelle, 146, 147, 148, 149, 152, 154, 162, 163, 164

Celexa, 12, 106, 107, 110, 118, 147, 150, 153, 157, 159, 161, 163

Cipriani, Andrea, 115, 116, 117, 136

Citalopram, see Celexa, 12, 60, 114, 115, 174

Crespi, David, 96, 99,

Crespi, Kim, 99

## D

Dolin, Stewart, 93, 94

Dolin, Wendy, 86, 89, 93, 94

Doshi, Peter, 81, 83, 84, 85, 185

Drake, Nick, 11

## F

FDA, 13, 19, 20, 22, 27, 30, 31, 32, 33, 34, 35, 42, 48, 57, 58, 60, 63, 64, 65, 67, 68, 69, 71, 73, 74, 75, 78, 80, 81, 86, 88, 89, 90, 91, 92, 103, 106, 107, 109, 110, 116, 117, 142, 143, 144, 145, 170, 178, 179, 181, 187

Fluoxetine, see Prozac, 12, 22

Fluvoxamine, see Luvox, 12

Forsyth, William, 39, 40, 41, 42, 43

## G

Gibbons, Robert, 143, 144, 145, 146, 170, 183

## H

Harris, Eric, 19, 172

Healy, David, ii, vii, 2, 17, 40, 41, 42, 43, 44, 45, 46, 47, 49, 50, 51, 54, 55, 59, 60, 61, 67, 73, 77, 79, 81, 83, 84, 85, 86, 89, 90, 94, 99, 121, 122, 124, 125, 141, 142, 168, 170, 171, 172, 186

## I

Imipramine, 8

Iproniazid, 4,

## J

Jofre, Shelley, 58, 59, 133, 134, 168

Jureidini, Jon, 56, 78, 79, 81, 85

## K

Keller, Martin, 52, 53, 55, 56, 64, 77, 83, 84, 858

Kirsch, Irving, ii, vii, 104, 105, 106, 107, 108, 109, 110, 111, 112, 113, 114, 115, 116, 117, 123, 178, 183, 186

Klebold, Dylan, 172

Kramer, Peter, 22, 23, 113

## L

Lacuzong, Reynaldo, 70

# Endnotes

1    John Cornwell, *The Power to Harm* (New York: Viking, 1996): 13-27.

2    Ibid., 15.

3    Ibid., 20.

4    Ibid., 22-23.

5    Ibid., 39.

6    David Urbinato, "Jury Rules Prozac Maker Not Liable for Man's Deadly Rampage," Associated Press, December 13, 1994, https://www.apnews.com/9350e89fb1d872b5c876fbfce4138aa8

7    David Healy, *Let Them Eat Prozac* (New York: New York University Press, 2004), 85.

8    David Healy, "Psychopharmacology and the Government of the Self," accessed November 19, 2018, https://www.pharmapolitics.com/feb2healy.html

9    Mick Brown, "Nick Drake: The Fragile Genius," *Telegraph*, November 25, 2014, https://www.telegraph.co.uk/culture/music/worldfolkand-jazz/11250728/Nick-Drake-the-fragile-genius.html

10    Ibid.

11    Ibid.

12    Peter Paphides, "Stranger to the World," *Guardian*, April 24, 2004, https://www.theguardian.com/music/2004/apr/25/folk

13    Ibid.

14    Steven Mitchell, *Gilgamesh: A New English Version* (New York: Free Press, 2006), 6.

15    Ibid., 1.

16    Fischer also played a prominent role in developing the class of psychiatric drugs known as barbiturates. See Francisco López-Muñoz, Ronaldo Ucha-Udabe, and Cecilia Alamo, "The History of Barbiturates a Century After Their Clinical Introduction," *Neuropsychiatric Disease and Treatment* 1, no. 4 (December 2005): 329-343.

17    Martin Sandler, "Monoamine Oxidase Inhibitors in Depression: History and Mythology," *Journal of Psychopharmacology* 4, no. 3 (1990): 136.

18    E. Grunberg and R.J. Schnitzer, "Studies on the Activity of Hydrazine Derivatives of Isonicotinic Acid in the Experimental Tuberculosis of Mice," *Quarterly Bulletin of Sea View Hospital* 13, no. 1 (1952): 3-11.

19    Irving J. Selikoff, Edward H. Robitzek, and George G. Ornstein, "Toxicity of Hydrazine Derivatives of Isonicotinic Acid in the Chemotherapy of Human Tuberculosis," *Quarterly Bulletin of Sea View Hospital* 13, no. 1 (January 1952): 17-26; Edward H. Robitzek, Irving J. Selikoff, and George G. Ornstein, "Chemotherapy of Human Tuberculosis With Hydrazine Derivatives of Isonicotinic Acid," *Quarterly Bulletin of Sea View Hospital* 13, no. 1 (January 1952): 27-51; Irving Selikoff, Edward H. Robitzek, and George G. Ornstein, "Treatment of Pulmonary Tuberculosis With Hydrazide Derivatives of Isonicotinic Acid," *JAMA* 150, no. 10 (November 8, 1952): 973-980; Irving Cheifetz et al., "Iproniazid in Pulmonary Tuberculosis," *Diseases of the Chest* 25, no. 4 (April 1954): 390-396, https://doi.org/10.1378/chest.25.4.390; George Crane, "The Psychiatric Side Effects of Iproniazid," *American Journal of Psychiatry* 112, no. 7 (January 1956): 494-501.

20    Emma Harrison, "TB Drug is Tried In Mental Cases: Use of Iproniazid at Rockland Indicates Energizing Effect in Cases of Depression," *New York Times*, April 7, 1957, 86.

21    Cheifetz et al., "Iproniazid," 392; George Crane, "Psychiatric Side Effects," 500.

22    Jackson A. Smith, "The Use of the Isopropyl Derivative of Isonicotinyl-hydrazine (Marsilid) in the Treatment of Mental Disease," *American Practitioner and Digest of Treatment* 4, no. 8 (August 1953): 519-520.

23    Gordon Kamman, John G. Freeman, and Rubel Lucero, "The Effect of 1-Isonicotinyl 2-Isopropyl Hydrazide (IIH) on the Behavior of Long-Term Mental Patients," *Journal of Nervous and Mental Diseases* 118, no. 5 (November 1953): 391-407.

24    Nathan S. Kline, "Monoamine Oxidase Inhibitors: An Unfinished Picaresque Tale," in *Discoveries in Biological Psychiatry*, ed. F.J. Ayd and B. Blackwell (Philadelphia: Lippincott, 1970), 197.

25    H.P. Loomer, J.C. Saunders, and Nathan S. Kline, "Iproniazid, an Amine Oxidase Inhibitor as an Example of a Psychic Energizer," *Hearings Before the Subcommittee of the Committee on Appropriations*, United States Senate, 85th Congress, First Session on HR 6287, pp. 1382-1390, Washington DC, US Government Printing Office 1957.

26    Andrea Cipriani, email 25 February 2018. See also Andrea Cipriani et al., "Comparative Efficacy and Acceptability of 21 Antidepressant Drugs for the Acute Treatment of Adults With Major Depressive Disorder: A Systematic Review and Meta-Analysis," *Lancet* 391, no. 10128 (April 7, 2018): 1357-1366, https://doi.org/10.1016/S0140-6736(17)32802-

27    Kline, "Monoamine Oxidase Inhibitors," 202.

28    Albert and Mary Lasker Foundation, "1964 Albert Lasker Clinical Medical Research Award: Iproniazid for the Treatment of Severe Depression," 2018, http://www.laskerfoundation.org/awards/show/iproniazid-for-the-treatment-of-severe-depression/

29    E.A. Zeller et al., "Influence of Isonicotinic Acid Hydrazide (INH) and 1-Isconicotinyl-2-Isopropyl Hydrazide (IIH) on Bacterial and Mammalian Enzymes," *Experientia* 8, no. 9 (September 1952): 349-350.

30    David Healy, "The Three Faces of Antidepressants: A Critical Commentary on the Clinical-Economic Context of Diagnosis," *Journal of Nervous and Mental Disease* 187, no. 3 (1999): 174-180.

31    Roland Kuhn, "The Imipramine Story," in *Discoveries in Biological Psychiatry*, ed. Frank J. Ayd and Barry Blackwell (Philadelphia: Lippincott, 1970), 205-217.

32    Harold S. Koplewicz, *It's Nobody's Fault: New Hope and Help for Difficult Children* (New York: Random House, 1996).

33    Kuhn, "Imipramine Story," 214.

34    Chaitra T. Ramachandrai et al., "Antidepressants: From MAOIs to SSRIs and More," *Indian Journal of Psychiatry* 53, no. 2 (2011): 180-182, https://www.doi:10.4103/0019-5545.8256

35    Arvid Carlsson, "Rationale and Design of a Selective Inhibitor of 5-HT Re-Uptake," *British Journal of Clinical Practice: A Symposium* 19, (1982): 20; Julius Axelrod, "An Unexpected Life in Research," *Annual Review of Pharmacology and Toxicology* 28, (1988): 1-23.

36    Leo E. Hollister, "Drugs in Emotional Disorders: Past and Present," *Annals of Internal Medicine* 51, no. 5 (November 1959): 1045.

37    Carlsson himself said of the serotonin hypothesis in his 1982 paper, "We were, of course, aware of the fact that such a statement is necessarily an over-simplification; nevertheless, it may have heuristic value." Since then, years of work by scientists with impeccable credentials have failed to yield any convincing evidence for the chemical imbalance theory of mental illness. It is beyond the scope of the present work to provide a comprehensive account of this research. Interested readers are referred to David Healy, "The Structure of Psychopharmacological Revolutions," *Psychiatric Development* 4, (1987): 349-376; Eliot S. Valenstein, *Blaming the Brain: The Truth About Drugs and Mental Health* (New York: Free Press, 1998); Jeffrey R. Lacasse and Jonathan Leo, "Serotonin and Depression: A Disconnect Between Advertisements and the Scientific Literature," *PLoS Medicine* 2, no. 12 (November 8, 2005), e92. https://doi.org.10.1371/journal.pmed.0020392; and Irving Kirsch, *The Emperor's New Drugs: Exploding the Antidepressant Myth* (New York: Basic Books, 2010).

38    Terry Lynch, *The Depression Delusion: The Myth of the Brain Chemical Imbalance Volume 1* (Mental Health Publishing, 2015).

39    George Krieder, "Suicides, Drugs, and the Open Hospital," *Hospital and Community Psychiatry* 17, no. 7 (July 1966): 20-23.

40 David Avery and George Winokur, "Suicides, Attempted Suicides, and Relapse Rates in Depression," *Archives of General Psychiatry* 35, (June 1978): 749-753.

41 Simon Cassidy and John Henry, "Fatal Toxicity of Antidepressant Drugs in Overdose," *British Medical Journal* 295, no. 6605 (October 24, 1987): 1021-1024.

42 Ibid., 1023.

43 Paul Cole, "The Last 10 Days of Singer-Songwriter Nick Drake's Life Are Revealed in His Father's Heartbreaking Diary," *Birmingham Mail*, November 22, 2014, https://www.birminghammail.co.uk/news/midlands-news/last-10-days-singer-songwriter-nick-8153684

44 *MOJO* Staff, "The 20 Most Important Artists of the Last 20 Years," *MOJO*, January 10, 2014, https://www.mojo4music.com/articles/10647/the-20-most-important-music-artists-of-the-last-20-years

45 David Healy, Joanna Le Noury, and Julie Wood, *Children of the Cure: Missing Data, Lost Lives, and Antidepressants*, Samizdat Health Writers' Co-operative Inc., Chapter 5, Kindle.

46 David T. Wong, Frank P. Bymaster, and Eric A. Engleman, "Prozac (Fluoxetine, Lilly 11040), the First Selective Serotonin Uptake Inhibitor as an Antidepressant Drug: Twenty Years Since Its First Publication," *Life Sciences* 57, no. 5 (1995): 411-441.

47 Personal observations.

48 Zimelidine was removed from the market a year after it was introduced after being linked to cases of Guillain-Barre Syndrome. The second SSRI, indalpine, was removed after being linked to cases of liver failure. The third, fluvoxamine, was introduced under the trade name Luvox and still is available. Prozac was the fourth SSRI to be released on to the market.

49 Peter D. Kramer, *Listening to Prozac: A Psychiatrist Explores Antidepressant Drugs and the Remaking of the Self* (New York: Penguin Books, 1993), xvii.

50      Fran Schumer, "Bye-Bye Blues: The New Wonder Drug for Depression," *New York*, December 18, 1989, 46-53.

51      Ibid., 48.

52      Ibid., 50.

53      Ibid., 52.

54      Ibid., 53.

55      Ibid., 48.

56      Ibid., 48-53.

57      Ibid., 49.

58      Geoffrey Cowley, "The Promise of Prozac," *Newsweek*, March 26, 1990.

59      Ibid.

60      Ibid.

61      Ibid.

62      Natalie Angier, "New Antidepressant Is Acclaimed but Not Perfect," *New York Times*, March 29, 1990, B9.

63      Martin H. Teicher, Carol Glod, and Jonathan O. Cole, "Emergence of Intense Suicidal Preoccupation During Fluoxetine Treatment," *American Journal of Psychiatry* 147, no. 2 (February 1990): 207-210, https://doi10.1176/ajp.147.2.207

64      Prakash Makand et al., "Suicidal Ideation Related to Fluoxetine Treatment," *New England Journal of Medicine* 324, no. 6 (February 7 1991): 420.

65      Robert A. King et al., "Emergence of Self-Destructive Phenomena in Children and Adolescents During Fluoxetine Treatment," *Journal of the American Academy of Child and Adolescent Psychiatry* 30, no. 2 (March 1991): 179-185, https://doi.org/10.1097/00004583-199103000-00003

66      W. Creaney, I. Murray, and David Healy, "Antidepressant Induced Suicidal Ideation," *Human Psychopharmacology* 6, (August 1991): 329-332.

67    Ibid., 330-331.

68    Anthony J. Rothschild and Carol A. Locke, "Reexposure to Fluoxetine After Serious Suicide Attempts by Three Patients: The Role of Akathisia," *Journal of Clinical Psychiatry* 52, no. 12 (December 1991): 491-493.

69    Ibid., 492.

70    Ibid., 494.

71    William Wirshing et al., "Fluoxetine, Akathisia, and Suicidality: Is There a Causal Connection?" *Archives of General Psychiatry* 49, no. 7 (July 1992): 580-581, https://doi:10.1001/archpsyc.1992.01820070074012

72    Ibid., 580-581.

73    David Healy, "Lines of Evidence on the Risks of Suicide with Selective Serotonin Reuptake Inhibitors," *Psychotherapy and Psychosomatics* 72, (2003): 74, https://doi.10.1159/000068691

74    David Healy, "A Failure to Warn," *International Journal of Risk and Safety in Medicine* 12, (1999):151-156.

75    David Healy, "Science, Rhetoric, and the Causality of Adverse Effects," *International Journal of Risk and Safety in Medicine* 24, (2011): 1-14, https://doi.10.3233/JRS-2011-534

76    Reuters, "Warning on Suicide in Prozac Use is Sought," *New York Times*, May 24, 1991, A17; Associated Press, "Warning Label on Antidepressant is Opposed," *New York Times*, September 21, 1991, 001022.

77    Allison Bass, *Side Effects: A Prosecutor, a Whistleblower, and a Bestselling Antidepressant on Trial* (Chapel Hill: Algonquin Books, 2008), 35.

78    FDA, "Psychopharmacological Drugs Advisory Committee, Friday, September 20, 1991," https://upload.wikimedia.org/wikipedia/commons/7/7a/1991_FDA_Psychopharmacological_Drugs_Advisory_Committee.pdf, 59.

79    Ibid., 76.

80    Ibid., 79.

81    Ibid., 116-117, 119.

82    Associated Press, "Warning Label," 0010022.

83    FDA, "Psychopharmacological Drugs," 10-12.

84    Healy, *Prozac*, 61.

85    Peter Huber, "Junk Science in the Courtroom," *Forbes*, July 8, 1991.

86    Ibid.

87    Ibid.

88    Ibid.

89    Henry Friedlander, *The Origins of Nazi Genocide* (Chapel Hill: University of North Carolina Press, 1995), 155.

90    E.A. West, "FDA's Support of Prozac a Milestone in a 'Sordid Controversy,'" *Saint Petersburg Times*, August 8, 1991, 21A.

91    Ibid.

92    John Read, Nick Haslam, L. Sayce, and E. Davies, "Prejudice and Schizophrenia: A Review of the 'Mental Illness is an Illness Like Any Other' Approach," *Acta Psychiatrica Scandinavica* 114, no. 5 (November 2006): 303-318, https://doi.org/10.1111/j.1600-0447.2006.00824.x; John Read, Nick Haslam, and Lorenza Magliano, "Prejudice, Stigma, and 'Schizophrenia': The Role of Bio-Genetic Ideology," in *Models of Madness: Psychological, Social, and Biological Approaches to Schizophrenia*, ed. John Read and Jacqui Dillon (Abingdon: Routledge, 2013), 157-177; Erlend P. Kvaale, Nick Haslam, and William H. Gottdeiner, "The 'Side Effects' of Medicalization: A Meta-Analytic Review of How Biogenetic Explanations Affect Stigma," *Clinical Psychology Review* 33, no. 6 (August 2013): 782-794, https://doi.org/10.1016/j.cpr.2013.06.002

93    Charles H. Beasley et al., "Fluoxetine and Suicide: A Meta-Analysis of Controlled Trials of Treatment for Depression," *BMJ* 303, (September 21, 1991): 685-692.

94    Ibid., 685.

95    Kramer, *Listening to Prozac*, xv.

96    Ibid., 13.

97    Ibid., xvi.

98    Sharon Begley and Debra Rosenberg, "One Pill Makes You Larger, and One Pill Makes You Small," *Newsweek*, February 7, 1994.

99    Ibid.

100   Cornwell, *Power*, 71-72.

101   Ibid., 74.

102   Peter R. Breggin, *Toxic Psychiatry: Why Therapy, Empathy, and Love Must Replace the Drugs, Electroshock, and Biochemical Theories of the "New Psychiatry"* (New York: Saint Martin's Griffin, 1991).

103   Cornwell, *Power*, 72-73.

104   Ibid., 58-61.

105   Ibid., 62, 65.

106   Ibid., 62-70.

107   Ibid., 2-3, 40, 66-67, 248.

108   Ibid., 83.

109   Ibid., 6, 88-89.

110   Ibid., 86, 89.

111   Ibid., 92-93.

112   Ibid., 6, 186.

113   Ibid., 7-8.

114   Ibid., 8.

115   Ibid., 104-105.

116   Ibid., 103-105.

117   Ibid., 57.

118   Ibid., 57.

119   Ibid., 46-47.

120   Ibid., 123.

121   Peter R. Breggin and Ginger Ross Breggin, *Talking Back to Prozac* (New York: Saint Martin's Press, 1994).

122   Melvin Konner, "Good Health: Out of the Darkness," *New York Times Magazine,* October 2, 1994, 72.

123   See Chapter 5 of this volume.

124   Konner, "Darkness," 72.

125   Ibid., 72.

126   Ibid., 73.

127   Christine Gorman, "Prozac's Worst Enemy," *Time*, October 10, 1994, http://content.time.com/time/magazine/article/0,9171,981579,00.html

128   John Read and Nick Argyle, "Hallucinations, Delusions, and Thought Disorder Among Adult Psychiatric Inpatients With a History of Child Abuse," *Psychiatric Services* 50, no. 11 (November 1999): 1467-1472, https://doi.org/10.1176/ps.50.11.1467; John Read et al., "Childhood Trauma, Psychosis and Schizophrenia: A Literature Review With Theoretical and Clinical Implication," *Acta Psychiatric Scandinavica* 112, no. 5 (October 2005): 330-350, https://doi.org/10.1111/j.1600-0447.2005.00634.x; John Read et al., "Child Maltreatment and Psychosis: A Return to a Genuinely Integrated Bio-Psycho-Social Model," *Clinical Schizophrenia and Related Psychoses* 2, no. 3 (October 2008): 235-254, https://doi.org/10.3371/CSRP.2.3.5; John Read et al., "Time to Abandon the Bio-Bio-Bio Model of Psychosis: Exploring the Epigenetic and Psychological Mechanisms by Which Adverse Life Events Lead to Psychotic Symptoms," *Epidemiologia e Psichiatria Sociale* 18, no. 4 (2009): 299-310.

129   E.g., Theo van Erp et al., "Cortical Brain Abnormalities in 4474 Individuals With Schizophrenia and 5098 Control Subjects Via the Enhanced Neuro Imaging Genetics Through Meta Analysis (ENIGMA) Consor-

25

tium," *Biological Psychiatry*, May 14, 2018, https:doi.org.10.1016/j. biopsych.2018.04.023 [Epub ahead of print].

130   Gorman, "Enemy."

131   Cornwell, *Power*, 270.

132   Leslie Scanlon and Todd Murphy, "Wesbecker Rampage Not Linked to Prozac," *Courier-Journal*, December 13, 1994, 1, 5.

133   Cornwell, *Power*, 289.

134   Ibid., 289-290.

135   Ibid., 295-297.

136   John Gibeaut, "Mood-Altering Verdict: Judge Suspects Prozac Settlement Though Case Went to Jury," *ABA Journal* 82, 8 (August 1994): 18.

137   Cornwell, *Power*, 293.

138   Richard Zitrin and Carol M. Langford, *The Moral Compass of the American Lawyer* (New York: Ballantine Books, 1999): 200-201.

139   Andrew Wolfson, "Prozac Maker Secretly Paid Millions to Secure Favorable Verdict in Mass Shooting Lawsuit," *Courier-Journal*, September 11, 2019, https://www.courier-journal.com/story/news/investiga-tions/2019/09/11/standard-gravure-shooting-drugmakers-secret-pay-ment-revealed-mass-shooting-lawsuit/2263776001/

140   Ibid.

141   Helen Altonn, "Prozac's Role in Maui Deaths Going to Court," *Honolulu Star-Bulletin*, January 9, 1998, http://archives.starbulletin.com/98/01/09/ news/story2.html; Lori Tighe, "Decision in Family's Lawsuit Against Prozac Rests With Jury," *Honolulu Star-Bulletin*, January 9, 1998, http:// archives.starbulletin.com/98/01/09/news/story2.html

142   Healy, "Failure to Warn," 152.

143   Susan S. Jick, Alan D. Dean, and Herschel Jick, "Antidepressants and Suicide," *BMJ* 310, no. 6974 (January 28, 1995): 215-218.

144   Healy, *Prozac*, 87.

145　David Healy, "Emergence of Antidepressant Induced Suicidality," *Primary Care Psychiatry* 6, no. 1 (2000): 23-28.

146　Ibid., 26-27.

147　Ibid., 24-25.

148　Healy, *Prozac*, 190.

149　Susan Kreifels, "Family Hopes Prozac Case Leads to Awareness: They Lost Their Lawsuit, but Still Believe the Drug Caused Their Parents' Deaths," *Honolulu Star-Bulletin*, April 1, 1999.

150　Healy, *Prozac*, 170-171.

151　Ibid., 171.

152　Ibid., 171.

153　Ibid., 171.

154　Healy, "Failure to Warn," 151.

155　Healy, *Prozac*, 159-160.

156　David Healy, "Good Science or Good Business?" *Hastings Center Report* 30, no. 2 (March-April 2000): 19-22, https://doi.org/10.2307/3528308

157　David Healy, "Conflicting Interests in Toronto: Anatomy of a Controversy at the Interface of Academia and Industry," *Perspectives in Biology and Medicine* 45, no. 2 (Spring 2002): 255.

158　Arif Khan, Heather A. Warner, and Walter A. Brown, "Symptom Reduction and Suicide Risk in Patients Treated With Placebo in Antidepressant Clinical Trials," *Archives of General Psychiatry* 57, (April 2000): 311-317.

159　Ibid., 317.

160　Robert M. A. Hirschfeld, "Suicide and Antidepressant Treatment," *Archives of General Psychiatry* 57, (April 2000): 325-326.

161　Healy, *Prozac*, 209-210.

162　Ibid., 209-210.

163    Sarah Boseley, "Bitter Pill," *Guardian*, May 7, 2001, https://www.theguardian.com/education/2001/may/07/medicalscience.highereducation

164    Healy, "Conflicting Interests," 252-253.

165    Healy, "Psychopharmacology."

166    Healy, *Prozac*, 216.

167    Healy, "Conflicting Interests," 253-254.

168    *News and Current Affairs*, "Hard to Swallow," Narr. Peter Mansfield, CBC, June 12, 2001.

169    David Healy, *The Antidepressant Era* (Cambridge, MA: Harvard University Press, 1999).

170    Ann Silversides, "Hospital Denies That Withdrawal of MD's Job Offer was Related to Drug Company Funding," *Canada Medical Association Journal* 164, no. 14 (June 26, 2001): 1879.

171    Healy, *Prozac*, 217.

172    Healy, "Conflicting Interests," 254.

173    Ryan Kelly, "Slayings Suspect is One of Dead," *Wyoming Tribune-Eagle*, February 6, 1998, A1.

174    Bloomberg News, "British Drug Shares Get a Lift," *New York Times*, January 1, 1993, D3.

175    Michael W. Otto and Andrew A. Nierenberg, "Assay Sensitivity, Failed Clinical Trials, and the Conduct of Science," *Psychotherapy and Psychosomatics* 71, (2002): 242, https://www.karger.com/Article/Pdf/64813

176    *Panorama*, "Secrets of Seroxat," Narr. Shelley Jofre, BBC, October 13, 2002.

177    David Healy, "One Side of the Background to an Academic Freedom Dispute," Academy for the Psychoanalytic Arts, accessed December 7, 2018, http://www.academyanalyticarts.org/healy-academic-freedom-dispute

178   Ibid.

179   Ibid.

180   Ibid.

181   Becky Orr, "Anti-Depressant Lawsuit Begins in Cheyenne," *Wyoming Tribune-Eagle*, May 22, 2001, A3.

182   *Panorama*, "Secrets of Seroxat."

183   Ibid.

184   Becky Orr, "Paxil Verdict: $6.4 Million," *Wyoming Tribune-Eagle*, June 7, 2001, A1.

185   David Healy, email 10 December 2019.

186   Martin B. Keller et al., "Efficacy of Paroxetine in the Treatment of Adolescent Major Depression: A Randomized, Controlled Trial," *Journal of the American Academy of Child and Adolescent Psychiatry* 40, no. 7 (July 2001): 762-772, https://doi.org/10.1097/00004583-200107000-00010

187   *Panorama*, "Secrets of the Drug Trials," Narr. Shelley Jofre, BBC, January 29, 2007.

188   Alison Bass, "Drug Companies Enrich Brown Professor," *Boston Globe*, October 4, 1999, 1.

189   Alison Bass, "Brown Researcher Faced Billing Questions in the Past," *Boston Globe*, January 21, 1996, 21.

190   Alison Bass, "State Paid School $218,000 on Falsely Billed DMH Study," *Boston Globe*, January 7, 1996, 1.

191   Peter J. Howe and Alison Bass, "Probe of Brown Mental Health Contract Handed Over to AG," *Boston Globe*, March 29, 1996, 34.

192   Alison Bass, "5 Ex-Employees Allege Harassment by Brown," *Boston Globe*, June 24, 1996, 17.

193   Howe and Bass, "Probe."

194   Bass, "Drug Companies," A1.

195    Keller et al., "Efficacy of Paroxetine," 763-764.

196    Ibid., 764-766.

197    Ibid., 764-766.

198    Ibid., 768-769.

199    Ibid., 762.

200    *Lancet* Editorial Staff, "Is GSK Guilty of Fraud?" *Lancet* 363, no. 9425 (July 12, 2004): 1919, https://doi.org/10.1016/S0140-6736(04)16435-0

201    *News and Current Affairs,* "Hard to Swallow."

202    Ibid.

203    Clark Campbell, "Top Scientists Allege U of T Academic Chill," *Globe and Mail Canada*, September 6, 2001, https://www.theglobeand-mail.com/news/national/top-scientists-allege-u-of-t-academic-chill/article4152673/

204    Healy, "Conflicting Interests in Toronto," 9.

205    "'A Complete Vindication' for David Healy," Canadian Association of University Teachers, May 2002, https://bulletin-archives.caut.ca/bulletin/articles/2002/05/'a-complete-vindication'-for-david-healy

206    Janice Paskey, "Psychiatrist and University of Toronto Settle Dispute," *Chronicle of Higher Education*, May 17, 2002, https://www.chronicle.com/article/PsychiatristUniversity-of/15145

207    Canadian Association of University Teachers, "Complete Vindication."

208    Mitch Parsons, "Paroxetine in Adolescent Major Depression," *Journal of the American Academy of Child and Adolescent Psychiatry* 41, no. 4 (April 2002): 364.

209    Martin B. Keller et al., "Paroxetine in Adolescent Major Depression," *Journal of the American Academy of Child and Adolescent Psychiatry* 41, no. 4 (April 2002): 364.

210  Jon Jureidini and Anne Tonkin, "Paroxetine in Major Depression," *Journal of the American Academy of Child and Adolescent Psychiatry* 42, no. 5 (May 2002): 514.

211  Ibid., 514.

212  Martin B. Keller et al., "Paroxetine in Major Depression," *Journal of the American Academy of Child and Adolescent Psychiatry* 42, no. 5 (May 2002): 515.

213  "GlaxoSmithKline PLC Annual Report for the Year Ended 31st December 2000," April 12, 2001, https://www.gsk.com/media/4698/annual-report-2000.pdf; "GlaxoSmithKline PLC Annual Report for the Year Ended 31st December 2001," March 28, 2002, https://www.gsk.com/media/2659/annual-report-2001.pdf; "GlaxoSmithKline PLC Annual Report for the Year Ended 31st December 2002," March 28, 2003, https://www.gsk.com/media/2663/annual-report-2002.pdf; All currency exchange rates via XE: The World's Trusted Currency Authority, accessed December 26, 2018, https://www.xe.com/

214  David Healy, "Study 329," accessed December 9, 2018, https://study329.org/wp-content/uploads/2014/12/Famous-Grouse-Lecture-Transcript.pdf

215  Pat Wingert, "Young and Depressed," *Newsweek*, October 6, 2002.

216  Ibid.

217  Ibid.

218  Healy, "Study 329."

219  *Panorama*, "Secrets of Seroxat."

220  Ibid.

221  Ibid.

222  Ibid.

223  *Panorama*, "Seroxat: Emails From the Edge," Narr. Shelley Jofre, BBC, May 11, 2003; *Panorama*, "Taken on Trust," Narr. Shelley Jofre, BBC, September 21, 2004; *Panorama*, "Secrets of the Drug Trials."

224    *Panorama*, "Emails."

225    Healy, "Lines of Evidence," 71-79.

226    Ibid., 72.

227    Ibid., 73.

228    Ibid., 73.

229    Ibid., 73.

230    David Healy, *Mania: A Short History of Bipolar Disorder* (Baltimore: Johns Hopkins University Press, 2008), 110.

231    Hans Melander et al., "Evidence-B(i)ased Medicine—Selective Reporting From Studies Sponsored by Pharmaceutical Industry: Review of Studies in New Drug Applications," *BMJ* 326, May 31, 2003, https://doi.org.10/1136/bmj.326.7400.1171

232    Ibid.

233    David Healy, "Study 329.org: Science With a Conscience," September 3, 2015, https://davidhealy.org/study329-org-science-with-a-conscience/

234    Ibid.

235    Ibid.

236    Ibid.

237    Ibid.

238    Ibid.

239    Healy, "Study 329."

240    Alliance for Human Research Protection, "FDA Issues Public Health Advisory," October 27, 2003, http://ahrp.org/fda-issues-public-health-advisory-entitled-reports-of-suicidality-in-pediatric/

241    Ibid.

242    "Complaint Ex 1," United States Department of Justice, accessed December 15, 2018, https://www.justice.gov/usao-ma/file/872511/download

243    Ibid.

244    Ibid.

245    American College of Neuropsychopharmacology, "Executive Summary: Preliminary Report of the Task Force on SSRIs and Suicidal Behavior in Youth," January 21, 2004, https://acnp.org/wp-content/uploads/2017/10/Task-Force-Report-on-SSRIs-and-Suicide-in-Youth-Exec-Summary.pdf

246    Ibid., 7.

247    Ibid., 18.

248    Ibid., 6.

249    Rob Waters, "Drug Report Barred by FDA/Scientist Links Antidepressants to Suicide in Kids," *San Francisco Chronicle*, February 1, 2004, https://www.sfgate.com/health/article/Drug-report-barred-by-FDA-Scientist-links-2825996.php

250    Waters, "Drug Report"; Rob Waters, "FDA Was Urged to Limit Kids' Antidepressants/Advice Citing Risk of Suicide Rejected," *San Francisco Chronicle*, April 16, 2004, https://www.sfgate.com/health/article/FDA-was-urged-to-limit-kids-antidepressants-2767075.php

251    Waters, "Drug Report."

252    FDA, "Psychopharmacologic Drugs Advisory Committee, Monday, February 2, 2004," http://psychrights.org/research/digest/AntiDepressants/FDA2-2-2004Hearing.htm, 85-87.

253    Ibid., 88-89.

254    Ibid., 101-102.

255    Ibid., 149.

256    Ibid., 155.

257    Ibid., 170-171.

258    David Healy, *Pharmageddon* (Berkeley: University of California Press, 2012), 148.

259    Wayne Kondro and Barbara Sibbald, "Drug Company Experts Advised Staff to Withhold Data About SSRI Use in Children," *Canada Medical Association Journal* 170, no. 5 (March 2, 2004), 783.

260    Gardiner Harris, "Regulators Want Antidepressants to List Warning," *New York Times*, March 23, 2004, A1.

261    Rob Waters, "Lawmakers Open Probe of FDA/Agency Accused of Barring Safety Data on Antidepressants," *San Francisco Chronicle*, March 31, 2004, https://www.sfgate.com/health/article/Lawmakers-open-probe-of-FDA-Agency-accused-of-2773090.php

262    Bass, *Side Effects*, 167.

263    Gardiner Harris, "Spitzer Sues a Drug Maker, Saying it Hid Negative Data," *New York Times*, June 30, 2004, A1.

264    Robert Preston and Cynthia Pfeifer, "Garnier Hits Back at Spitzer Over Allegations of Fraud at GSK," *Sunday Telegraph*, June 6, 2004, https://www.telegraph.co.uk/finance/2887277/Garnier-hits-back-at-Spitzer-over-allegations-of-fraud-at-GSK.html

265    Ibid.

266    Ibid.

267    Ibid.

268    Barry Meier, "Glaxo Plans Public Listing of Drug Trials on Web Site," *New York Times*, June 19, 2004, C2; Barry Meier, "Glaxo to Begin Posting Drug Trial Results," *New York Times*, September 1, 2004, C2.

269    Harris, "Spitzer Sues a Drug Maker," A1.

270    Laurel K. Leslie et al., "The Food and Drug Administration's Deliberations on Antidepressant Use in Pediatric Patients," *Pediatrics* 11, no. 6 (July 2005): 195-204, https://doi.org.10.1542/peds.2005-0074; Tarak A. Hammad et al., "Suicidality in Pediatric Patients Treated With Antidepressant Drugs," *Archives of General Psychiatry* 63, no. 3 (March 2006): 332-339, https://doi.org.1001.archpsych.63.3.332; this point has since been confirmed in an expanded data set by Steven Julious, "Efficacy and

Risk for Antidepressants in Paediatric and Adolescent Patients," *Statistical Methods in Mental Health Research* 22, no. 2 (2013): 190-218, https://doi.org.10.1177.0962280211432210

271   Gardiner Harris, "FDA Panel Urges Stronger Warning on Antidepressants," *New York Times*, September 15, 2004, A1.

272   Gardiner Harris, "Warning Called Likely on Drug Risk for Suicide," *New York Times*, September 24, 2004, A16.

273   Peter R. Breggin, "How GlaxoSmithKline Suppressed Data on Paxil-Induced Akathisia: Implications for Suicidality and Violence," *Ethical Human Psychology and Psychiatry* 8, no. 2 (Summer 2006): 91-100, http://dx.doi.org/10.1891/ehpp.8.2.91

274   "Police Suspect Murder-Suicide in Deaths of Father and 2 Kids," SFGate, May 1, 1997, https://www.sfgate.com/news/article/Police-Suspect-Murder-Suicide-In-Deaths-of-Father-2841957.php

275   Breggin, "Suppressed Data," 91.

276   Ibid., 96-97.

277   Ibid., 96-98.

278   Benedict Carey, "Panel to Weigh Expansion of Antidepressant Warnings," *New York Times*, December 13, 2006, A30.

279   FDA, "Psychopharmacologic Drugs Advisory Committee, Tuesday, December 13, 2006," https://breggin.com/antidepressant-drugs-resources/FDA-2006-drug-companies-allowed-to-hide-adult-suicide-data.pdf, 16.

280   Ibid., 24-25.

281   Ibid., 106-108.

282   Ibid., 112.

283   Ibid., 138-139.

284   Ibid., 170-171.

285   Ibid., 180-181.

286  Ibid., 183-184.

287  YouTube, "David Healy Antidepressant Testimony," January 18, 2012, https://www.youtube.com/watch?v=VjXDDMK-Awg

288  YouTube, "Peter Breggin Antidepressant Testimony," January 12, 2012, https://www.youtube.com/watch?v=zjHtBAkncgk

289  Benedict Carey, "Panel Wants Broader Antidepressant Labeling," *New York Times*, December 14, 2006, A36.

290  Richard A. Friedman and Andrew C. Leon, "Expanding the Black Box—Depression, Antidepressants, and the Risk of Suicide," *New England Journal of Medicine* 356, no. 23 (June 7, 2007): 2343-2346, https://doi.org.10.1056/NEJMp078015

291  *Panorama*, "Secrets of the Drug Trials."

292  Ibid.

293  Ibid.

294  Ibid.

295  Keller et al., "Efficacy of Paroxetine," 2001.

296  *Panorama*, "Secrets of the Drug Trials."

297  Ibid.

298  Ibid.

299  Jon Jureidini et al., "Clinical Trials and Drug Promotion: Selective Reporting of Study 329," *International Journal of Risk and Safety in Medicine* 20, (2008): 73-81, https://doi.org.10.3233/JRS-2008-0426

300  Gardiner Harris, "Top Psychiatrist Didn't Report Drug Makers' Pay," *New York Times*, October 3, 2008, A1.

301  Robert J. Valuck, Heather D. Orton, and Anne Libby, "Antidepressant Discontinuation and Risk of Suicide Attempt: A Retrospective, Nested Case-Control Study," *Journal of Clinical Psychiatry* 70, no. 8 (August 2009): 1069-1077, https://doi.org/10.4088/JCP.08m04943

302   Robert Langreth and Roberta Ruiz, "The Forgotten Patients," *Forbes*, September 13, 2010, 32-36.

303   Thomas J. Moore, Joseph Glenmullen, and Curt D. Furberg, "Prescription Drugs Associated With Violence Towards Others," *PLoS One* 5, no. 12 (December 2010): e15337, https://doi.org.1371/journal.pone.0015337

304   Ibid.

305   United States Department of Justice, "GlaxoSmithKline to Plead Guilty and Pay $3 Billion to Resolve Fraud Allegations and Failure to Report Safety Data: Largest Health Care Fraud Settlement in U.S. History," July 2, 2012, https://www.justice.gov/opa/pr/glaxosmithkline-plead-guilty-and-pay-3-billion-resolve-fraud-allegations-and-failure-report

306   Katie Thomas and Michael S. Schmidt, "Glaxo Agrees to Pay $3 Billion in Fraud Settlement," *New York Times*, July 2, 2012, A1.

307   Ibid.

308   Ibid.

309   Charles Riley and Emily Jane Fox, "GlaxoSmithKline in $3 Billion Fraud Settlement," *CNN Money*, July 2, 2012, https://money.cnn.com/2012/07/02/news/companies/GlaxoSmithKline-settlement-index.htm

310   Peter Doshi et al., "Restoring Invisible and Abandoned Trials: A Call for People to Publish the Findings," *BMJ* 346, (June 13, 2013): f2865, https://doi.org.10.1136/bmj.f2865

311   Ibid.

312   Joanna LeNoury et al., "Restoring Study 329: Efficacy and Harms of Paroxetine and Imipramine in Treatment of Major Depression in Adolescence," *BMJ* 351, (September 16, 2015): h4320, https://doi.org.10.1136/bmj.h4320

313   Healy et al., *Children of the Cure*, Chapters 9 and 12, Kindle.

314   LeNoury et al., "Restoring Study 329."

315   Healy et al., *Children of the Cure*, Chapter 10, Kindle.

316 LeNoury et al., "Restoring Study 329."

317 Peter Doshi, "No Correction, No Retraction, No Apology, No Comment: Paroxetine Trial Reanalysis Raises Questions About Institutional Responsibility," *BMJ* 351, (September 16, 2015): h4629, https://doi.org.10.1136/bmj.h4629

318 Paul Basken, "Landmark Analysis of an Infamous Medical Study Points out the Challenges of Research Oversight," *Chronicle of Higher Education*, September 17, 2015, chronicle.com/article/Landmark-Analysis-of-an/233179

319 Martin B. Keller et al., "Letter From Keller et al.," accessed December 16, 2018, https://study329.org/responses-keller-et-al/

320 Ibid.

321 David Healy, "Response," accessed April 17, 2019, https://study329.org/responses-keller-et-al/

322 Martin B. Keller et al., "Re: Restoring Study 329: Efficacy and Harms of Paroxetine in Treatment of Major Depression in Adolescence. Response from the Authors of the Original Study 329," January 18, 2016, https://www.bmj.com/content/351/bmj.h4320/rr-27

323 Jon Jureidini et al., "Re: Restoring Study 329: Response to Keller and Selected Colleagues," February 3, 2016, https://www.bmj.com/content/351/bmj.h4320/rr-29

324 Sydney Ember, "Longtime Psychiatry Chair Resigns," *Brown Daily Herald*, April 7, 2009, http://www.browndailyherald.com/2009/04/07/longtime-psychiatry-chair-resigns/

325 Isobel Heck, "Controversial Paxil Paper Still Under Fire 13 Years Later," *Brown Daily Herald*, April 2, 2014, http://www.browndailyherald.com/2014/04/02/controversial-paxil-paper-still-fire-13-years-later/

326 Hana Park, "U. Professors Among 'Most Influential Minds,'" *Brown Daily Herald*, March 11, 2016, http://www.browndailyherald.com/2016/03/11/u-professors-among-most-influential-scientific-minds/

327   Shannon Hughes et al., "Differences in Reporting Serious Adverse Events in Industry Sponsored Clinical Trial Registries and Journal Articles on Antidepressant and Antipsychotic Drugs: A Cross-Sectional Study," *BMJ Open* 2014;4:e005535.

328   Wendy Dolin, "About MISSD," 2019, https://missd.co

329   Ameet Sachdev, "Stewart Dolin 1952-2010," *Chicago Tribune*, July 18, 2010, https://www.chicagotribune.com/living/ct-xpm-2010-07-18-ct-met-dolin-obit-0718-20100718-story.html

330   Roni Caryn Rabin, "A Suicide Leaves Tough Questions," *New York Times*, September 11, 2017, D3.

331   Natalie Blazer, "Federal Court Allows Claims Against Branded Drug Maker for Injuries Caused by Generic Pill," *Product Liability Monitor*, March 10, 2014, https://product-liability.weil.com/pharma-medical-devices/federal-court-allows-claims-against-branded-drug-maker-for-injuries-caused-by-generic-pill/

332   Ibid.

333   Ibid.

334   Baum, Hedlund, Aristei, & Goldman, PC, "Damning Testimony from Former GlaxoSmithKline CEO Jean-Pierre Garnier in Paxil Suicide Case," March 17, 2017, https://www.youtube.com/watch?v=EZlzzN-AQ2fQ

335   S.A. Montgomery, D.L. Dunner, and G.C. Dunbar, "Reduction in Suicidal Thoughts With Paroxetine in Comparison with Reference Antidepressants and Placebo," *European Neuropsychopharmacology* 5, no. 1 (March 1995): 5-13. This paper analyzed completed suicides in terms of patient exposure years, rather than per-patient, biasing the results toward those patients who did well on the drug. The paper also analyzed data on suicidal ideation using a technique called Last Observation Carried Forward, which assumes that patients who dropped out of the trial for any reason maintained the same level of improvement in depressive symptoms

they displayed on the drug—an indefensible assumption, and one that biases the results toward the active drug and against placebo.

336 Law360, "Widow's Trial Against GSK Ends With $39M Damages Plea," April 21, 2017, https://www.law360.com/articles/914039/widow-s-trial-against-gsk-wraps-with-39m-damages-plea

337 *Sun-Times* Media Wire, "Drug Firm to Pay $3 M to Widow of Man Who Jumped in Front of Train," *Chicago Sun-Times*, April 21, 2017, https://chicago.suntimes.com/health/gsk-must-pay-3m-to-widow-of-man-who-jumped-in-front-of-cta-train/

338 Tina Bellon, "US Appeals Court Says GSK Cannot Be Sued Over Generic Drug Verdict," Reuters, August 22, 2018, https://www.reuters.com/article/us-gsk-lawsuit/u-s-appeals-court-says-gsk-cannot-be-sued-over-generic-drug-suicide-idUSKCN1L72D1

339 Wendy Dolin, "Akathisia," 2019, https://missd.co

340 Dolin, "About MISSD."

341 David Carmichael, "Calm, Organized, Homicidal Behavior—My Connection to School Shooters," March 27, 2018, https://www.madinamerica.com/2018/03/calm-organized-homicidal-behaviour-connection-school-shooters/

342 Ibid.

343 Ibid.

344 Ibid.

345 David Carmichael, "Three Weeks to Prescripticide," May 12, 2016, https://rxisk.org/three-weeks-to-prescripticide/

346 Ibid.

347 Ibid.

348 Ibid.

349 Joe Friesen, "Man Not Criminally Responsible in Son's Death," *Globe and Mail Canada*, October 1, 2005, https://www.theglobeandmail.com/news/

national/man-not-criminally-responsible-in-sons-death/article987568/; David Carmichael, "David Carmichael," accessed December 22, 2018, www.davidcarmichael.com

350    Carmichael, "Homicidal Behavior."

351    Carmichael, "Three Weeks."

352    Kim Crespi, "Crespi Family Hope," 2012, http://www.crespifamilyhope. org/about-us/

353    Ibid.

354    Ibid.

355    Crespi, "Crespi Family Hope"; Gary L. Wright, "Crespi to Plead Guilty to Murder: Father Expected to Serve Life in Prison for Killing Twin Daughters," *Charlotte Observer*, July 16, 2006.

356    Crespi, "Crespi Family Hope."

357    M. Bandettini di Poggio et al., "Clarithromycin-Induced Neurotoxicity in Adults," *Journal of Clinical Neuroscience* 18, no. 3 (March 2011): 313-318, https://doi.org.10.1016/j.jocn.2010.08.014

358    FDA, "Ambien (zolpidem tartrate)," February 2008, https://www.access-data.fda.gov/drugsatfda_docs/label/2008/019908s027lbl.pdf

359    FDA, "Lunesta (eszoplicone)," May 2014, https://www.accessdata.fda. gov/drugsatfda_docs/label/2014/021476s030lbl.pdf

360    FDA, "Prozac (fluoxetine hydrochloride)," 2011, https://www.accessdata. fda.gov/drugsatfda_docs/label/2011/018936s091lbl.pdf

361    FDA, "Desyryl (trazadone hydrochloride)," June 17, 2017, https://www. accessdata.fda.gov/drugsatfda_docs/label/2017/018207s032lbl.pdf

362    Crespi, "Crespi Family Hope."

363    Ibid.

364    Ibid.

365    Wright, "Crespi to Plead Guilty."

366    Crespi, "Crespi Family Hope."

367    Carl N. Brownsberger, "Yes, Prozac Has Risks—So Do All Drugs," *Boston Globe*, May 16, 2000, A16.

368    Harris, "Regulators," A1.

369    Gardiner Harris, "Antidepressant Study Seen to Back Expert," *New York Times*, August 20, 2004, A16.

370    Gardiner Harris, "F.D.A. Links Drugs to Being Suicidal," *New York Times*, September 14, 2004, A1.

371    Kirsch, *Exploding the Antidepressant Myth*, 1.

372    Ibid., 2.

373    Irving Kirsch and Guy Sapirstein, "Listening to Prozac but Hearing Placebo: A Meta-Analysis of Antidepressant Medication," *Prevention & Treatment* 1, no. 2 (June 1998): ArtID: 2a.

374    Ibid.

375    Ibid.

376    Ibid.

377    Ibid.

378    Ibid.

379    Ibid.

380    Breggin and Breggin, *Talking Back*, 56-57.

381    Donald F. Klein, "Listening to Meta-Analysis but Hearing Bias," *Prevention & Treatment* 1, no. 2 (June 1998): ArtID: 6c.

382    Kirsch, *Exploding the Antidepressant Myth*, 25.

383    Irving Kirsch et al., "The Emperor's New Drugs: An Analysis of Antidepressant Medication Data Submitted to the U.S. Food and Drug Administration," *Prevention & Treatment* 5, (July 15, 2002): Article 23.

384    Kirsch, *Exploding the Antidepressant Myth*, 27.

385    Kirsch, "Emperor's New Drugs."

386    Ibid.

387    Ibid.

388    Kirsch, *Exploding the Antidepressant Myth*, 29-30.

389    Kirsch, "Emperor's New Drugs."

390    Ibid.

391    David O. Antonuccio et al., "Antidepressants: A Triumph of Marketing Over Science," *Prevention & Treatment* 5, (July 15, 2002): Article 25.

392    Ibid.

393    Michael E. Thase, "Antidepressant Effects: The Suit May Be Small, but the Fabric Is Real," *Prevention & Treatment* 5, (July 15, 2002): Article 32.

394    Ibid.

395    Irving Kirsch and Joanna Moncrieff, "Clinical Trials and the Response Rate Illusion," *Contemporary Clinical Trials* 28, no. 4 (July 2007): 348-351, https://doi.org.10.1016/j.cct.2006.10.012

396    E.g., Steven D. Hollon, "The Emperor's New Drugs: Effect Size and Moderation Effects," *Prevention & Treatment* 5, (July 15, 2002): Article 28; Thase, "Antidepressant Effects."

397    Maurizio Fava et al., "The Problem of the Placebo Response in Clinical Trials for Psychiatric Disorders: Culprits, Possible Remedies, and a Novel Study Design Approach," *Psychotherapy and Psychosomatics* 72, (2003): 115-127, https://doi.org/10.1159/000069738

398    Irving Kirsch et al., "Initial Severity and Antidepressant Benefits: A Meta-Analysis of Data Submitted to the Food and Drug Administration," *PLoS Medicine* 5, no. 2 (February 2008): 260-268, https://journals.plos.org/plosmedicine/article/file?id=10.1371/journal.pmed.0050045&type=printable

399    Ibid, 261-263.

400    Ibid., 263-266.

401    Kirsch, *Exploding the Antidepressant Myth*.

402    *PLoS*, "Responses to Article," accessed December 31, 2018, archive.li/t0yH0

403    Ibid.

404    Ibid.

405    Ibid.

406    Irving Kirsch, "Dr. Irving Kirsch: The Emperor's New Drugs: Exploding the Antidepressant Myth," accessed December 31, 2018, https://www.youtube.com/watch?v=UC5RZRG7-QQ

407    Stefan Leucht et al., "What Does the HAM-D Mean?" *Journal of Affective Disorders* 148, (2013): 243-248, https://doi.org/10.1016/j.jad.2012.12.001

408    Kirsch, *Exploding the Antidepressant Myth*, 61-62.

409    Ibid., 96.

410    Ibid., 60-61.

411    Ibid., 116.

412    Ibid., 97-98.

413    Ibid., 150.

414    Ibid., 157-176.

415    Peter Kramer, "In Defense of Antidepressants," *New York Times*, July 9, 2011, SRI1.

416    The NNT, "Statins in Persons at Low Risk of Cardiovascular Disease," accessed December 31, 2018, http://www.thennt.com/nnt/statins-persons-low-risk-cardiovascular-disease/

417    Irving Kirsch, "Antidepressants and the Placebo Effect," *Zeitschrift für Psychologie* 222, no. 3 (2014): 128-134, https://doi.org.1027/2151-2604/a00176

418    F. Hieronymous, A. Lisinski, S. Nilsson, and E. Eriksson, "Efficacy of Selective Serotonin Reuptake Inhibitors in the Absence of Side Effects: A Mega-Analysis of Citalopram and Paroxetine in Adult Depression,"

*Molecular Psychiatry* 23, (2018): 1731-1736, https://doi.org.10.1038/mp2017.147

419   Ibid.

420   Mark Brown, "Antidepressants Work, so Why Do We Shame People for Taking Them?" *Guardian*, September 1, 2017, https://www.theguardian.com/commentisfree/2017/sep/01/antidepressants-work-shame-people-ssri

421   Cipriani et al., "Efficacy and Acceptability."

422   Abi Rimmer, "Large Meta-Analysis Ends Doubts About Efficacy of Antidepressants," *BMJ* 360, (February 22, 2018), https://doi.org.10/10.1136/bmj.k847

423   Cipriani et al., "Efficacy and Acceptability."

424   Ibid.

425   Ibid.

426   Ibid.

427   Mark Rice-Oxley, "It's Official: Antidepressants Are Not Snake Oil or a Conspiracy—They Work," *Guardian*, February 21, 2018, https://www.theguardian.com/society/2018/feb/21/its-official-antidepressants-are-not-snake-oil-or-a-conspiracy-they-work

428   Newspapers.ink: Newspapers in PDF, accessed January 1, 2019, https://newspapers.ink/sun-22-february-2018/

429   Katherine Hignett, "Antidepressants Do Work, and Many More People Should Take Them," *Newsweek*, February 22, 2018, https://www.newsweek.com/antidepressants-major-depressive-disorder-study-815415

430   Marc Stone et al., "Components and Trends in Treatment Effects in Randomized Placebo-controlled Trials in Major Depressive Disorder from 1979-2016," poster presented at the American Society of Clinical Psychopharmacology, Miami, May 28-June 1, 2018.

431   Ibid.

432    Breggin and Breggin, *Talking Back*, xxviii.

433    National Institute of Mental Health, "Sequenced Treatment Alternatives to Relieve Depression Study," accessed January 5, 2019, https://www.nimh.nih.gov/funding/clinical-research/practical/stard/index.shtml

434    A. John Rush et al., "Acute and Longer-Term Outcomes in Depressed Outpatients Requiring One or Several Treatment Steps: A STAR*D Report," *American Journal of Psychiatry* 163, no. 11 (November 2006): 1906, https://doi.org/10.1176/ajp.2006.163.11.1905

435    Ibid., 1906-1909.

436    Ibid., 1914-1915.

437    Brandi L. O'Neal et al., "Sequenced Treatment Alternatives to Relieve Depression: Patient Education Manual, February 1, 2001," accessed January 5, 2019, https://www.madinamerica.com/wp-content/uploads/2011/12/STAR_D%20Patient%20Education%20Plan%20Manual.pdf

438    Madhukar H. Trivedi et al., "Evaluation of Outcomes With Citalopram for Depression Using Measurement-Based Care in STAR*D: Implications for Clinical Practice," *American Journal of Psychiatry* 163, no. 1 (January 2006): 30-31, https://doi.org/10.1176/appi.ajp.163.1.28

439    H. Edmund Pigott et al., "Efficacy and Effectiveness of Antidepressants: Current Status of Research," *Psychotherapy and Psychosomatics* 79, (July 9, 2010): 271, https://doi.org/10.1159/000318293

440    Trivedi et al., "Evaluation," 30-31.

441    Ibid., 30-31.

442    Rush et al., "Outcomes," 1908.

443    Pigott et al., "Efficacy and Effectiveness," 271.

444    Trivedi et al., "Evaluation," 30.

445    Pigott et al., "Efficacy and Effectiveness," 273-274.

446    Rush et al., "Outcomes," 1910-1911.

447 Pigott et al., "Efficacy and Effectiveness," 276.

448 David Healy et al., "Service Utilization in 1896 and 1996: Morbidity and Mortality Data From North Wales," *History of Psychiatry* 16, no. 1 (2005): 28-29, https://doi.org.10.1177/0957/154X05044604

449 Ibid., 33, 36.

450 Ibid., 33-37.

451 Ibid., 35-36.

452 Robert Whitaker, *Anatomy of an Epidemic: Magic Bullets, Psychiatric Drugs, and the Astonishing Rise of Mental Illness in America* (New York: Broadway Books, 2010), 151.

453 Ibid., 170.

454 Ibid., 152-153.

455 Ibid., 157-164.

456 Investigative Reporters and Editors, "2010 IRE Awards Winners," accessed January 3, 2019, https://www.ire.org/awards/ire-awards/winners/2010-ire-awards-winners/#book

457 Marcia Angell, "The Epidemic of Mental Illness: Why?" *New York Review of Books*, June 23, 2011, https://www.nybooks.com/articles/2011/06/23/epidemic-mental-illness-why/; Marcia Angell, "The Illusions of Psychiatry," *New York Review of Books*, July 14, 2011, https://www.nybooks.com/articles/2011/07/14/illusions-of-psychiatry/

458 John Oldham et al., "'The Illusions of Psychiatry': An Exchange," *New York Review of Books*, August 18, 2011, https://www.nybooks.com/articles/2011/08/18/illusions-psychiatry-exchange/

459 CBC Radio, "Listener Mail—Dr. Jeffrey Lieberman," May 1, 2015, https://www.cbc.ca/radio/thesundayedition/men-will-be-boys-the-refugee-problem-christiana-pflug-ve-day-1.3055705/listener-mail-dr-jeffrey-lieberman-1.3057807

460 See Chapter 10 of this volume.

461  Ramin Mojtabai and Mark Olfson, "Proportion of Antidepressants Prescribed Without a Psychiatric Diagnosis is Growing," *Health Affairs* 30, no. 8 (August 2011): 1434-1442, https://doi.org/10.1377/hlthaff.2010.1024

462  Whitaker, *Epidemic*, 164-165.

463  Paul W. Andrews et al., "Blue Again: Perturbational Effects of Antidepressants Suggest Monoaminergic Homeostasis in Major Depression," *Frontiers in Psychology* 2, (July 7, 2011), https://doi.org/10.3389/fpsyg.2011.00159

464  Ibid.

465  Jeffrey R. Vittengl, "Poorer Long-Term Outcomes Among Persons With Major Depressive Disorder Treated with Medication," *Psychotherapy and Psychosomatics* 86, (2017): 302-304, https://doi.org/10.1159/000479162

466  National Institute for Health and Clinical Excellence, "Depression in Adults: Recognition and Treatment," October 28, 2009, https://www.nice.org.uk/guidance/cg90, 10.

467  Ibid., 25.

468  American Psychiatric Association, "Practice Guidelines for the Treatment of Patients With Major Depressive Disorder, Third Edition," October 2010, https://psychiatryonline.org/pb/assets/raw/sitewide/practice_guidelines/guidelines/mdd.pdf, 16.

469  NICE, "Depression," 35.

470  APA, "Guidelines," 39.

471  James Davies and John Read, "A Systematic Review into the Incidence, Severity, and Duration of Antidepressant Withdrawal Effects: Are Guidelines Evidence-Based?" *Addictive Behaviors*, September 4, 2018, https://doi.org/10.1016/j.addbeh.2018.08.027 [Epub ahead of print].

472  Ibid.

473  Ibid.

474  Ibid.

475   Ibid.

476   Tom Stockman et al., "SSRI and SNRI Withdrawal Symptoms Reported
      on an Internet Forum," *International Journal of Risk and Safety in Medicine*
      29, no. 3-4 (2018): 175-180, https://doi.org/10.3233/JRS-180018

477   Ibid.

478   All-Party Parliamentary Group for Prescribed Drug Dependence,
      "Antidepressant Withdrawal: A Survey of Patients' Experience by the
      All-Party Parliamentary Group for Prescribed Drug Dependence,"
      September 2018, http://prescribeddrug.org/wp-content/uploads/2018/10/
      APPG-PDD-Survey-of-antidepressant-withdrawal-experiences.pdf

479   Ibid., 5.

480   Ibid., 5.

481   Ibid., 5.

482   Ibid., 5.

483   Ibid., 5.

484   Ibid., 13.

485   Ibid., 13.

486   Ibid., 13.

487   Ibid., 15.

488   Ibid., 16.

489   Ibid., 17.

490   Ibid., 17.

491   Ibid., 17.

492   Ibid., 17.

493   Ibid., 17.

494   Ibid., 23.

495   Ibid., 24.

496    Ibid., 24.

497    Ibid., 25.

498    Ibid., 25.

499    *Panorama*, "Secrets of Seroxat."

500    *Panorama*, "Emails."

501    John Read, Claire Cartwright, and Kerry Gibson, "Adverse Emotional Effects Reported by 1829 New Zealanders While Taking Antidepressants," *Psychiatry Research* 216, (2014): 67-73, http://dx.doi.org/10.1016/j.psychres.2014.01.042

502    Ibid., 71.

503    Chris Smyth, "More People Should Get Pills to Beat Depression," *Times*, February 22, 2018, https://www.thetimes.co.uk/article/more-people-should-get-pills-to-beat-depression-sv5vhczss

504    James Davies et al., "Stigma and Efficacy of Taking Antidepressants," *Times*, February 23, 2018, https://www.thetimes.co.uk/article/stigma-and-efficacy-of-taking-antidepressants-0zvsg560x

505    David Baldwin and Wendy Burn, "Pills for Depression," *Times*, February 24, 2018, https://www.thetimes.co.uk/article/86afb2fc-18c7-11e8-a427-78e8af199a96

506    John Read et al. to the Royal College of Psychiatrists, March 9, 2018, http://cepuk.org/wp-content/uploads/2018/03/Complaint-to-RCPsych.pdf

507    Ibid.

508    John Read et al. to the Royal College of Psychiatrists, May 1, 2018, https://www.madinamerica.com/2018/05/royal-college-dismisses-complaint/

509    Chris Smyth, "Drugs Adviser David Baldwin Quits After Being Branded 'Worse Than Hitler' in Online Abuse Row," *Times*, September 25, 2018, https://www.thetimes.co.uk/article/drugs-adviser-david-baldwin-quits-after-being-branded-worse-than-hitler-in-online-abuse-row-srtqltmfs

510    Ibid.

511    Royal College of Psychiatrists, "RCPsych Calls Upon NICE to Update its Antidepressant Withdrawal Advice," May 29, 2019, https://www.rcpsych. ac.uk/news-and-features/latest-news/detail/2019/05/29/rcpsych-calls-on-nice-to-update-its-antidepressant-withdrawal-advice

512    Helen McArdle, "U-turn as Psychiatrists Say Patients Should be Warned of Antidepressant Withdrawal Risk," *Herald*, May 30, 2019, https://www. heraldscotland.com/news/17673220.antidepressants-u-turn-as-psychia-trists-say-patients-should-be-warned-of-withdrawal-risk/

513    Public Health England, "Prescribed Medicines Review: Summary," September 10, 2019, https://www.gov.uk/government/publications/ prescribed-medicines-review-report/prescribed-medicines-review-sum-mary

514    Gareth Iacobucci, "NICE Updates Antidepressant Guidelines to Reflect Severity and Length of Withdrawal Symptoms," *BMJ* 2019 Oct 18;367:l6103, https://doi.org/10.1136/bmj.l6103

515    David Healy and David O. Antonuccio, "Relabeling the Medications We Call Antidepressants," *Scientifica*, 2012, 6 pages, Article ID 965908, http://dx.doi.org/10.6064/2012/965908

516    Ibid., 4.

517    Robert Gibbons et al., "Early Evidence on the Effects of Regulators' Suicidality Warnings on SSRI Prescriptions and Suicide in Children and Adolescents," *American Journal of Psychiatry* 164, no. 9 (September 2007): 1356-1363, https://doi.org/10.1176/appi.ajp.2007.07030454

518    Ibid., 1361-1362.

519    Shankar Vendantam, "Youth Suicide Rates Increased as Antidepressant Use Fell," *Washington Post*, September 6, 2007, http://www.washington-post.com/wp-dyn/content/article/2007/09/05/AR2007090502303.html

520    Jordan Lite, "Warning May Be Killing Kids," *New York Post*, September 7, 2007, 7.

521   Judith Graham, "As Youth Suicides Rise, FDA's Label Rule Criticized," *Chicago Tribune*, September 7, 2007, https://www.chicagotribune.com/news/ct-xpm-2007-09-07-0709061231-story.html

522   Ibid.

523   Gibbons et al., "Early Evidence," 1358.

524   CDC, "Fatal Injury Reports: National, Regional, and State 1981-2016," page last updated February 19, 2017, https://webappa.cdc.gov/sasweb/ncipc/mortrate.html

525   Christian J. Bachman et al., "Trends and Patterns of Antidepressant Use in Children and Adolescents From Five Western Countries, 2005-2012," *European Neuropsychopharmacology* 26, (2016): 411-419, https://dx.doi/10.1016/j.euroneuro.2016.02.001

526   Stephen Soumeri and Ross Koppel, "FDA's Continuing Use of 'Black Box' Warning for Antidepressants Ignores the Harms of this Warning," *STAT*, August 29, 2018, https://www.statnews.com/2018/08/29/fda-antidepressants-black-box-warnings-harms/?utm_source=*STAT*+Newsletters&utm_campaign=f6cc09a85d-MR_COPY_08&utm_medium=email&utm_term=0_8cab1d7961-f6cc09a85d-143355333

527   Ibid.

528   Ibid.

529   Ibid.

530   Austin Bradford Hill, "The Environment or Disease: Association of Causation?" *Proceedings of the Royal Society of Medicine* 58, no. 5 (May 1965): 297.

531   Soumeri and Koppel, "Harms."

532   Robert Whitaker, "Adolescent Suicide and the Black Box Warning: STAT Gets it All Wrong," August 31, 2018, https://www.madinamerica.com/2018/08/adolescent-suicide-and-the-black-box-warning-stat-gets-it-all-wrong/

533 Joe Fitzgerald, "Knox Seeks Sympathy Where None Deserved," *Boston Herald*, November 18, 2017, https://www.bostonherald.com/2017/08/05/fitzgerald-knox-seeks-sympathy-where-none-deserved/

534 *New York Post* Editorial Board, "The Michelle Carter Case: A Horrible Window on the Way We Live Now," *New York Post*, June 16, 2017, https://nypost.com/2017/06/16/the-michelle-carter-case-a-horrible-window-on-the-way-we-live-now/

535 Patrick Knox, "Texts on Trial: Who Is Michelle Carter, What Happened to Conrad Roy, and Why Did She Encourage Her Boyfriend to Kill Himself?" *Sun*, August 4, 2017, https://www.thesun.co.uk/news/3741960/michelle-carter-guilty-encouraging-conrad-roy-boyfriend-suicide/

536 Peter R. Breggin, "Michelle Starts Prozac and Sees the Devil," August 7, 2017, https://www.madinamerica.com/2017/08/michelle-carter-starts-prozac-sees-devil/

537 Peter Schworm, "Plainville Teen Accused of Urging Friend to Kill Himself," *Boston Globe*, February 27, 2015, https://www.bostonglobe.com/metro/2015/02/27/plainville-teen-charged-with-manslaughter-friend-suicide/WM5yHKA5IpobG2WXEWHLFM/story.html

538 Ibid.

539 Ibid.; *Boston Globe* Staff, "Read the Texts at the Center of the Massachusetts Teen Suicide Case," *Boston Globe*, June 6, 2017, https://www.google.com/url?q=https://www.bostonglobe.com/metro/2017/06/05/read-texts-center-massachusetts-teen-suicide-case/YIjOPc1K0ICLoyUx97uwLL/story.html&sa=U&ved=0ahUKEwjDhq6ltuTfAhUBneAKHfBWCMEQFggFMAA&client=internal-uds-cse&cx=006376928391721581342:dttdzxtrxse&usg=AOvVaw1qlpNR0_cFAjAxaaf6sdAz

540 Schworm, "Accused."

541 Ibid.

542 Cathy McCabe, "Mass. Woman Must Stand Trial in Teen Friend's Suicide," *Boston Globe*, July 1, 2016, https://www.bostonglobe.com/

metro/2016/07/01/sjc-rules-teen-charged-with-cajoling-friend-commit-suicide-must-stand-trial/J6bZdTPL6MNIaJ4iTlNLAJ/story.html

543  Jan Ransom and John R. Ellement, "Texting Suicide Came After 'Sick Game of Life and Death,'" *Boston Globe*, June 6, 2017, https://www.bostonglobe.com/metro/2017/06/06/woman-charged-with-cajoling-friend-commit-suicide-faces-involuntary-manslaughter-trial/8ylBhZifsAYU2ix71ZFQTJ/story.html

544  Jaclyn Reiss and Jan Ransom, "How the Testimony Unfolded on the First Day of the Texting Suicide Case," *Boston Globe*, June 7, 2017, https://www.bostonglobe.com/metro/2017/06/06/how-testimony-unfolded-first-day-texting-suicide-case/YeIFSnLft0BPhSgrKiYtDI/story.html

545  *Boston Globe* Staff, "'When Are You Doing It?' Read the Carter Case Texts," *Boston Globe*, June 8, 2017, https://www.bostonglobe.com/metro/2017/06/08/when-are-you-doing-read-latest-texts-michelle-carter-case/Ei7L2NXVxXozc6T7MU29BJ/story.html

546  Ibid.

547  Ibid.

548  Ibid.

549  *Boston Globe* Staff, "Teen Suicide."

550  Ransom and Ellement, "Texting Suicide."

551  Ibid.

552  Jan Ransom, "Michelle Carter 'Involuntarily Intoxicated' by Prescription Before Friend's Suicide, Psychiatrist Testifies," *Boston Globe*, June 12, 2017, https://www.bostonglobe.com/metro/2017/06/12/michelle-carter-ssri-hampered-her-ability-feel-empathy-make-good-decisions-psychiatrist-says/zCrOp77pYoDNZldPlT7TSI/story.html

553  Jan Ransom and Travis Anderson, "Michelle Carter Receives 15 Months in Jail; Will Remain Free Pending Appeal," *Boston Globe*, August 3, 2017, https://www.bostonglobe.com/metro/2017/08/03/will-michelle-car-

ter-sentenced-prison-maybe-not/iAB02N4H3jMojUi5DnxMQO/story.
html

554    Ibid.

555    Ibid.

556    Ibid.

557    Ibid.

558    Jack Tager, "'Murder by Counseling': The 1816 Case of George Bowen (Northampton)," *Historical Journal of Massachusetts* 38, no. 2 (Fall 2010): 103-119.

559    Kevin Cullen, "Three Little Words Sunk Michelle Carter," *Boston Globe*, June 16, 2017, https://www.bostonglobe.com/metro/2017/06/16/three-little-words-sunk-michelle-carter/7MgZibLEgQ7As6zvNOaDJI/story.html

560    Ibid.

561    *48 Hours*, "Death by Text: The Case Against Michelle Carter," Narr. Erin Moriarty, CBS, August 16, 2017.

562    Ibid.

563    Ibid.

564    FDA, "Celexa (citalopram hydrobromide) Tablets/Oral Solution," revised January 2009, https://www.accessdata.fda.gov/drugsatfda_docs/label/2009/020822s037,021046s015lbl.pdf

565    *48 Hours*, "Death by Text."

566    Keller et al., "Efficacy of Paroxetine," 762.

567    Ransom and Anderson, "Michelle Carter Receives 15 Months in Jail."

568    Ibid.

569    Matt Rochelau, "Appeal in Michelle Carter Case May Take Years to Resolve," *Boston Globe*, August 3, 2017, https://www.bostonglobe.com/metro/2017/08/03/appeal-michelle-carter-case-may-take-years-resolve-experts-say/GaXXZYfvCRSXpzJG9j5raI/story.html

570 Peter R. Breggin, "Michelle Carter: Did She Text Her Boyfriend to Death?" August 3, 2017, https://www.madinamerica.com/2017/08/michelle-carter-text-boyfriend-death/

571 Ibid.

572 Ibid.

573 Ibid.

574 Ibid.

575 Ibid.

576 Breggin, "Michelle Starts Prozac."

577 Ibid.

578 Ibid.

579 Ibid.

580 Ibid.

581 Peter R. Breggin, "How Adult Society Betrayed Michelle Carter and Conrad Roy," September 20, 2017, https://www.madinamerica.com/2017/09/part-vi-adult-society-betrayed-michelle-carter-conrad-roy/

582 Breggin, "Michelle Starts Prozac."

583 Ibid.

584 Ibid.

585 Ibid.

586 Ibid.

587 Ibid.

588 Ibid.

589 Peter R. Breggin, interview July 16, 2017.

590 Breggin, "Michelle Starts Prozac."

591 Jan Ransom and John R. Ellement, "I Love You. Kill Yourself," *Boston Globe*, June 9, 2017, https://www.bostonglobe.com/metro/2017/06/09/

michelle-carter-texting-trial-resume/kadMPvxS3sjEPK60EEWhKP/
story.html

592    Breggin, "Betrayed."

593    Ibid.

594    Breggin, "Michelle Starts Prozac."

595    Peter R. Breggin, "DA Goes After Her Expert Witness to Stop His Blog," August 30, 2017,  https://www.madinamerica.com/2017/08/michelle-carter-expert-witness-stop-blog/

596    Peter R. Breggin, interview July 16, 2017.

597    Ibid.

598    Timothy Wilens et al., "A Systematic Chart Review of the Nature of Psychiatric Adverse Events in Children and Adults Treated With Selective Serotonin Reuptake Inhibitors," *Journal of Child and Adolescent Psychopharmacology* 13, no. 2 (2003): 143-152, https://doi.org/10.1089/104454603322163862

599    Breggin, "Betrayed."

600    Peter R. Breggin, interview July 16, 2017.

601    Peter R. Breggin, "Did She Tell Conrad to 'Get Back in the Truck?'" September 6, 2017, https://www.madinamerica.com/2017/09/michelle-carter-part-iv-did-she-tell-conrad-get-back-in-the-truck/

602    Peter R. Breggin, interview July 16, 2017.

603    Breggin, "Get Back in."

604    Ibid.

605    Ibid.

606    Ibid.

607    Ibid.

608    Jeannie Suk, "ABA Criminal Justice Standards," August 15, 2017, https://h2o.law.harvard.edu/text_blocks/30177

609　Peter R. Breggin, "The Michelle Carter Texting Case Becomes a Witch Hunt," September 13, 2017, https://www.madinamerica.com/2017/09/part-v-michelle-carter-texting-trial-witch-hunt/

610　Breggin, "DA Goes After Her Expert Witness."

611　Ibid.

612　Ibid.

613　Ibid.

614　Ibid.

615　Breggin, "Get Back in."

616　Jan Ransom, "Mother of Conrad Roy III Seeks $4.2 Million in Wrongful Death Suit Against Michelle Carter," *Boston Globe*, August 4, 2017, https://www.bostonglobe.com/metro/2017/08/04/mother-conrad-roy-iii-seeks-wrongful-death-suit-against-michelle-carter/me1NraKa2NqdyZb-5HECC8I/story.html?event=event12

617　Danny McDonald, "Michelle Carter's Attorney Files Notice to Appeal Her Conviction," *Boston Globe*, September 1, 2017, https://www.boston-globe.com/metro/2017/08/31/michelle-carter-attorney-files-notice-appeal-her-conviction/DdjdfV4RZSHCWzhYlEB8fP/story.html

618　David Linton, "Prosecutor in Texting-Suicide Case Involving Plainville Woman Gets Judgeship," *Sun-Chronicle*, October 5, 2017, https://www.thesunchronicle.com/news/local_news/prosecutor-in-texting-suicide-case-involving-plainville-woman-gets-judgeship/article_deab9ec9-090b-5080-aff1-536c616da215.html

619　John R. Ellement and Travis Andersen, "Mass. High Court Upholds Carter Ruling," *Boston Globe,* February 6, 2019, https://www.bostonglobe.com/metro/2019/02/06/sjc-rule-case-michelle-carter-convicted-involuntary-manslaughter-death-year-old-man/jmOuFii7iTZFKrnEXPzzAM/story.html

620　Travis Anderson and Martin Finucane, "Judge Orders Michelle Carter to Begin Serving Sentence," *Boston Globe*, February 11, 2019, https://www.

bostonglobe.com/metro/2019/02/11/sjc-rejects-michelle-carter-bid-stay-sentence/mXl9rpxOwNxSoMVLS7zDHM/story.html

621 Marie Szaniszlo, "Wrongful Death Suit Against Michelle Carter 'Resolved,'" *Boston Herald*, April 9, 2019, https://www.bostonherald.com/2019/04/09/wrongful-death-suit-against-michelle-carter-resolved/

622 Katie Lannan, "Bill Calls for Coercion to be a Crime," *Lowell Sun*, July 25, 2019, http://www.lowellsun.com/todaysheadlines/ci_32747521/bill-calls-coercion-be-crime

623 Ann O'Neill, "Theater Shooter Holmes Gets 12 Life Sentences Plus 3,318 Years," *CNN*, August 27, 2015, https://www.cnn.com/2015/08/26/us/james-holmes-aurora-massacre-sentencing/index.html

624 Shelley Jofre, "A Prescription for Murder?" *BBC News*, July 26, 2017, https://www.bbc.co.uk/news/resources/idt-sh/aurora_shooting

625 Ann O'Neil, "Victims: James Holmes' Bullets Tore Huge Holes in Their Lives," *CNN*, August 11, 2015, https://www.cnn.com/2015/08/26/us/james-holmes-aurora-massacre-sentencing/index.html

626 Ibid.

627 Ibid.

628 Ibid.

629 Jofre, "Prescription."

630 Ibid.

631 Ibid.

632 Ibid.

633 Ibid.

634 Ibid.

635 Ibid.

636 Ibid.

637 Ibid.

638    Ibid.

639    Ibid.

640    Ibid.

641    Ibid.

642    David Healy, "Prescription for Murder," RxISK.org, July 26, 2017, https://rxisk.org/prescription-for-murder/

643    Jofre, "Prescription."

644    Ibid.

645    *Independent* Staff, "Antidepressants Linked to 28 Murders in Three Decades, BBC Investigation Finds," *Independent*, July 25, 2017, https://www.independent.co.uk/life-style/health-and-families/health-news/antidepressants-ssris-muders-suicide-panorama-depression-anxiety-side-effects-a7859876.html

646    Ellen Scott, "Can We Please Stop Demonising Antidepressants?" *Metro News*, July 25, 2017, https://metro.co.uk/2017/07/25/can-we-please-stop-demonising-antidepressants-6804436/

647    Hannah Osborne, "BBC, SSRIs, and 'A Prescription for Murder': Experts Slam Panorama Documentary on Antidepressants," *Newsweek*, July 26, 2017, https://www.newsweek.com/bbc-panorama-antidepressants-murder-james-holmes-642068

648    Wendy Burn, "Stop This Dangerous Scaremongering Over Antidepressants," *Times*, July 27, 2017, Opinion and Editorial 28.

649    Peter Hitchens, "How to Be a Scaremonger—Reflections on BBC Panorama's Study of the Aurora Mass Murders," July 27, 2017, https://hitchensblog.mailonsunday.co.uk/2017/07/how-to-be-a-scaremonger-reflections-o-bbc-panoramas-study-of-the-aurora-mass-murders-.html

650    Carmine Pariente, "Panorama's Prescription," *Lancet* 4, July 28, 2017, e21, https://doi.org.10.1016/S2215-0366(17)30312-7

651    See Chapter 7 of this volume.

652    Sam Howe Verhovek, "15 Bodies Are Removed From School in Colorado," *New York Times*, April 22, 1999, 1.

653    Dave Cullen, *Columbine* (Grand Central Publishing 2009), https://books.google.com/books?id=ZQONT3jE1-sC&printsec=frontcover&d-q=Columbine&hl=en&sa=X&ved=0ahUKEwi84fiQoP3fAhWIGt-8KHa9mAsYQ6AEIKjAA#v=snippet&q=Luvox&f=false

654    Susan Klebold, "I Will Never Know Why," *Oprah Magazine*, November 2009, https://www.oprah.com/omagazine/susan-klebolds-o-magazine-es-say-i-will-never-know-why/all

655    Klaus Linde et al., "Saint John's Wort for Major Depression," *Cochrane Database of Systematic Reviews*, October 8, 2008, https://doi.org/10.1002/14651858.CD000448.pub3

656    Jeremy Lennard, "Ten Dead in US School Shooting," *Guardian*, May 22, 2005, https://www.theguardian.com/world/2005/mar/22/usgunviolence.usa

657    Chuck Haga, "Relatives: Could Meds Play a Role?" *Minneapolis Star-Tribune*, March 25, 2005, A14.

658    Ministry of Justice, Finland, "Jokela Secondary School Shooting: Report of the Investigation Commission," February 26, 2009, https://turval-lisuustutkinta.fi/material/attachments/otkes/tutkintaselostukset/fi/poikkeuksellisettapahtumat/SbmrFqAo3/Jokela_School_Shooting_on_7_November_2007.pdf

659    Abbie Boudreau and Scott Zamost, "Girlfriend: Shooter Was Taking Cocktail of 3 Drugs," *CNN*, February 20, 2008, http://www.cnn.com/2008/CRIME/02/20/shooter.girlfriend/index.html

660    Gordon Rayner, "Finnish School Shooting: How Killer 'Calmly' Picked off His Victims," *Telegraph*, September 23, 2008, https://www.telegraph.co.uk/news/worldnews/europe/finland/3068671/Finnish-school-shoot-ing-how-killer-calmly-picked-off-his-victims.html

661    Ministry of Justice, Finland, "Kauhajoki School Shooting: On September 23 2008: Report of the Investigation Commission," February 17, 2010,

https://schoolshooters.info/sites/default/files/Kauhajoki%20School%20
Shooting.pdf

662   A.G. Sulzberger and Mark Binker, "Gunman Kills 8 at N. Carolina
Nursing Home," *New York Times*, March 29, 2009, A16.

663   WRAL, "Defense: Defendant Doesn't Remember Nursing Home
Shooting," August 1, 2011, https://www.wral.com/news/local/
story/9936931/

664   North Carolina Department of Public Safety Offender Public Information, "Robert K. Stewart," 2012, https://webapps.doc.state.nc.us/opi/
viewoffender.do?method=view&offenderID=1142611&searchLastNam-
e=Stewart&searchFirstName=Robert&searchGender=M&searchRa-
ce=1&searchDOB=09/23/1963&searchDOBRange=2&listurl=pagelist-
offendersearchresults&listpage=1

665   Ashley Halsey, Peter Merman, and Clarence Williams, "D.C. Navy
Yard Attack Kills 12, Injures 8; Alleged Shooter Dead, Is ID'd as Aaron
Alexis," *Washington Post*, September 13, 2013, https://www.washington-
post.com/local/dc-navy-yard-rampage-leaves-14-dead-alleged-shoot-
er-killed-idd-as-aaron-alexis/2013/09/16/d084842e-1ef9-11e3-94a2-
6c66b668ea55_story.html?utm_term=.ce7d67e6142c

666   Steve Vogel, Sari Horwitz, and David A. Fahrenthold, "Navy Yard
Gunman Aaron Alexis Told VA Doctors He Was Not Thinking of
Harming Others," *Washington Post*, September 18, 2013, https://www.
washingtonpost.com/politics/2013/09/18/aee01b22-20a6-11e3-b73c-
aab60bf735d0_story.html?utm_term=.aad4c67556b1

667   Le Bureau d'Enquêtes et d'Analyses pour la Sécurité de l'Aviation
Civile, "Final Report," March 2016, https://www.madinamerica.com/
wp-content/uploads/2016/04/Germanwings-crash-final-BEA-re-
port-2015-0125.en-LR.pdf

668   Erica Goode, "Role of Illness in Germanwings Crash Raises Worry
About Stigma," *New York Times*, March 30, 2015, A1.

669    Gardiner Harris, "Drug Makers Are Advocacy Group's Biggest Donors," *New York Times*, October 21, 2009, A23.

670    Goode, "Stigma," A1.

671    Moore et al., "Violence."

672    Tarang Sharma et al., "Suicidality and Aggression During Antidepressant Treatment: Systematic Review and Meta-Analysis Based on Clinical Study Reports," *BMJ* 2016; 352:165 http://dx.doi.10.1136/bmj/i65

673    Ibid., 6.

674    Andreas Ø. Bielefeldt et al., "Precursors to Suicidality and Violence on Antidepressants: Systematic Review of Trials in Adult Healthy Volunteers," *Journal of the Royal Society of Medicine* 109, no. 10 (October 2016): 381-392, https://doi.org/10.1177/0141076816666805

675    Markus Rütgen et al., "Antidepressant Treatment, Not Depression, Leads to Reductions in Behavioral and Neural Responses to Pain Empathy," *Translational Psychiatry* 9, Article 164 (2019), https://doi.org/10.1038/s41398-019-0496-4

676    United States Secret Service National Threat Assessment Center, "Mass Attacks in Public Spaces—2018," July 2019, https://www.secretservice.gov/data/press/reports/USSS_FY2019_MAPS.pdf

677    Sandy Hook Advisory Commission, "Final Report of the Sandy Hook Advisory Commission," March 6, 2015, http://www.shac.ct.gov/SHAC_Final_Report_3-6-2015.pdf

678    Able Child, "CT AAG Nervous About Releasing Adam Lanza's Medical Records: Disclosure 'Can Cause a Lot of People to Stop Taking Their Medications,'" http://ablechild.org/2013/09/01/ct-aag-nervous-about-releasing-adam-lanzas-medical-records-disclosur*e-can-cause-a-lot-of-people-to-stop-taking-their-medications/

679    Janssen, "Janssen Announces US FDA Approval of SPRAVATO™ (Esketamine) CIII Nasal Spray for Adults With Treatment-Resistant Depression (TRD) Who Have Cycled Through Multiple Treat-

ments Without Relief," March 5, 2019, https://www.janssen.com/janssen-announces-us-fda-approval-spravato-esketamine-ciii-nasal-spray-adults-treatment-resistant

680   Janssen, "Prescribing Information for SPRAVATO," March 2019, http://www.janssenlabels.com/package-insert/product-monograph/prescribing-information/SPRAVATO-pi.pdf

681   At least it is according to Janssen scientists. A minimum 6.4 point improvement on the MARSD is needed for a "clinically meaningful improvement" in depressive symptoms. See I. Turkoz et al., "Demonstration of the Relationships Among Clinical Global Impression of Severity of Depression Scale and Montgomery-Åsberg Depression Rating, Patient Health Questionnaire-9, and Sheehan Disability Scales," poster presented at the 14th Annual Meeting of the International Society of CNS Clinical Trials and Methodology, February 20-22, 2018, https://isctm.org/public_access/Feb2018/PDFs/Turkoz-poster.pdf

682   FDA, "FDA Briefing Document: Psychopharmacologic Drugs Advisory Committee (PDAC) and Drug Safety and Risk Management (DRaRM) Advisory Committee Meeting February 12, 2019," 23.

683   Carolyn Y. Johnson and Laurie McGinley, "In Biggest Advance for Depression in Years, FDA Approves Novel Treatment for Hardest Cases," *Washington Post*, March 5, 2019, https://www.washingtonpost.com/health/2019/03/06/biggest-advance-depression-years-fda-approves-novel-treatment-hardest-cases/?noredirect=on&utm_term=.c3e6e8f4a09a

684   United States Department of Justice, "Johnson & Johnson to Pay More Than $2.2 Billion to Resolve Criminal and Civil Investigations: Allegations Include Illegal Marketing and Kickbacks to Doctors and Pharmacists," November 4, 2013, https://www.justice.gov/opa/pr/johnson-johnson-pay-more-22-billion-resolve-criminal-and-civil-investigations

685   Chris Mondics, "Philadelphia Jury Pins $70m Verdict on Janssen for Its Risperdal Drug," *Inquirer*, July 1, 2016, https://www.philly.com/philly/

business/20160702_Philadelphia_jury_pins__70m_verdict_on_Janssen_
for_its_Risperdal_drug.htm

686    FDA, "Briefing Document," 21, 42.

687    Benedict Carey, "Nasal Spray, a Quick-Acting Treatment for Depression, Is Approved by the FDA," *New York Times*, March 5, 2019, A18.

688    Johnson and McGinley, "Advance."

689    CDC, "Antidepressant Use Among Persons Aged 12 and Over: United States, 2011-2014," August 2017, https://www.cdc.gov/nchs/data/databriefs/db283.pdf

690    Ibid.

691    Market Research Store, "Global Depression Drug Market Poised to Surge from USD $14.51 Billion in 2014 to USD $16.80 Billion by 2020," May 10, 2016, https://globenewswire.com/news-release/2016/05/10/838292/0/en/Global-Depression-Drug-Market-Poised-to-Surge-from-USD-14-51-Billion-in-2014-to-USD-16-80-Billion-by-2020-MarketResearch-Store-Com.html

692    M.M. Painter et al., "Antidepressants at Environmentally Relevant Concentrations Affect Predator Avoidance Behavior of Larval Fathead Minnows (*Pimephales promelas*)," *Environmental Toxicology and Chemistry* 28, no. 12 (December 2009): 2677-2684, https://www.doi.org10.1897/08-556.1

693    Robert Whitaker and Lisa Cosgrove, *Psychiatry Under the Influence: Institutional Corruption, Social Injury, and Prescriptions for Reform* (New York: Palgrave Macmillan, 2015), 112.

694    A. Schafer, "Biomedical Conflicts of Interest: A Defence of the Sequestration Thesis—Learning from the Cases of Nancy Olivieri and David Healy," *Journal of Medical Ethics* 30, no. 1 (February 2004): 8-24, http://dx.doi.org/10.1136/jme.2003.005702

695    Ben Goldacre, *Bad Pharma* (London: Fourth Estate, 2012), 309-312.

696    Ibid., 249-250

697   Ibid., 314-323.

698   Patrick D. Hahn, "Drug Companies Prey on Children," *Baltimore Sun*, December 25, 2016, https://www.baltimoresun.com/opinion/op-ed/bs-ed-youth-overmedication-20161225-story.html

699   Whitaker and Cosgrove, *Influence*, 33-39.

700   On Thursday 27 June 2019, Pfizer announced that Scott Gottlieb, the 23rd Commissioner of the FDA, had joined the company Board of Directors. According to the *Washington Post*, every FDA commissioner of the last 38 years except for David Kessler has joined the board of a major pharmaceutical company. See Pfizer, "Scott Gottlieb Elected to Pfizer's Board of Directors," June 27, 2019, https://investors.pfizer.com/investor-news/press-release-details/2019/Scott-Gottlieb-Elected-to-Pfizers-Board-of-Directors/default.aspx; Laurie McGinley, "Former FDA Head Gottlieb Joins Pfizer Board," *Washington Post*, June 28, 2019.

701   Robert Pear, "Drug Industry, Having Long Smiled on Republican, Now Splits Donations Equally," *New York Times*, October 14, 2008; Alex Ruoff, "AbbVie, Bristol-Myers Among Patient Advocacy Groups' Big Backers," Bloomberg Government, October 8, 2019, https://about.bgov.com/news/abbvie-bristol-myers-among-patient-advocacy-groups-big-backers/?fbclid=IwAR3A_1rf8Q0UsgHUhoxBh1pQtnFe3sfnlyMME0tBc-7j6odzY1yup8vgtloA

702   See Chapter 5 of this volume.

703   World Health Organization, "Depression," March 22, 2018, https://www.who.int/news-room/fact-sheets/detail/depression

704   Paul E. Greenberg et al., "The Economic Burden of Adults With Major Depressive Disorder in the United States (2005 and 2010)," *Journal of Clinical Psychiatry* 76, no. 2 (February 2015): 155-162, https://doi.org/10.4088//JCP.14m09298

705   Chelsea Whyte, "US Suicide Rate at its Highest Since the End of the Second World War," *New Scientist*, June 19, 2019, https://www.newscien-

tist.com/article/2207007-us-suicide-rate-at-its-highest-since-the-end-of-the-second-world-war/

706    Jonas Forsman et al., "Selective Serotonin Re-uptake Inhibitors and the Risk of Violent Suicide: A Nationwide Postmortem Study," *European Journal of Clinical Pharmacology* 75, no. 3 (March 2019): 393-400, https://doi.org/10.1007/s00228-018-2586-2

707    Brett Burnstein, Holly Agostino, and Brian Greenfield, "Suicidal Attempts and Ideation Among Children and Adolescents in US Emergency Departments, 2007-2015," *JAMA Pediatrics*, https://doi.org/10.1001/jamapediatrics.2019.0464 [Epub ahead of print].

708    Michael Hengartner and Martin Plöderl, "Newer-Generation Antidepressants and Suicide Risk in Randomized Controlled Trials: A Re-Analysis of the FDA Database," *Psychotherapy and Psychosomatics*, June 24, 2019, https://doi.org/10.1159/000501215 [Epub ahead of print].

709    Gemma Mullin, "'Rare but Serious' Risk of Suicide for Patients on Antidepressants, New Findings Reveal," *Sun*, June 25, 2019, https://www.thesun.co.uk/news/9367136/antidepressants-rare-serious-risk-suicide/

710    Ben Spencer, "New Health Alert over Antidepressants as Study Finds a 'Rare but Serious Risk' of Suicide for Patients on Pills," *Daily Mail*, June 24, 2019, https://www.dailymail.co.uk/news/article-7176689/New-study-finds-rare-risk-suicide-patients-antidepressants.html

711    P.B. Danborg, M. Valdersdorf, and Peter C. Gøtzsche, "Long-Term Harms from Previous Use of Selective Serotonin Reuptake Inhibitors: A Systematic Review," *International Journal of Risk and Safety in Medicine* 30, no. 2 (July 26, 2019): 59-71, https://doi.org/10.3233/JRS-180046

712    Christina Maxouris et al., "El Paso Vigils Bring Together a City in Mourning After Mass Shooting," *CNN*, August 5, 2019, https://www.cnn.com/2019/08/05/us/el-paso-shooting-monday/index.html

713    Paul P. Murphy et al., "Dayton Shooter Had an Obsession With Violence and Mass Shootings, Police Say," *CNN*, August 7, 2019, https://www.cnn.com/2019/08/05/us/connor-betts-dayton-shooting-profile/index.html

714    William Wan, "White House Weighs Controversial Plan on Mental Illness and Mass Shootings," *Washington Post,* September 9, 2019, https://beta.washingtonpost.com/health/white-house-considers-controversial-plan-on-mental-illness-and-mass-shooting/2019/09/09/eb58b6f6-ce72-11e9-87fa-8501a456c003_story.html

715    Janus Christian Jakobsen, Christian Gluud, and Irving Kirsch, "Should Antidepressants be Used for Major Depressive Disorder?" *BMJ Evidence-Based Medicine* Published Online First: 25 September 2019, https://doi.org/10.1136/bmjebm-2019-111238, 3.

716    Ibid., 4.

717    CDC, "Death Rates Due to Suicide and Homicide Among Persons Aged 10-24: United States, 2000-2017," October 17, 2019, https://www.cdc.gov/nchs/data/databriefs/db352-h.pdf

718    William Wan, "Teen Suicides are Increasing at an Alarming Pace, Outstripping All Other Age Groups, a New Report Says," *Washington Post*, October 17, 2019, https://www.washingtonpost.com/health/teen-suicides-increasing-at-alarming-pace-outstripping-all-other-age-groups/2019/10/16/e24194c6-f04a-11e9-8693-f487e46784aa_story.html

719    Helen McArdle, "Mental Health Prescriptions Rising Fastest in 10-to-14 Year Old Scots: Sedatives Up 700% and Antidepressants Up 180%," *Herald*, October 27, 2019, https://www.heraldscotland.com/news/17994753.mental-health-prescriptions-rising-fastest-10-14-year-old-scots/?ref=fbshr&fbclid=IwAR28GngjBCLgFBerLXaY1XP08gDNxVONaDD8RaeX2NL4m3xnR9JUgYmbVjM

720    John Read, Beverly Thorpe, and Marion Brown, "Dangerous Opinions," *Herald*, November 3, 2019, https://www.heraldscotland.com/opinion/18011286.herald-sunday-letters-readers-talking-week/

721    Caleb Gardner and Arthur Kleinman, "Medicine and the Mind—The Consequences of Psychiatry's Identity Crisis," *New England Journal of Medicine* 381, (October 31, 2019):697-699, https://doi.org/ 10.1056/ NEJMp1910603

722    Udo Schulenk and Suzanne van de Vathorst, "Treatment-Resistant Major Depressive Disorder and Assisted Dying," *Journal of Medical Ethics* 41, no. 8 (2015): 577-583, http://dx.doi.org/10.1136/medethics-2014-102458

723    Paul S. Applebaum, "Should Mental Disorders Be a Basis for Physician-Assisted Death?" *Psychiatric Services* 68, no. 4 (April 2017): 315-317, https://doi.org/10.1176/appi.ps.201700013

724    *Economist*, "24 & Ready to Die," November 10, 2015, https://www.youtube.com/watch?v=SWWkUzkfJ4M; Linda Pressley, "The Troubled 29-Year-Old Helped to Die by Dutch Doctors," *BBC News*, August 9, 2018, https://www.bbc.com/news/stories-45117163

725    Breggin, *Medication Madness.*

726    Peter R. Breggin, *Guilt, Shame, and Anxiety: Understanding and Overcoming Negative Emotions* (New York: Prometheus Books, 2014).

# *About the Author*

Dr. Patrick D. Hahn is an Affiliate Professor of Biology at Loyola University Maryland, USA, and a freelance writer. He has a long-standing interest in iatrogenic harm and the medicalization of everyday life. His first book, *Madness and Genetic Determinism: Is Mental Illness in Our Genes?*, explores how genetic determinist views of so-called "mental illness" have obscured the well-established role of childhood sexual abuse and other adverse childhood experiences in the genesis of those conditions. His writing on mental health and other issues has appeared in the *Baltimore Sun, Mad in America,* the *Canada Free Press, Natural News Blogs,* and other venues.

Made in the USA
Coppell, TX
27 January 2021